Fundamentals of
NEUROLOGY

ERNEST GARDNER, M.D.

Professor of Anatomy and Dean
Wayne State University School of Medicine

FIFTH EDITION
ILLUSTRATED

W. B. SAUNDERS COMPANY
Philadelphia · London · Toronto

W. B. Saunders Company: West Washington Square
Philadelphia, Pa. 19105

12 Dyott Street
London, WC1A   1DB

1835 Yonge Street
Toronto 7, Ontario

Fundamentals of Neurology   SBN 0-7216-4001-X

Print No.:   9   8   7   6   5   4   3

To La Vearl Gardner

PREFACE TO THE FIFTH EDITION

The purpose of this volume was expressed in the preface to the first edition and in each of the subsequent editions. It is to select from the available data those facts necessary to present neurology as concepts which can be the foundation for more detailed studies. The last five years have seen major advances in our understanding of the nervous system. Many of these advances have been possible because of the development of elegant experimental methods involving particularly the electron microscope; biochemistry, histochemistry, and pharmacology; the use of microelectrodes in electrical recording; systems and statistical analyses; and increasingly sophisticated behavioral studies. The present edition, like the fourth, emphasizes recent work on conduction, transmission, and sensory mechanisms.

Certain arrangements are unchanged. The references cited are intended to provide the interested student with a starting point for further reading. The short biographical sketches are of those men whose names are mentioned in the text, or who were outstanding in neurology.

I am indebted to Mr. William Loechel of the Department of Medical Illustration, and to Marjorie Fodal of the same department, for their preparation of the illustrations.

I wish to thank Dr. Clem Fox, Department of Anatomy, Wayne State University, and Dr. Ray Brown, Department of Biochemistry, Wayne State University, who contributed valuable criticisms and suggestions during the preparation of the revision

Finally, I am indebted to the W. B. Saunders Company for the help and the many courtesies they extended me.

ERNEST GARDNER

Detroit, Michigan

CONTENTS

CHAPTER 1
DESCRIPTIVE AND ANALYTICAL METHODS 1

Orientation.. 3
Techniques for Gross and Microscopic Study.................... 3
Experimental Methods of Study................................. 5
Clinical Methods of Study 5
Names in Neurology 6
References 6

CHAPTER 2
THE CENTRAL NERVOUS SYSTEM 8

Location and Coverings of the Central Nervous System 9
The Brain.. 10
The Spinal Cord 24
Summary 25
Names in Neurology 26
References 27

CHAPTER 3
THE PERIPHERAL NERVOUS SYSTEM 28

Cranial Nerves 29
Spinal Roots and Spinal Nerves............................... 32
Spinal Nerves and Peripheral Nerves.......................... 33
Autonomic Nervous System 40
Summary 40
References 42

CHAPTER 4

BLOOD SUPPLY AND CEREBROSPINAL FLUID 43

Blood Supply of the Nervous System 44
Clinical Importance of Blood Supply 48
Formation and Circulation of Cerebrospinal Fluid 50
Clinical Importance of Cerebrospinal Fluid 52
Summary 54
Names in Neurology 54
References 55

CHAPTER 5

**FORMATION AND DEVELOPMENT OF THE NERVOUS
SYSTEM** 56

Embryonic and Fetal Periods 56
Development of the Nervous System 57
Congenital Defects of the Nervous System 65
Summary 65
References 66

CHAPTER 6

MICROSCOPIC ANATOMY OF THE NERVOUS SYSTEM ... 67

General Characteristics of Cells 67
The Neuron 67
    Structure of the Cell Body 68
    Structure of the Cell Process 73
Synapses 82
Neuroglia 83
Degeneration and Regeneration in the Nervous System 85
The Neuron Theory 91
Summary 91
Names in Neurology 92
References 94

CHAPTER 7

EXCITATION, CONDUCTION, AND TRANSMISSION 95

Methods of Study 97
Steady or Resting Potential 97

Changes in Potential 98
Recording of Potential Changes 104
Nerve Impulses and Stimuli 107
Synaptic Transmission 110
Summary 112
References 113

Chapter 8
CHEMISTRY OF THE NERVOUS SYSTEM 114

General Metabolism 114
Intermediary Metabolism 115
Inorganic Constituents 118
Chemistry of Cell Constituents 119
Chemistry and Behavior 120
Names in Neurology 121
References 121

Chapter 9
GENERAL PROPERTIES OF THE REFLEX ARC 122

Types of Reflexes 123
Coordination of Reflex Arcs 125
Reflexes and Behavior 130
Clinical Value of Reflexes 131
Summary 133
Names in Neurology 133
References 134

Chapter 10
STRUCTURES MEDIATING RECEPTION AND
RESPONSE 135

Receptors 136
Physiology of Receptors 142
Effectors 144
Neuroeffector Junctions 146
    Structure of Neuroeffector Junctions 146
    Physiology of Neuroeffector Junctions 148
Dependence on Nerve Supply 151
Summary 153

Names in Neurology 153
References 154

CHAPTER 11
THE CONTROL OF MUSCULAR ACTIVITY 155

Levels of Control 158
Muscular Activity in the Trunk and Limbs 160
Muscular Activity in the Head and Neck 164
Clinical Importance of Motor Areas and Pathways 167
    Upper Motor Neuron Lesions.................................... 167
    Lower Motor Neuron Lesions.................................... 170
Summary 172
References 173

CHAPTER 12
THE GENERAL SENSES AND THEIR AFFERENT
PATHWAYS 174

Sensory Paths from the Skin 175
Sensory Paths from the Subcutaneous and Deep Tissues..... 181
Sensory Paths from Viscera 183
Referred Pain and Projected Sensations 183
Clinical Importance of the Afferent Pathways 185
Primary Receptive Areas 187
Summary 188
Names in Neurology 188
References 189

CHAPTER 13
THE SPECIAL SENSES AND THEIR AFFERENT
PATHWAYS 190

Vision 191
    The Retina 194
    Central Connections of the Retina............................. 205
    Lesions of the Visual System.................................... 207
Hearing 208
    The External and Middle Ears.................................. 209
    The Inner Ear and Cochlea 211
    Lesions of the Auditory System 214

Balance or Equilibrium 215
   The Semicircular Ducts 216
   The Utricle and Saccule 217
   Central Vestibular Connections 217
   Functions of the Vestibular System 219
   Lesions of the Vestibular System 219
Taste 219
Smell 221
Summary 223
Names in Neurology 223
References 224

CHAPTER 14
CONTROL OF VISCERAL ACTIVITY 226

Autonomic Nervous System 228
   Levels of Organization 228
   Levels of Outflow 230
   Functions of the Various Levels 236
General Functions of the Autonomic Nervous System 241
Summary 242
Names in Neurology 243
References 243

CHAPTER 15
THE SPINAL CORD, SPINAL NERVES, AND PERIPHERAL
  NERVES 244

The Spinal Cord 244
Functions of the Spinal Cord 247
   Spinal Man 249
Spinal Nerves 252
   Nerve Components 252
Peripheral Nerves 253
Summary 254
References 255

CHAPTER 16
THE BRAIN STEM 256

General Features of the Brain Stem 256
   The Medulla Oblongata 256

The Pons and Midbrain 258
Cranial Nerve Components 260
Motor Functions of the Brain Stem 263
Static Reflexes in Decerebrate Rigidity 266
Functions of the Midbrain 267
Autonomic Functions of the Brain Stem 268
Control of Respiration 268
Control of Movements in the Alimentary Canal 271
Reticular Formation 272
Summary 273
Names in Neurology 273
References 274

CHAPTER 17
✓THE CEREBELLUM 275

Connections with the Cerebral Cortex 278
Connections with the Spinal Cord 280
Connections with Brain Stem and Cranial Nerves 281
Localization in the Cerebellum 282
Functions of the Cerebellum....................................... 282
Disorders of the Cerebellum 284
Summary 285
Names in Neurology 285
References 285

CHAPTER 18
THE PROSENCEPHALON OR FOREBRAIN 286

General Features of the Forebrain.................................. 288
Fishes... 288
Amphibians... 289
Reptiles 289
Birds 289
Mammals 289
Basal Ganglia 292
Thalamus 294
✓Cerebral Cortex 294
Electrical Activity 296
Summary 298
Names in Neurology 299
References 299

CHAPTER 19
MOTOR AND SENSORY FUNCTIONS OF THE
  FOREBRAIN 300

  Motor Functions 300
    Stimulation 303
  Extirpation 306
    Relation to Sensory Areas and to the Cerebellum 307
    Basal Ganglia 308
    Motor Disorders 311
  Sensory Functions 312
  Epilepsy and the Convulsive States 316
  Summary 317
  Names in Neurology 318
  References 319

CHAPTER 20
ASSOCIATIVE AND INTEGRATIVE FUNCTIONS
  OF THE FOREBRAIN 320

  Learning 322
    Learning and Sensorimotor Functions 322
    Learning and Language Mechanisms 328
    Learning and Conditioned Responses 332
  Frontal Association Areas 333
    The Affective Component of Behavior 334
  Emotional and Visceral Functions of Subcortical Centers ... 334
  Summary 336
  Names in Neurology 337
  References 338

GLOSSARY OF NEW TERMS 339

INDEX 347

CHAPTER 1

DESCRIPTIVE AND
ANALYTICAL METHODS

The material in this volume is based upon dissection and microscopic study of the nervous system, analysis by experimental methods, and the study of neurological disorders. This knowledge has accumulated over many centuries, owing to the efforts of countless investigators, working in many countries, using many different languages. One of the results has been an expanding and, at the same time, confusing terminology. Names were often given to portions of the body before the functions of these parts were known. For instance, an area of the brain which in general configuration somewhat resembles a sea horse was named the *hippocampus*. Often the name of the investigator who first described a structure became associated with that structure, as, for example, the *vein of Galen* (p. 6).

The first attempt to clarify and simplify anatomical terminology was made in 1895 by a group consisting chiefly of German anatomists meeting at Basle. The terminology they adopted is the *Basle Nomina Anatomica* (B. N. A.). Later revisions were the *Birmingham Revision* (B. R., 1933) and the *Jena Nomina Anatomica* (I. N. A , 1936). In Paris in 1955, international agreement was reached on a Latin system of nomenclature based largely on the B. N. A. This *Nomina Anatomica*, as amended in 1960 and 1965, is used throughout this book where applicable, and translated into English where appropriate.

1

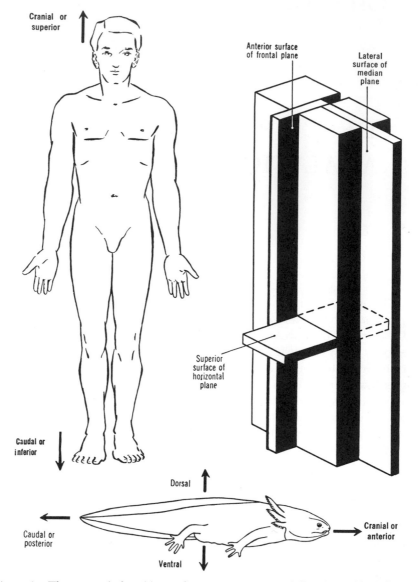

Figure 1. The anatomical position and synonymous terms of direction; a block diagram showing the primary planes and surfaces; and an amphibian, illustrating comparative anatomical nomenclature.

ORIENTATION

Information as to the position of any object, such as a house in a city, is expressed in terms of direction, such as east and west, or right and left. When the human body is in the *anatomical position,* that is to say, when it is upright, with the upper limbs at the sides and the palms facing forward, three primary planes may be defined (Fig. 1). These are the *sagittal, coronal* or *frontal,* and *horizontal* planes. A sagittal plane divides the body into right and left parts. The *median* plane is that sagittal plane which divides the body into right and left halves. A coronal or frontal plane is a vertical plane at right angles to the sagittal that divides the body into front and back parts. A *horizontal* plane is any plane at right angles to the preceding ones that divides the body into upper and lower parts.

Structures toward the front of the body are *anterior;* toward the back, *posterior. Cranial,* or *superior,* refers to upper; and *caudal,* or *inferior,* to lower structures. The fact that man stands upright has led to a difference from the terminology used in comparative anatomy. In lower forms, structures which in man are toward the front of the body are *ventral,* those toward the back, *dorsal.* Cranial and anterior become synonymous, as do caudal and posterior (Fig. 1). In connection with the nervous system, the comparative anatomical nomenclature is often followed, particularly as regards "dorsal" and "ventral." For instance, the roots of the spinal cord usually are termed "dorsal" and "ventral" rather than "posterior" and "anterior" (pp. 24 and 32). "Ventral" is sometimes used to indicate structures at the base of the human brain; the comparable surface in animals that walk on all fours is ventral.

Other important terms are *medial,* nearer the median plane, and *lateral,* farther from that plane. *Proximal,* in referring to a limb, indicates a position nearer the trunk, or central axis of the body; *distal,* a more peripheral position. For other terms of position and directions one should consult the textbooks of anatomy cited at the end of this chapter.

TECHNIQUES FOR GROSS AND MICROSCOPIC STUDY

Many important characteristics of the nervous system, such as size, shape, position and surface markings, may be noted by ordinary inspection. Details may be revealed by dissection of the nervous system, that is, by separating it from other tissues or organs, or by cutting it in various ways so as to obtain access to structures not apparent on the surface. The minute anatomy can be studied by examining portions of the nervous system under the microscope. Tissues examined by this means must be thin and transparent so that light can pass through them into the microscope and eventually to the eye. Although it is desirable to study tissues in the living state, thin sections are difficult to obtain and structures in the tissues may not be readily distinguishable. Therefore, special techniques are used to kill tissues and obtain thin slices to which dyes are applied so as to color structures differentially.

In order to preserve a structure in a state resembling the living as closely as possible, small pieces of fresh tissue are *fixed* in a chemical solution that simultaneously kills them and preserves them from alteration during subsequent treatment. Formalin or alcohol are the fixatives that are most commonly used for nerve tissue. After fixation, water in the tissues is slowly removed by transferring them through increasing concentrations of alcohol. Water-free tissues are then infiltrated with some substance which can be hardened later. Melted paraffin or a solution of nitrocellulose (celloidin) is used for such purposes. The hardened blocks can be cut into thin slices (as thin as 1 or 2 *microns*) without marked damage or distortion. This is done with a sharp knife and a special machine, the *microtome*. The thin slices or sections are then stained. Because all parts of tissues are not of the same chemical composition, some stains will color one structure, some another. Numerous dyes are available, and their choice depends upon the structures being studied. The stained sections are then made transparent by immersing them in a substance such as xylene. To prevent the drying and destruction which occur on exposure to air, they are placed on glass slides, covered with a solution of a transparent resin, and sealed with a thin piece of glass. As the resin dries, it remains clear and forms a hard, protective coat for the sections that will last for many years.

In hospitals, where a rapid method is often necessary, fresh pieces of tissue can be quickly frozen into hard blocks, and sections cut immediately, stained and mounted

Many details of structure are beyond the resolution of the light microscope. In recent years, however, significant advances in our knowledge of the structure of the nervous system have resulted from the use of the electron microscope. Special methods of fixation and embedding, coupled with the use of a special type of microtome and knife, enable sections a fraction of a micron in thickness to be prepared The study of these sections under the electron microscope, which permits an enormous magnification, has led to a substantial increase in our understanding of *ultrastructure*. The most significant advances have been made in connection with the structure of membranes of cells and fibers, and of myelin, synapses, receptors, and special sense organs.

EXPERIMENTAL METHODS OF STUDY

There are many methods of studying the living nervous system. Most of them are carried out in animals other than man. The function of a particular portion or structure in the nervous system may be adduced by stimulating it with an electric current and observing the results directly. A part of the nervous system may be removed surgically and any effect or loss of function noted. Habit formation, behavior, reactions to stimuli, and the like may be observed before and after surgical procedures in animals and in man. Drugs may be given which affect or stimulate certain elements of the nervous system and thereby alter their functions. The inception of function may be observed by correlating physiological and morphological development during embryonic, fetal, and infant life. Finally, there are methods involving special techniques. Some of these will be discussed in subsequent chapters. For instance, living tissue, especially that of the nervous system, undergoes electrical changes during an alteration in activity. These changes can be studied and recorded, usually by means of special electronic equipment, and the methods allow one to examine a variety of phenomena, among which are nerve conduction, the localization of active nerve centers, and the tracing of pathways in the central nervous system. The effect of various drugs, such as anesthetics, on electrical activity can also be included.

In recent years, biochemical studies of the nervous system have constituted an increasingly important avenue of experimental study. General biochemical studies, histochemical studies which combine microscopic and biochemical procedures, and special methods of studying cytochemistry have all yielded important information about chemical composition and general and intermediary metabolism. In combination with studies of ultrastructure and the use of radioisotopes, they have led to major advances in our understanding of neural functions and disorders.

CLINICAL METHODS OF STUDY

A disease or injury of the nervous system usually causes a loss of function or may give rise to an abnormal condition. If a patient with a neurological disorder dies, the signs and symptoms which that patient presented during life may be correlated with pathological changes found after death. Over many years the study of great numbers of such cases has yielded considerable information. Data may also be obtained when operations are necessary. Clinical methods are often the only comprehensive ones available for neurological studies in man, if one excludes special tests used by psychologists and psychiatrists.

Names in Neurology

GALEN OF PERGAMUM (ABOUT A.D 130-200)

Galen was a Greek physician who, after many years of study, settled in Rome. Here, as the founder of experimental physiology, he did an incredible amount of work. He knew of the effects of cutting the spinal cord, with its resulting sensory losses and motor disturbances. Galen studied the heart and knew that the arteries contained blood. He saw and described the cerebral aqueduct His knowledge of anatomy was comprehensive and accurate. He set so high a standard that for thirteen centuries his works were the only authoritative sources. We now recognize Galen as one of the great scientific figures of all times.

REFERENCES

The first of the following textbooks is a general anatomical one and presents anatomy on a regional basis. It contains extensive references to textbooks, monographs, and periodicals. The next four textbooks are concerned chiefly with the gross and microscopic anatomy of the nervous system.

Crosby, E. C., Humphrey, T., and Lauer, E. W.: Correlative Anatomy of the Nervous System. New York, The Macmillan Company, 1962.
Gardner, E., Gray, D. J., and O'Rahilly, R.: Anatomy. 2nd ed. Philadelphia, W. B. Saunders Company, 1963.
Peele, T. L.: The Neuroanatomic Basis for Clinical Neurology. 2nd ed. New York, McGraw-Hill Book Company, Inc., 1961.
Ranson, S. W., and Clark, S. L.: Anatomy of the Nervous System. 10th ed. Philadelphia, W. B. Saunders Company, 1959.
Truex, R. C.: Strong and Elwyn's Human Neuroanatomy. 5th ed. Baltimore, Williams & Wilkins Company, 1964.

The following three textbooks deal primarily with mammalian physiology, but emphasize human physiology and clinical applications.

Best, C. H., and Taylor, N. B.: Physiological Basis of Medical Practice. 7th ed. Baltimore, Williams & Wilkins Company, 1961.
Guyton, A. C.: Textbook of Medical Physiology. 3rd ed. Philadelphia, W. B. Saunders Company, 1966.
Ruch, T. C., and Fulton, J. F.: Medical Physiology and Biophysics. 18th ed. Philadelphia, W. B. Saunders Company, 1960.

The Handbook of Physiology, American Physiological Society, Washington, D.C., 1959, has published Section 1, which consists of 3 volumes of Neurophysiology. Each volume contains detailed chapters with extensive bibliographies on various aspects of neurophysiology. The three volumes comprise a most extensive treatment of the subject.

The following textbook is one of the best on comparative anatomy in the English language. The chapters on sense organs and the nervous system are of particular interest here.

Romer, A. S.: The Vertebrate Body, 3rd ed. Philadelphia, W. B. Saunders Company, 1962.

The following textbook for the beginning student presents elementary facts about the structure and function of the human body.

King, B. G., and Showers, M. J.: Human Anatomy and Physiology. 5th ed. Philadelphia, W. B. Saunders Company, 1963.

For excellent accounts of famous names in neurology, see the following:

Haymaker, W.: The Founders of Neurology. Springfield, Ill., Charles C Thomas, 1953.

The *Nomina Anatomica* cited below was adopted with the following principles in mind: (1) Every term in the official list shall be in Latin, with each country at liberty to translate the official Latin terms into its own vernacular for teaching purposes. (2) With but few exceptions, each structure shall be designated by one term only. (3) Terms shall be primarily memory signs, but shall have some informative or descriptive value. (4) Eponyms shall not be used.

Nomina Anatomica, 3rd ed. Amsterdam, Excerpta Medica Foundation, 1966.

CHAPTER 2

THE CENTRAL
NERVOUS SYSTEM

During the course of development in the embryo, the nervous system becomes a tubular structure, and this tubular arrangement is found in the adult in a considerably modified form (Chapter 5). The part of the tube in the head region develops into the *brain* and its various subdivisions. The rest of the tube becomes the *spinal cord.* The brain and spinal cord constitute the *central nervous system.*

Nerve cells in the brain and spinal cord have processes of various lengths. Many of these processes connect parts of the brain and spinal cord, while others collect in bundles, leave the brain and spinal cord as cranial and spinal nerves, and are distributed to muscles and glands. Other nerve cells lie adjacent to the brain and spinal cord, and their processes convey sensory impulses from non-nervous structures to the brain and spinal cord. The *cranial* and *spinal nerves,* their peripheral combinations, and the peripheral portions of the *autonomic nervous system,* constitute the *peripheral nervous system.*

In order to pave the way for more detailed anatomical and physiological discussions, this and the next two chapters will be devoted to a general presentation of the gross or macroscopic anatomy of the nervous system.

8

LOCATION AND COVERINGS OF THE CENTRAL NERVOUS SYSTEM

The brain and spinal cord are protected by the *skull*, the *vertebrae*, and their ligamentous connections. The brain occupies the cranial cavity in the interior of the skull. This cavity is commonly of 1200 to 1500 cc capacity. There are numerous openings or *foramina* in the base of the skull for blood vessels and nerves. Through an especially large one, the *foramen magnum*, the medulla oblongata of the brain is continuous with the spinal cord (Fig. 2).

The vertebrae are irregularly shaped bones joined so as to form a long column. Each vertebra has a heavy body from which an arch ex-

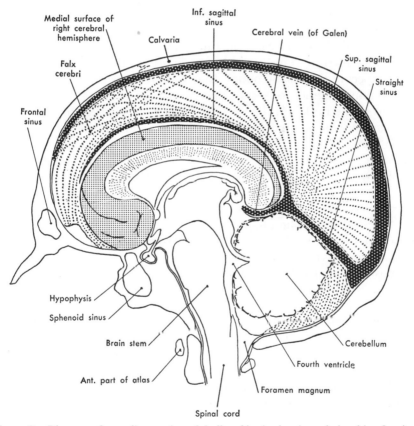

Figure 2. Diagram of a median section of skull and brain showing relationship of various parts of brain to skull and dura mater. The falx cerebri and its contained sinuses are also shown in Figure 3. Veins in the cerebral hemispheres empty into the sinuses. Blood flows posteriorly and, from the junction of straight sinus and superior sagittal sinus, is carried by other sinuses (not shown) to the internal jugular veins.

tends backward, enclosing a large opening, the *vertebral foramen*. The vertebrae are arranged so that the foramina form a continuous channel, the *vertebral canal*. The spinal cord occupies the vertebral canal and extends from the foramen magnum to about the level of the first or second lumbar vertebra.

There are lateral openings between the vertebrae, the *intervertebral foramina*, through which nerves and blood vessels run (Fig. 20, p. 32).

Seven *cervical* vertebrae are present in the neck; twelve *thoracic* vertebrae in the chest or thorax; five *lumbar* vertebrae in the abdomen; a *sacrum* in the pelvis (the sacrum develops before birth as five sacral vertebrae that later fuse into a single bone). At the lower end of the column is a small bone, the *coccyx*, representing several vertebral segments.

The brain and spinal cord are surrounded and protected by layers of non-nervous tissue collectively called *meninges*. The outer layer is the *dura mater* (Figs. 2 and 3), which is a tough fibrous membrane that is lined on its inner aspect by flat cells. When bone is removed preparatory to entering the cranial cavity, the dura mater is the first meningeal layer to be encountered. The dura mater serves as the periosteum for the inner aspect of the cranial bones. In certain regions the dura mater contains venous channels or *sinuses* that carry venous blood from the brain to veins in the neck and thence to the heart. In the vertebral canal, the dura mater is separated from bone by an interval, the *epidural space*, which contains fat and many small veins. A comparable space is not found in the cranial cavity except when artificially produced, for example, by bleeding between skull and dura mater after trauma (p. 46).

Just internal to the dura mater is a thin membrane of reticular fibers, the *arachnoid*, the outer and inner aspects of which are lined by flat and oval cells. The potential space between the arachnoid and the dura mater is termed the *subdural space*. Around the brain, a delicate network of connective tissue trabeculae connects the arachnoid to the innermost meningeal layer, the *pia mater*. The pia mater is a delicate membrane of reticular and elastic fibers that is closely applied to the brain and spinal cord. The outer part of the pia mater consists of loosely arranged connective tissue. This outer part, which is more prominent around the spinal cord, contains the blood vessels which supply the brain and spinal cord. The space between the arachnoid and the pia mater, the *subarachnoid space*, contains the extraventricular cerebrospinal fluid. Meningeal arrangements are shown in Figure 29 and cerebrospinal fluid is discussed on page 50.

THE BRAIN

The part of the neural tube that develops in the head region forms the brain. Three enlargements of this tube are found early in develop-

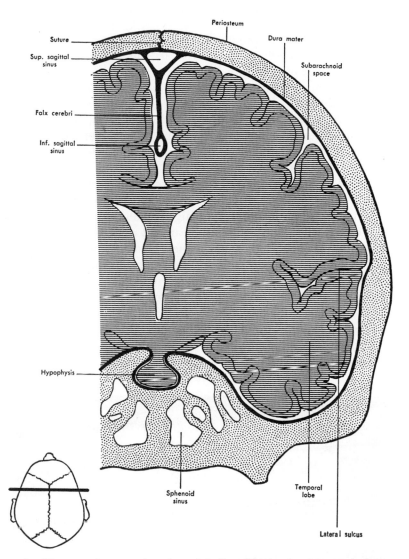

Figure 3.   Diagram of a coronal section of skull and brain, showing certain features of the dura mater (the arachnoid and pia mater are not shown). The small figure shows the plane of section. Note that the dura mater forms a fold (falx cerebri) between the cerebral hemispheres, and contains two venous sinuses. This plane is at right angles to that of Figure 2. Note also that the dura mater is continuous through the suture with periosteum on the outer surface of the skull.

ment. These are the forebrain, midbrain, and hindbrain, and from these
the subdivisions of the adult brain *(cerebrum)* are formed (Table 1, p. 60).
The cavity of the neural tube persists in the adult as cavities called *ventricles.*

The forebrain forms the endbrain *(telencephalon),* and the *interbrain
(diencephalon).* The endbrain gives rise to the two *cerebral hemispheres*
that form the bulk of the brain.

The midbrain *(mesencephalon)* persists as the *midbrain* of the adult.

The hindbrain forms the *pons, medulla oblongata,* and *cerebellum.*

The term *brain stem* refers to the midbrain, pons, and medulla oblongata, and often includes the diencephalon as well. These regions
collectively form a stem or stalk between the expanded cerebral hemispheres and the spinal cord.

Cerebral Hemispheres. The huge size of the hemispheres relative
to the rest of the brain is due, in man, to the development of regions
concerned with motor, sensory, and higher mental functions.

A prominent longitudinal fissure partially divides the cerebrum into
two hemispheres. This fissure is occupied by a downward projection or
fold of dura mater, the *falx cerebri.* When the arachnoid and pia mater
are removed, it is seen that the hemispheres are folded or convoluted.
The convolutions are called *gyri,* the depressions or intervals between
gyri, *sulci.* Most gyri and sulci are named, and the more constant of these
are shown in Figures 4 and 5.

Thus, between the *central sulcus* and *precentral sulcus* is the precentral
gyrus, a region concerned in motor activities. There is considerable indi-

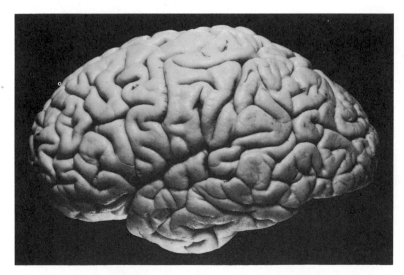

Figure 4. Photograph of lateral surface of human cerebral hemisphere. The arachnoid
and pia mater have been removed.

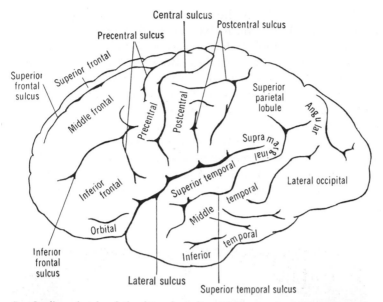

Figure 5. Outline sketch of the lateral surface of the cerebral hemisphere shown in Figure 4. The gyri are directly labeled (except the superior frontal), while the sulci are indicated by leaders.

vidual variation in size, shape, and position of gyri and sulci, and none can be identified with certainty unless arachnoid and pia mater are removed.

Some sulci separate parts of the hemispheres called *lobes*. Each lobe supposedly has specific functions. To a certain extent this is true; the occipital lobe, for example, is concerned with vision. However, the assignment of clear-cut functional properties to lobes may be quite arbitrary. The lobes are shown in Figure 5. The *frontal lobe* is in front of the central sulcus, the *parietal lobe* behind it and above the lateral sulcus. The *temporal lobe* is below the lateral sulcus. The *occipital lobe* is posterior to temporal and parietal lobes, but there is usually no definite sulcus separating them on the lateral surface of the hemisphere. Figure 12 shows how the various lobes extend to the medial surface of the hemisphere.

The two hemispheres are united by several bands (commissures) of nerve fibers that cross the midline. The most prominent of these is the *corpus callosum* (Fig. 13).

Diencephalon. The diencephalon or interbrain lies between cerebrum and midbrain. Its largest part is the *thalamus* (Fig. 14), a region concerned with sensory functions. Just below the thalamus is the *hypothalamus*, concerned with visceral functions (Fig. 13).

Base of Cerebrum and Diencephalon. The nerves connected to the brain, and the blood vessels supplying the brain, enter or leave from below, that is, from the inferior or ventral aspect. Hence the brain must be removed and its base studied. Figures 6 and 7 show the base of the brain. The only lobes readily visible in this view are parts of the frontal and temporal lobes. Between the two temporal lobes is a part of the brain marked by two prominences, the *mamillary bodies* (Figs. 8 and 9). These are parts of the diencephalon. Just behind the mamillary bodies are two large bundles of nerve fibers, the *cerebral peduncles,* which form part of the midbrain.

The *olfactory nerves,* the first of twelve pairs of cranial nerves, are groups of tiny nerve filaments that ascend through openings in the front part of the floor of the cranial cavity. They end in *olfactory bulbs,* from which *olfactory tracts* are directed backward to the base of each of the frontal lobes (Fig. 7).

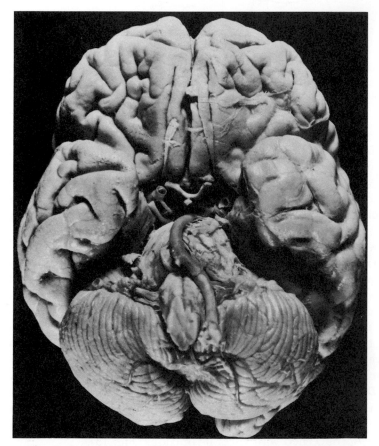

Figure 6. Photograph of the base of a human brain, with the arachnoid and pia mater largely removed. One vertebral artery is enlarged; the other, smaller one is cut at the beginning of the basilar artery. The right olfactory bulb is removed.

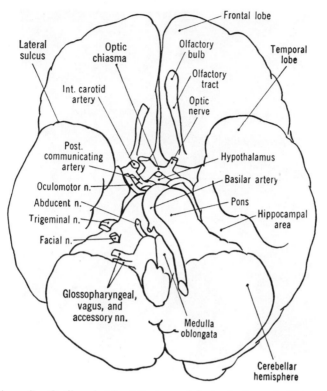

Figure 7. Outline sketch of the base of the brain shown in Figure 6.

The *optic nerves*, the second pair of cranial nerves, leave the orbital cavities through the *optic canals* and join to form the *optic chiasma*, from which *optic tracts* proceed backward around the cerebral peduncles.

Close to each optic nerve, near the chiasma, is a large blood vessel, the *internal carotid artery*, which supplies the orbit and brain. Just behind the optic chiasma is a stalk of tissue connecting the base of the brain with the *hypophysis (pituitary gland)*, which is contained in a fossa in the base of the skull (Figs. 2 and 3). Near the optic nerves, and entering the orbit where they supply muscles that move the eye, are the *oculomotor, trochlear,* and *abducent* nerves, the third, fourth, and sixth pairs of cranial nerves respectively.

Also at the base of the brain is the *arterial circle* (circle of Willis, see Chapter 4), formed by communications between branches of the internal carotid and basilar arteries, and from which branches are distributed to the brain.

Midbrain. The front of the midbrain or mesencephalon is formed by the two cerebral peduncles, which contain nerve tracts connecting the cerebrum with brain stem and spinal cord. On the posterior surface

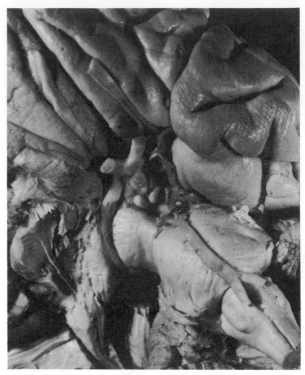

Figure 8. Photograph of the base of the brain. Most of the cranial nerves have been removed, as well as one olfactory bulb. The temporal lobe on one side has been cut away to expose the right optic tract as it winds around the cerebral peduncle.

of the midbrain are four rounded eminences. The upper two are the *superior colliculi*, the lower two the *inferior colliculi.* The superior colliculi are concerned with visual functions, the inferior with auditory functions. The posterior limit of the diencephalon, at the junction of the diencephalon and midbrain, is marked by a small, oval body, the *pineal body* or *epiphysis,* which is attached in the midline just above the superior colliculi. The pineal body often becomes calcified with advancing age, and hence more radiopaque. It thereby becomes visible in radiograms and thus serves as a useful landmark or reference point in interpreting radiograms of the brain and skull. The functions of the pineal body in mammals are obscure, but may be neuroendocrine in part.

The oculomotor nerves attach to the front of the midbrain, between the cerebral peduncles. The trochlear nerves arise in the midbrain, but leave from its posterior surface.

Pons. The midbrain continues below into a massive, rounded structure, the *pons.* The pons serves in part as a bridge or connection between the two cerebellar hemispheres, and contains various nerve

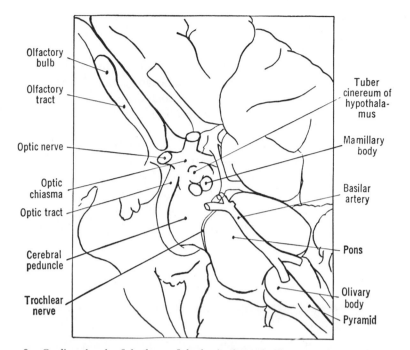

Olfactory bulb

Olfactory tract

Optic nerve

Optic chiasma

Optic tract

Cerebral peduncle

Trochlear nerve

Tuber cinereum of hypothala-mus

Mamillary body

Basilar artery

Pons

Olivary body

Pyramid

Figure 9. Outline sketch of the base of the brain shown in Figure 8. The trochlear nerve, having been cut anteriorly, has fallen on the brain stem.

tracts and collections of nerve cells. The fifth pair of cranial nerves, the *trigeminal nerves,* is attached to the sides of the pons. The *abducent nerves* are attached to the front of the pons, just above its junction with the medulla oblongata. The seventh and eighth pairs of cranial nerves, the *facial* and the *vestibulocochlear* (often called *acoustic* or *auditory*), are attached at the sides, at the junction of pons and medulla oblongata.

Medulla Oblongata. The pons continues below into the medulla oblongata, which in turn continues into the spinal cord, the junction being at the level of the foramen magnum.

The front of the medulla oblongata is marked by the longitudinally directed *anterior median fissure,* on each side of which is an elevation, the *pyramid.* Lateral to the upper part of each pyramid and separated from it by the *anterior lateral sulcus,* is an ovoidal elevation, the *olive.* Details of the posterior surface of the medulla oblongata are discussed with the ventricular system (p. 19).

The ninth, tenth, and eleventh pairs of cranial nerves, the *glosso-pharyngeal, vagus,* and *accessory* nerves respectively, are attached to the side of the medulla oblongata, between the olive and *inferior cerebellar peduncle.* The *hypoglossal nerves,* the twelfth pair, emerge on each side between pyramid and olive, from the anterior lateral sulcus.

The medulla oblongata contains, in addition to various nerve tracts, important collections of nerve cells dealing with vital functions, such as respiration, circulation, and special senses.

Two vertebral arteries enter the cranial cavity through the foramen magnum, ascend in front of the medulla oblongata, and unite to form the basilar artery. This in turn ascends in front of pons and midbrain and ends by dividing into the two posterior cerebral arteries, which enter the arterial circle (Fig. 27, p. 44).

Cerebellum. The cerebellum is a deeply fissured structure behind the brain stem, formed of two hemispheres connected by a median portion, the *vermis*. The cerebellum is connected to the brain stem by paired peduncles, whose position and direction are shown in Figure 10. The *superior cerebellar peduncles* connect the cerebellum and midbrain, the *middle cerebellar peduncles* connect cerebellum and pons, and the *inferior cerebellar peduncles* connect cerebellum and medulla oblongata.

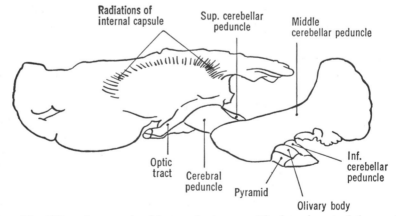

Figure 10. *Upper,* photograph of human brain stem. The lateral part of the cerebral hemisphere is removed to show the internal capsule, and the cerebellum is dissected to show its peduncles. Only a small part of the superior peduncle is visible, because it extends longitudinally on the dorsal aspect of the brain stem (see Fig. 19, p. 30). *Lower,* outline sketch of the photograph.

The cerebellum is an important organ that is concerned with various aspects of control of muscular activity.

The Ventricular System.   Figures 11 and 12 show a brain separated into right and left halves by a median cut. This cut exposes some of the *ventricles,* the adult derivatives of the cavity in the embryonic neural tube. The ventricles contain cerebrospinal fluid (Chapter 4). There is a *lateral ventricle* in the interior of each cerebral hemisphere. Each lateral ventricle joins the front end of the *third ventricle* by an *interventricular foramen.* The third ventricle is a narrow space within the diencephalon. Posteriorly it is continuous with the *cerebral aqueduct (aqueduct of Sylvius).* The aqueduct is a narrow channel within the midbrain, continuous below with the *fourth ventricle,* between the cerebellum behind, and pons and medulla oblongata in front. The fourth ventricle continues below into a narrow channel, the *central canal,* which is present in the lower part of the medulla oblongata and throughout the length of the spinal cord.

Below the cerebellum, the fourth ventricle is roofed by a thin membrane in which there is an opening, the *median aperture,* by means of which the ventricle communicates with the subarachnoid space. A *lateral aperture* on each side also provides a communication between the fourth ventricle and the subarachnoid space. Cerebrospinal fluid circulates through the ventricles, into the subarachnoid space (Chapter 4). In the lateral, third, and fourth ventricles there are complex tufts of small

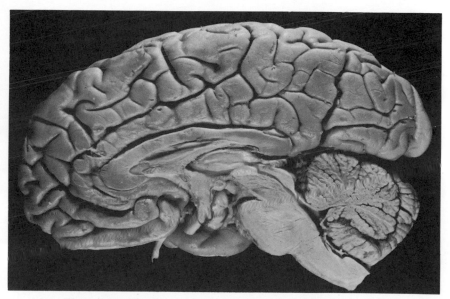

Figure 11. Photograph of a brain sectioned in the median plane.

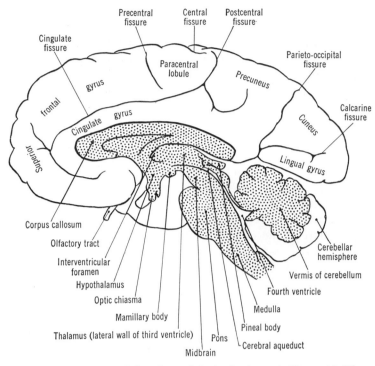

Figure 12. Sketch of the medial surface of the brain shown in Figure 11. The gyri are directly labeled, while other structures are indicated by leaders.

blood vessels, the *choroid plexuses*. These are concerned with the formation of cerebrospinal fluid and are discussed in Chapter 4.

The floor of the fourth ventricle is formed by the pons and medulla oblongata (Fig. 19). There is, in the midline, a *median sulcus*, lateral to which are various elevations. Below the lower end of the fourth ventricle are two elevations on each side of the midline, the *fasciculus gracilis* and *fasciculus cuneatus*, marking nerve tracts ascending from the spinal cord.

Gray and White Matter of the Brain. If a cerebral hemisphere is cut into slices (Figs. 13 and 14), certain structural features are evident. The surface or *cortex,* in fresh brains, is grayish in appearance, and is accordingly termed *gray matter,* in contrast to *white matter.* Gray matter is composed largely of bodies of nerve cells, whereas white matter is formed largely by processes or fibers of nerve cells. More detailed explanations of these differences are given later (p. 74). Figures 13 and 14 also show that the interior of the hemispheres is composed partly of white matter, and partly of well demarcated areas of gray matter known collectively as *basal nuclei* or *basal ganglia.* In each hemisphere,

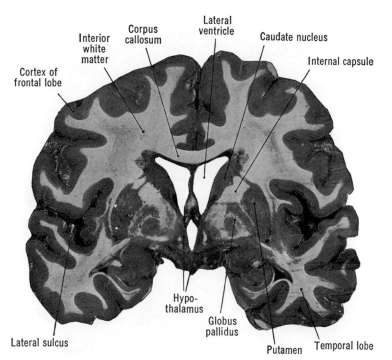

Figure 13. Photograph of a coronal slice of brain, stained by a method that colors gray matter and leaves white matter relatively unstained.

these masses of gray matter form a medial group, including the *caudate nucleus, thalamus, hypothalamus,* and the *subthalamic nucleus,* and a lateral group formed by the *lentiform nucleus* (composed of *putamen* and *globus pallidus*). These lateral and medial groups are separated by a band of white matter known as the *internal capsule.* Each internal capsule emerges from the base of the brain as a cerebral peduncle. Although technically the term basal nuclei applies to all the masses of gray matter listed, as well as several smaller masses not listed, in common usage the thalamus and hypothalamus are often excluded.

Nerve fibers in the internal capsule that connect caudate nucleus and lentiform nucleus are arranged in parallel groups so that this region has a striated appearance. Hence these structures are collectively termed the *corpus striatum.*

The thalamus and hypothalamus belong to the diencephalon, and are often included with the brain stem. Most of the other basal nuclei belong to the cerebral hemisphere, and are concerned with important aspects of motor activity and behavior (Chapter 18).

Figure 15 illustrates a slice through the midbrain. There are two masses of gray matter in an intermediate position. In the fresh condi-

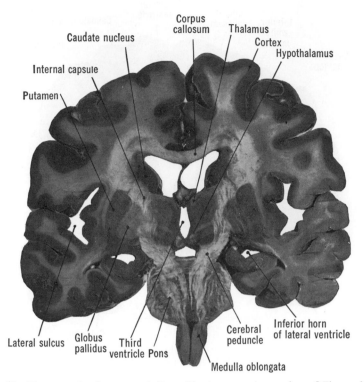

Figure 14. Photograph of a coronal slice of brain, posterior to that of Figure 13, and stained by the same method. This is in approximately the same plane and same region as the microscopic sections of Figures 147 and 148 (pp. 292, 293).

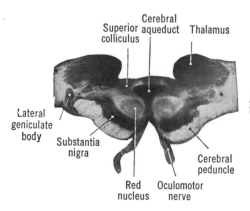

Figure 15. Horizontal slice of midbrain. Staining method as for Figure 13.

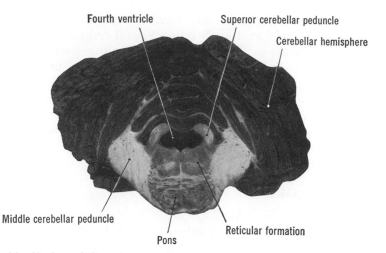

Figure 16. Horizontal slice of pons and cerebellum. Staining method as for Figure 13.

tion, they are pinkish and are accordingly named the *red nuclei.* Just in front of each nucleus, in the cerebral peduncle, is an area, *the substantia nigra,* in which the nerve cells contain a dark pigment (melanin).

Figures 16 and 17 are slices of pons and medulla oblongata. These show that white matter is found anteriorly; mixtures of white and gray

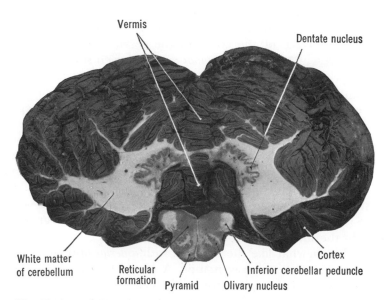

Figure 17. Horizontal slice of medulla oblongata and cerebellum. Staining method as for Figure 13.

matter, the *reticular formation,* are intermediate; and gray matter is next to cerebral aqueduct, fourth ventricle, and central canal.

The slices shown in Figures 16 and 17 include parts of the cerebellum. As is true of the cerebral cortex, the cortex of the cerebellum is composed of gray matter. The cerebellar peduncles and the interior of the cerebellum are composed of white matter. But within the interior of the cerebellum, in and near the roof of the fourth ventricle, are paired masses of gray matter, among which are the *dentate nuclei* (Fig. 17) and several others known collectively as *roof nuclei*

THE SPINAL CORD

The spinal cord does not occupy the whole length of the vertebral canal, but ends at the level of the lower part of the first lumbar vertebra or the upper part of the second. Below this level the vertebral canal is occupied by meninges, including subarachnoid space, and nerve roots. A thin, fibrous strand, the *filum terminale,* continues downward from the spinal cord as a prolongation of the pia mater. Below, it is fused with the dura and continues to the back of the coccyx.

In the midline of the spinal cord posteriorly, there is a slight longitudinal groove, the *posterior median sulcus.* A continuous series of nerves, the *dorsal roots,* enters the *posterior lateral sulcus* of the spinal cord at regular intervals (Fig. 18). A *posterior intermediate sulcus* is commonly present between the lateral and median sulci, in the upper half of the spinal cord. A variable number of small arteries and veins is present on the posterior surface of the cord. In the cervical region the arteries are usually present as a *posterior spinal artery* on each side.

Anteriorly, in the midline, the spinal cord has an *anterior median fissure,* occupied by the *anterior spinal artery,* and one or two small veins. *Ventral roots* leave at regular intervals from the anterolateral region of the spinal cord.

The spinal cord has *cervical* and *lumbar enlargements,* corresponding to the attachments of dorsal and ventral roots supplying the limbs. The collection of roots in the spinal canal below the spinal cord resembles the tail of a horse, hence the name *cauda equina* given to this collection.

A slice through any level of the spinal cord reveals a characteristic structure (Fig. 18). In contrast to the cerebral hemispheres, gray matter is found in the interior, surrounded by white matter. The gray matter is arranged somewhat like the letter H, with *anterior* and *posterior horns,* and a connecting bar of gray matter. A *lateral horn* is also present in the thoracic part of the spinal cord The central canal lies in the connecting bar. Not uncommonly, in the adult, the canal is obliterated at various levels.

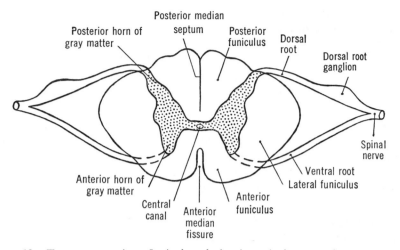

Figure 18. Transverse section of spinal cord, showing spinal roots and arrangement of white and gray matter. Note that a septum continues inward from the posterior median sulcus to divide the white matter into two posterior funiculi. Compare with Figure 134 (p. 246).

Nerve fibers leaving the anterior horns enter ventral roots. Nerve fibers of dorsal roots, entering the spinal cord at the posterior lateral sulcus, reach the posterior horns.

The white matter of the spinal cord is arranged into *funiculi.* A septum extending inward from the posterior median sulcus divides the white matter into two *posterior funiculi.* In the upper half of the spinal cord, and especially in the cervical region, a thin septum extending inward from each posterior intermediate sulcus divides each posterior funiculus into a laterally placed *fasciculus cuneatus* and a medially placed *fasciculus gracilis.* These are continuous with the corresponding fasciculi of the medulla oblongata.

Each *lateral funiculus* is the white matter between dorsal and ventral root fibers. Each *anterior funiculus* is the white matter between the ventral root fibers of that side and the anterior median fissure.

The white matter of the spinal cord contains nerve tracts connecting dorsal and ventral root fibers with various parts of the spinal cord, and with the brain. The gray matter contains cells concerned with sensory impulses, with the activity of muscles, and with the functions of various viscera, glands, and blood vessels.

SUMMARY

The central nervous system includes the brain and spinal cord. It is surrounded by the meninges, which are, from without inward, the dura mater, arachnoid, and pia mater. The subarachnoid space lies between the arachnoid and the pia mater and contains cerebrospinal fluid.

The brain includes the convoluted cerebral hemispheres, the brain stem, and the cerebellum. The hemispheres (frontal, temporal, parietal and occipital lobes) have a surface, or cortex, composed of gray matter. They contain the lateral and third ventricles, and the internal masses of gray matter known as the basal ganglia. The internal capsules lie between portions of the basal ganglia and emerge at the base of the hemispheres as the cerebral peduncles.

The brain stem is composed of diencephalon, midbrain, pons, and medulla oblongata. The cerebellum is connected to the brain stem by three pairs of peduncles. Between the cerebellum and the pons and medulla oblongata lies the fourth ventricle. The fourth ventricle communicates with the third through the cerebral aqueduct, which runs through the midbrain. The interior of the brain stem is composed of gray and white matter in varying proportions. The cerebellum has an interior of white matter and a surface of gray matter.

The spinal cord is continuous with the medulla oblongata at the foramen magnum. It terminates at the upper border of the second lumbar vertebra. Its interior gray matter is arranged like the letter H, surrounded by white matter arranged into funiculi. Ventral roots of the spinal nerves arise from the anterior horn of gray matter, and the dorsal roots terminate in the posterior horn of the gray matter. The cord is larger in the cervical and lumbar regions.

Names in Neurology

ALEXANDER MONRO (1697-1767)

In 1700, J. Monro settled in Edinburgh. At the age of 22, he became professor of anatomy, the first of a long line of distinguished anatomists. His son, Alexander Monro, followed in his father's footsteps as professor of anatomy, and it is his name that is attached to the interventricular foramina. The grandson, also named Alexander, held the same chair as professor of anatomy. The three Monros occupied this chair for a period of 126 years (1720-1846), and the first two Monros themselves taught at least 12,800 students.

SYLVIUS (also known as Jacques DeBois) (1478-1555)

Sylvius was a Parisian teacher and such a devoted follower of Galen's teachings that he would not admit the possibility of errors in Galen's descriptions, believing rather that the human body had changed since Galen's time. He named the jugular, subclavian, renal, and other blood vessels, but the cerebral aqueduct that bears his name was *not* first described by him. Galen, more than 1000 years before, had seen and described it.

REFERENCES

Detailed descriptions of the anatomy of the central nervous system are available in the textbooks cited on p. 6.

CHAPTER 3

THE PERIPHERAL
NERVOUS SYSTEM

The peripheral nervous system includes the cranial nerves, the spinal nerves with their dorsal and ventral roots and peripheral branches, and certain portions of a special division, the autonomic nervous system. The term *peripheral nerve* ordinarily refers to those nerves arising from plexuses formed by spinal nerves. This terminological distinction between spinal and peripheral nerves is important from the standpoint of differences in the distribution of these two types of nerves. These differences are discussed in the section on Spinal Nerves and Peripheral Nerves (p. 33).

A *nerve* is a collection of nerve fibers visible to the naked eye. Each fiber is so small that it cannot be seen with the naked eye, and hundreds or thousands are necessary to form a nerve. Thus, according to the number of constituent fibers, a nerve may be as large as a man's finger, or so small as to be barely visible. The nature of these fibers is discussed in Chapter 6. An idea of their function can nevertheless be introduced at this time. Each fiber in a nerve is a process of a nerve cell; a nerve cell with all its processes is termed a *neuron*. Nerve fibers conduct nerve impulses between non-nervous tissues and the central nervous system, and between various parts of the central nervous system. Those impulses that travel toward or into the central nervous system are *sensory* or *afferent;* those that leave are *motor* or *efferent*. Nearly all nerves contain both afferent and efferent fibers and are, therefore, mixed nerves.

28

Many nerves are distinguished by the presence of a local enlargement called a *ganglion*, consisting mainly of cell bodies of neurons. Ganglia associated with afferent fibers are located nearer the central nervous system than those in efferent paths. Ganglia associated with efferent fibers are always a part of the autonomic system.

CRANIAL NERVES

Cranial nerves follow complicated paths to the peripheral structures they serve. Detailed descriptions of their distributions can be found in anatomical textbooks. At this time only the general areas that they supply will be indicated. The usual method of description groups the cranial nerves into twelve pairs.

I. Olfactory Nerve. The filaments composing this nerve arise in the olfactory mucous membrane of the upper part of the nasal cavity. The fibers end in the olfactory bulb. The olfactory tract runs backward from the bulb and ends at the base of the brain near the optic chiasma (Fig. 9, p. 17). The olfactory nerve and its central connections are associated with the sense of smell (Chapter 13).

The *nervus terminalis* is a collection of nerve filaments that may be present near the olfactory bulb, descending to the mucosa of the nasal cavity. It is present in many lower forms, in which it is associated with the olfactory system. Its significance in man is obscure.

II. Optic Nerve. This nerve arises from the *retina* of the eye (p. 194). It runs posteriorly and, in joining the other optic nerve, forms the optic chiasma (Fig. 9, p. 17). Two bundles, the *optic tracts,* extend posteriorly from the chiasma, proceed around the cerebral peduncles, and end near the superior colliculi. These structures are concerned with vision (Chapter 13). The optic nerves and tracts are not true peripheral nerves, but are fiber tracts of the central nervous system, connecting the retina and the brain. The retina is a part of the central nervous system.

III. Oculomotor Nerve. After its origin from the midbrain (Fig. 15, p. 22), the oculomotor nerve runs anteriorly into the orbit, where it ends in muscles that attach to the eyeball and move it in various directions. A portion of the nerve is distributed to certain smooth muscles within the eye.

IV. Trochlear Nerve. The trochlear nerve is a bundle of fibers that arises from the back of the midbrain, around which it winds to run anteriorly into the orbit (Fig. 19). Here it ends in a single muscle attached to the eyeball.

V. Trigeminal Nerve. The trigeminal nerve has a *motor* and a

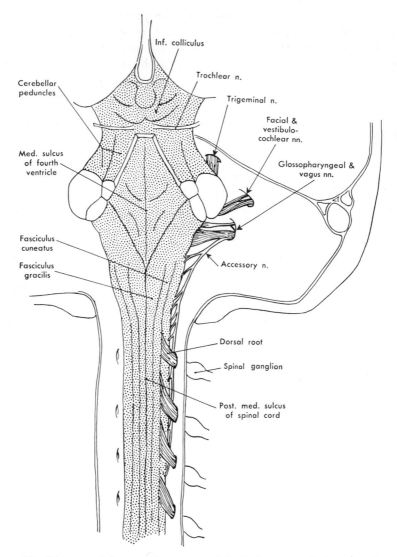

Figure 19. Diagram of the posterior aspect of the brain stem, spinal cord, and certain cranial and spinal nerves. The cerebellum has been removed to expose the floor of the fourth ventricle. The glossopharyngeal, vagus, and accessory nerves leave the skull through the same foramen (jugular foramen). The upper one or two filaments constitute the glossopharyngeal nerve.

sensory root, both attached to the side of the pons. Near the pons, the sensory root has an enlargement, the *trigeminal,* or semilunar, *ganglion,* from which three large branches arise to be distributed to the muscles of mastication, to the skin of the face and part of the scalp, to the mucous membrane of the mouth and nasal cavity, to the eye (especially the cornea), to the teeth, and to the dura mater. The motor root joins the branch which is distributed to the muscles of mastication.

VI. Abducent Nerve.   The abducent nerve arises from the front of the pons, just above its junction with the medulla oblongata (Fig. 7, p. 15). It enters the orbit, where it supplies a single muscle attached to the eyeball.

VII. Facial Nerve.   This nerve is attached laterally, just at the junction of the pons and medulla oblongata (Fig. 7, p. 15). Its main distribution is to the muscles of expression (the facial muscles), located around the mouth, nose and eyes, and on the forehead and scalp. Some fibers are also distributed to the mucous membrane of the anterior two-thirds of the tongue (for taste), and some to certain of the salivary glands and to the lacrimal gland. The *geniculate ganglion* is found on the nerve in its course through the skull.

VIII. Vestibulocochlear Nerve.   Formerly called auditory or acoustic, the new term better reflects its function, but for simplicity it can be called the *eighth nerve.* It is attached, laterally, at the junction of the pons and medulla oblongata (Figs. 19 and 118, p. 208). It has *cochlear* and *vestibular* divisions, each of which arises in the inner ear. Each has a small ganglion along its course in the inner ear, called *spiral* and *vestibular ganglia,* respectively. These nerves are associated with the sense of hearing and of balance or equilibrium.

IX. Glossopharyngeal Nerve.   This nerve is closely associated with, and hard to distinguish from, the vagus nerve. There is a series of nerve rootlets attached to the lateral surface of the medulla oblongata (Fig. 19). The upper one or two of these rootlets form the glossopharyngeal nerve, which supplies the mucous membrane and a muscle of the throat (pharynx), a salivary gland, and the mucous membrane of the posterior third of the tongue (for taste). There are two ganglia along its course, the *superior* and the *inferior.*

X. Vagus Nerve.   The majority of the rootlets just mentioned form the vagus nerve, which supplies the mucous membrane of the pharynx and larynx and also the muscles of these organs. In addition, it has a complex distribution to viscera in the thorax and abdomen. It has two main ganglia, the *superior* and the *inferior,* which are found on the nerve within and just below its foramen of exit. The position of the vagus is shown in Figure 19.

XI. Accessory Nerve.   The lower of the nerve rootlets from the medulla oblongata joins others which have ascended through the foramen magnum from the cervical spinal cord. The accessory nerve formed by this mingling of fibers (Fig. 19) then divides. One division, which is composed of fibers arising from the medulla oblongata, joins the vagus nerve and is distributed with it to the muscles of pharynx and larynx. The other division, which is composed of fibers arising from the spinal cord, ultimately supplies two muscles, the *trapezius* and the *sterno-cleidomastoid.*

XII. Hypoglossal Nerve. This nerve is formed from a number of rootlets attached to the ventrolateral surface of the medulla oblongata, between the pyramid and olive. It supplies the muscles of the tongue.

SPINAL ROOTS AND SPINAL NERVES

Ordinarily a pair of dorsal roots and a pair of ventral roots can be traced to the foramina between adjacent vertebrae. Near or in each fora-men is an ovoid swelling of each dorsal root, the *spinal ganglion.* Just beyond the ganglion, each dorsal root is joined by the corresponding ventral root. The spinal nerve formed by this junction then makes its

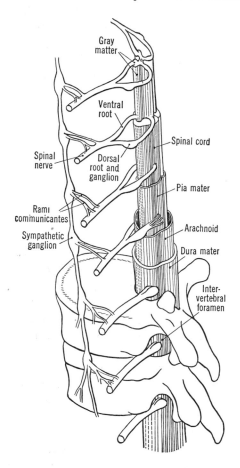

Figure 20. The spinal cord and me-ninges within the vertebral canal. The rami communicantes join the ventral rami of spinal nerves. The dorsal rami are not shown.

exit through the foramen. The first pair of spinal nerves leaves between the first cervical vertebra and the base of the skull; consequently the remaining cervical spinal nerves leave above the corresponding vertebrae, with the exception of the eighth cervical nerve. Since there are but seven cervical vertebrae, the eighth nerve leaves above the first thoracic vertebra. Below this level the spinal nerves leave below the corresponding vertebrae. There are, then, seven cervical vertebrae and eight pairs of cervical spinal nerves; twelve thoracic vertebrae and twelve pairs of thoracic nerves; five lumbar vertebrae and five pairs of lumbar nerves; one sacrum but five pairs of sacral nerves, because embryologically there are five sacral vertebrae; and for the coccyx, usually one pair of coccygeal nerves. The remainder, if any, are rudimentary. The part of the spinal cord from which a pair of spinal nerves arises is sometimes called a segment (first thoracic nerves from first thoracic segment), mainly because of correspondence with the segmented vertebral column.

The nerve fibers in the dorsal roots carry afferent impulses to the spinal cord, while those of the ventral roots carry efferent impulses away from the spinal cord. The spinal nerves, because they are formed by dorsal and ventral roots, are mixed nerves, and carry both types of impulses.

SPINAL NERVES AND PERIPHERAL NERVES

The spinal cord may be regarded as segmented, with one pair of spinal nerves for each segment. In the distribution of spinal nerves to the body this segmentation is more or less retained, in spite of the fact that in the brachial and lumbosacral regions the spinal nerves enter into complicated *plexuses*.

After leaving the intervertebral foramen, each spinal nerve divides into a dorsal and ventral ramus (Fig. 21). These are not distributed haphazardly, but in a fairly definite pattern over the body.

Distribution of the Dorsal Rami. These branches supply the muscles of the back, and the skin of the back in the areas indicated in Figure 22.

Distribution of the Ventral Rami. The ventral rami of the first four cervical nerves supply the muscles of the front of the neck: those, for instance, which bend the head forward and turn it to one side or the other. Branches also supply the skin areas indicated in Figure 22.

The ventral rami of the last four cervical nerves, and a part of the ventral ramus of the first thoracic nerve, form the *brachial plexus* by a series of communicating branches (Fig. 23). Peripheral nerves emerge

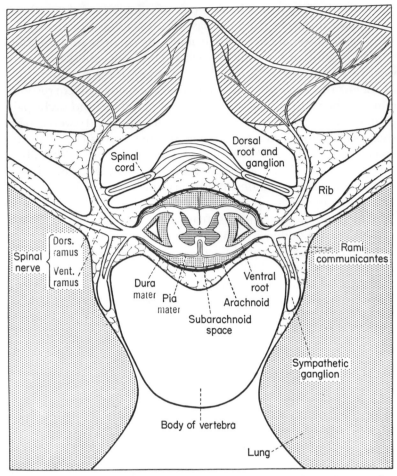

Figure 21. Drawing of a horizontal section of the spinal cord, meninges and spinal nerves.

from this plexus and supply the skin and muscles of the shoulder and upper limb.*

It might be supposed that spinal nerves would lose their identity in this or in any plexus. As a matter of fact, the spinal nerves are still distributed in a segmental manner, and this is particularly true for the innervation of skin. That is to say, the upper spinal nerves entering the brachial plexus eventually supply the lateral part of the upper limb, while the lower spinal nerves supply the medial part. The distribution

---

*Those who are interested in the names of these nerves, their course and distribution, should refer to the textbooks cited on page 6.

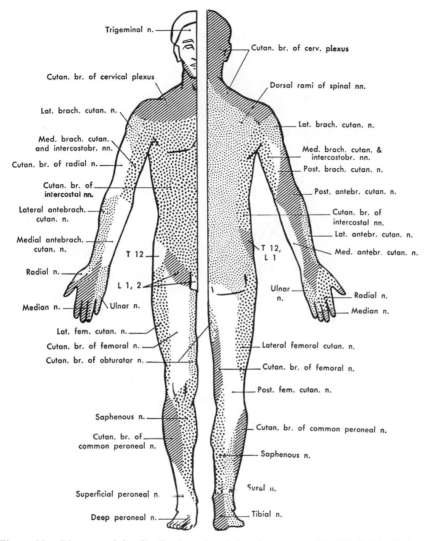

Trigeminal n.

Cutan. br. of cerv. plexus

Cutan. br. of cervical plexus

Dorsal rami of spinal nn.

Lat. brach. cutan. n.

Lat. brach. cutan. n.

Med. brach. cutan. and intercostobr. nn.

Med. brach. cutan. & intercostobr. nn.

Cutan. br. of radial n.

Post. brach. cutan. n.

Cutan. br. of intercostal nn.

Post. antebr. cutan. n.

Lateral antebrach. cutan. n.

Cutan. br. of intercostal nn.

Medial antebrach. cutan. n.

Lat. antebr. cutan. n.

T 12

Med. antebr. cutan. n.

Radial n.

T 12, L 1

L 1, 2

Ulnar n.

Median n.

Ulnar n.

Radial n.

Median n.

Lat. fem. cutan. n.

Cutan. br. of femoral n.

Lateral femoral cutan. n.

Cutan. br. of obturator n.

Cutan. br. of femoral n.

Post. fem. cutan. n.

Saphenous n.

Cutan. br. of common peroneal n.

Cutan. br. of common peroneal n.

Saphenous n.

Superficial peroneal n.

Sural n.

Deep peroneal n.

Tibial n.

Figure 22. Diagram of the distribution of peripheral nerves to skin. The left half of the figure represents the anterior surface of the body, the right half the posterior. Note the differences between this type of distribution and that illustrated for spinal nerves in Figure 24. Only in the trunk are the patterns similar. The skin of the trunk is supplied segmentally by intercostal and subcostal nerves, by cutaneous branches of the lumbar plexus and by dorsal rami of spinal nerves.

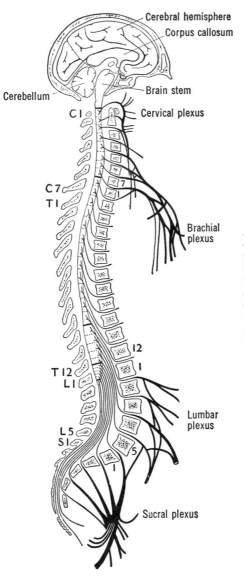

Cerebral hemisphere

Corpus callosum

Brain stem

Cerebellum

C I   Cervical plexus

C 7

T I

Brachial plexus

12

I

T 12

L I

Lumbar plexus

L 5

S I

5

Sacral plexus

Figure 23. Drawing of the brain and cord in situ. The brain is shown in the median plane (see Fig. 11, p. 19). Although not illustrated, the first cervical vertebra articulates with the base of the skull. The letters along the vertebral column indicate cervical, thoracic, lumbar, and sacral. Note that the cord ends at the upper border of the second lumbar vertebra.

is shown in Figure 24. This segmental supply cannot be determined accurately by dissection because the fibers from the spinal nerves are too intermingled in the plexus. It has been possible, however, to trace their ultimate distribution only by noting specific effects after disease, surgical operation, and animal experiments in which specific spinal nerves are destroyed. It is on the findings by such methods that the distribution shown in Figure 24 is based. This figure also indicates that the areas supplied by peripheral nerves (see Fig. 22) are usually quite different, except in the thorax and abdomen, from the areas supplied by spinal nerves. The differences are illustrated in Figure 25, which shows that any one spinal nerve may contribute to several peripheral nerves, and that any one peripheral nerve may carry fibers from several spinal nerves. Such distinctions are of the utmost importance in determining the location of neurological disorders affecting these structures. There is, however, considerable overlap between sensory nerve distribution. The area which any one spinal or peripheral nerve supplies overlaps into the area supplied by its neighbor. When a nerve is cut or otherwise destroyed, the area in which function is completely lost is smaller than the area to which the nerve is distributed.

The ventral rami of the first eleven thoracic nerves form *intercostal nerves*. These, together with the *subcostal nerve*, which is the ventral ramus of the twelfth thoracic nerve, and certain branches of the ventral rami of the upper lumbar nerves, supply the skin and muscles of the thorax and abdomen. The nerves do not form plexuses, but, instead, remain separate so that their segmental distribution is quite apparent.

The ventral rami of the remaining lumbar and the sacral nerves unite to form the *lumbar, sacral,* and *pudendal plexuses* (Fig. 23), from which peripheral nerves arise to supply the skin and muscles of the pelvis, hip region, and lower limbs. Here, again, Figure 24 illustrates the segmental nature of the spinal nerves in contrast to the peripheral nerves (Fig. 22).

The Segmental Supply of Muscles.   Segmental distribution is less apparent in muscles than in skin because muscles, as they form in the embryo and fetus, may migrate some distance from their place of origin. For instance, the diaphragm, which separates the thoracic and abdominal cavities, was originally formed in part in the cervical region. It later descends, but, in so doing, carries along its nerve supply from the cervical spinal cord. The complex nerve supply of many other muscles results from their development in areas supplied by two or more spinal nerves. There is, nevertheless, a craniocaudal sequence in that the distal parts of limbs are supplied by more caudally situated spinal nerves. For example, muscles of the shoulder are largely supplied by the cervical nerves of the brachial plexus, whereas the muscles of the hand are

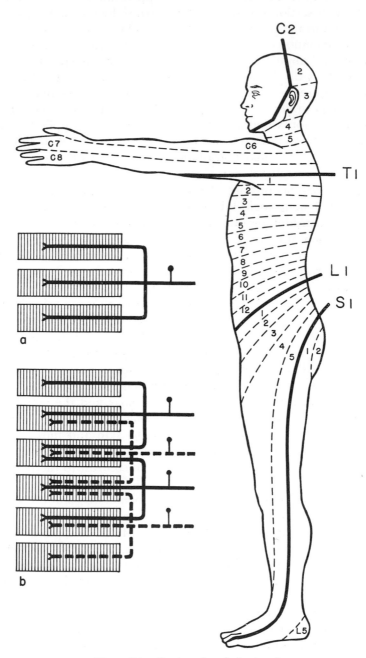

Figure 24.   *(See legend on facing page.)*

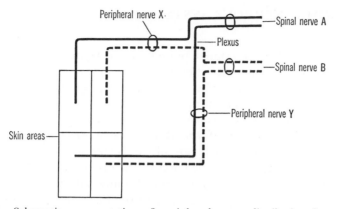

Figure 25. Schematic representation of peripheral nerve distribution from a plexus formed by spinal nerves. Spinal nerve *A* enters a plexus and reaches a different area of skin by way of peripheral nerves *X* and *Y*. Spinal nerve *B* also enters the plexus and reaches a different area of skin by way of peripheral nerves *X* and *Y*. Peripheral nerves *X* and *Y*, therefore, each contain parts of the two spinal nerves.

mainly supplied by the first thoracic spinal nerve. Since most muscles are supplied by two or more spinal nerves, section of one such nerve will result in weakness, not total paralysis, of a muscle.

Differences Between Cranial and Spinal Nerves. Cranial nerves are attached to the brain at irregular rather than regular intervals. Although not apparent by gross examination, the optic nerves are not true peripheral nerves, but are extensions of brain substance. Cranial nerves are not formed of dorsal and ventral roots; as a consequence, there is a marked variation in afferent and efferent components between them. Some cranial nerves have more than one ganglion, while others have none. There are other marked differences which, however, cannot be discussed until certain functional aspects are considered in subsequent chapters.

Figure 24. Schematic representation of the distribution of spinal nerves to skin. Each numbered zone refers to an area of skin supplied by the spinal nerve of the corresponding number. The letters refer to cervical, thoracic, lumbar and sacral. Thus, the zones between C 2 and T 1 are supplied by cervical nerves. The first cervical nerve rarely gives any significant supply to skin. Skin above C 2 is supplied by the trigeminal nerve. The diagram does not show variation or overlap. The latter is illustrated in *a* and *b*, showing, for example, that in the trunk region each spinal nerve sends branches to at least three segmental areas of skin *(a)*, and each area has branches from at least three spinal nerves *(b)*. Therefore, if a single spinal nerve is cut, the area it supplies will still receive fibers from adjacent nerves. Sensation will be diminished but not lost. The difficulties of accurately determining spinal nerve distribution in man are illustrated by the fact that this diagram, which is based on data from J. J. Keegan and F. D. Garrett, Anat. Rec., *102*:409-437, 1948, differs in many ways, particularly with respect to the neck and upper limb, from those of O. Foerster, Brain, *56*:1-39, 1933.

AUTONOMIC NERVOUS SYSTEM

Some branches of cranial nerves and certain branches of many spinal nerves contain motor fibers that supply viscera in the thorax, abdomen and pelvis, and most of the glands and blood vessels in the body. These special fibers supplying visceral structures comprise the peripheral portions of the *autonomic nervous system* (p. 228).

Sympathetic Division of the Autonomic Nervous System. There is a long nerve trunk on each side of the vertebral bodies that extends from the base of the skull to the coccyx. Each is known as the *sympathetic trunk.* Ganglia are present at fairly regular intervals along these trunks. Three or more pairs of ganglia occur in the neck, usually ten to twelve in the thorax, and a variable number of pairs in the abdomen and pelvis. Branches of the trunks are distributed to the organs of these areas and form extensive plexuses. Ganglia also occur in the plexuses, and in the abdomen have been given the name *celiac, mesenteric, splanchnic, renal, phrenic,* and *aorticorenal.* They are of the same structure and function as those in the sympathetic trunks.

Branches to and from the sympathetic trunks connect the trunks with each spinal nerve just after it emerges from the intervertebral foramen. These branches are called *rami communicantes* (Figs. 20 and 21).

The sympathetic trunks, their connections with the rest of the nervous system, and their branches to viscera constitute the sympathetic, or thoracolumbar, division of the autonomic nervous system.

Parasympathetic Division of the Autonomic Nervous System. Part of this division includes those cranial nerves supplying visceral structures. These are the oculomotor, facial, glossopharyngeal, vagus, and accessory nerves. There is also a sacral portion composed of branches of the second and third (sometimes third and fourth) sacral nerves that supply viscera in the pelvis. Numerous ganglia occur in the parasympathetic division, but are not located in a definite trunk. Instead, they are scattered, being found in or near the organs supplied.

During the course of their distribution, sympathetic and parasympathetic fibers become intermingled. This is especially true in the thorax and abdomen, where branches of the sympathetic trunks and of the vagus nerves cannot be easily separated by dissection.

SUMMARY

Attached to the base of the brain and to the brain stem are twelve pairs of cranial nerves, which have complex distributions to cranial,

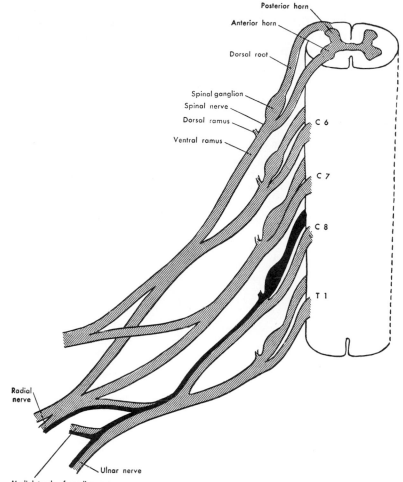

Figure 26. Diagram of the manner in which dorsal and ventral roots form spinal nerves, which in turn form a plexus (brachial). C 6, sixth cervical segment of the spinal cord, etc. Also shown is the fact that sensory fibers from a single dorsal root (C 8, solid black) may be distributed in several peripheral nerves. Many branches of the plexus are not shown.

cervical, thoracic, and abdominal structures.

Thirty-one pairs of dorsal and ventral roots are attached to the spinal cord at regular intervals. Each dorsal root joins the ventral root of the corresponding side and from the same cord segment to form a spinal nerve. Each spinal nerve leaves the vertebral canal and divides into a dorsal and a ventral ramus. The dorsal rami supply the skin and muscles of the back. Ventral rami supply the limbs and the sides and front of the body. In the cervical, brachial, lumbar, and sacral regions they enter into plexuses.

Certain branches of spinal nerves, plus sympathetic trunks and associated ganglia, supply motor fibers to viscera, and constitute the sympathetic division of the autonomic nervous system. Branches of certain of the cranial nerves, plus branches of the second and third sacral nerves to the pelvis, form the parasympathetic division.

REFERENCES

The textbooks cited on p. 6 contain descriptions of the anatomy of the peripheral nervous system and also contain sections dealing with the segmental distribution of spinal nerves and the anatomy of the autonomic system.

CHAPTER 4

BLOOD SUPPLY AND CEREBROSPINAL FLUID

The blood vascular system is designed to bring blood to or away from the *capillaries*. All exchanges between blood and cells take place through the walls of these tiny vessels. The arteries, which proceed from the heart, distribute blood to various large regions of the body. The smallest of the arteries *(arterioles)* are highly contractile and are thus able to regulate the amount of blood entering a given region or organ. The capillaries themselves may also open or close and thus affect the amount of blood circulating in an area. From the capillaries, blood enters small vessels, the *venules*. These in turn form larger vessels, the veins, by which the blood is ultimately returned to the heart. The number of capillaries in the body is so great that, if all were open at once, there would not be enough blood to fill them In any given structure, such as a muscle, most capillaries are closed except during marked activity. In certain parts of the body, notably skin and intestine, direct anastomoses between arterioles and venules are common. These *arterio-venous anastomoses* bypass the capillary circulation. If open, they shunt blood past a given capillary network and thereby prevent exchange from occurring or, in the case of skin, prevent cooling of the blood.

The blood vessels supplying the nervous system form an extensive capillary bed, especially in gray matter such as the cerebral cortex. A significant part of the oxygen used by the body is for the metabolism of the brain. Here, the oxygen is chiefly for the oxidation of glucose

43

for energy. The utilization rate is high and oxygen lack can occur quickly. A few minutes' deprivation of blood suffices to kill some portions of the nervous system.

BLOOD SUPPLY OF THE NERVOUS SYSTEM

Blood Supply of the Brain. The blood supply of the cranial cavity is derived from two pairs of arteries in the neck. These are the *common carotid* and the *vertebral arteries.*

The common carotid arteries ascend in the neck; below the base of the skull, each divides into an *external* and an *internal carotid artery,* certain branches of which supply cranial structures. Each internal carotid artery enters the cranial cavity through a canal in the base of the skull, emerges alongside the optic chiasma and divides into an *anterior* and a

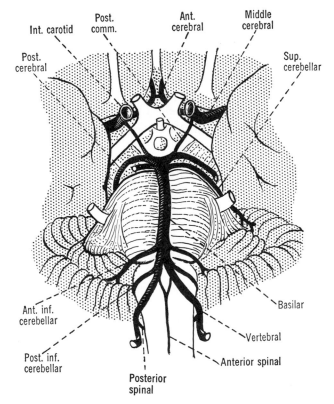

Figure 27. Drawing of the arterial circle at the base of the brain. All small branches and ramifications of various larger branches have been omitted. The anterior communicating artery is not labeled.

middle cerebral artery. The two anterior cerebral arteries are united by a small communicating branch.

The vertebral arteries ascend in foramina in the transverse processes of the cervical vertebrae and enter the cranial cavity through the foramen magnum. On the ventral surface of the medulla oblongata, they join to form a single arterial stem, the *basilar artery.* This artery ascends in front of the brain stem and ends by dividing into two *posterior cerebral arteries.* Each of these is joined to the corresponding internal carotid artery by a communicating branch. The various branches at the base of the brain thus form an *arterial circle, the circle of Willis* (p. 54). The arrangement of this circle and the branches issuing from it are illustrated in Figure 27. The cerebral arteries are distributed to those areas of the brain indicated in Figure 28, and to the interior and medial surface as well. The arterial circle may serve as an anastomotic channel if one of its component or contributing arteries is occluded.

As shown in Figure 29, all vessels lie in the subarachnoid space before entering brain substance. After repeated branchings the arteries form capillaries. The veins arising from the capillaries return to the sub-

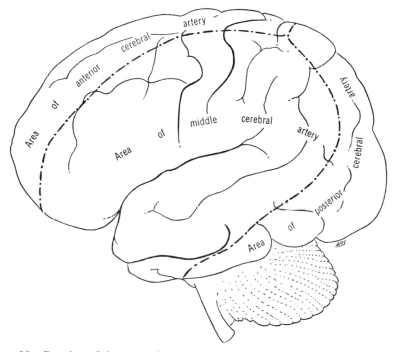

Figure 28. Drawing of the approximate areas on the lateral surface of the hemisphere supplied by the cerebral arteries. The brain stem and cerebellum are supplied by the vertebral and basilar arteries.

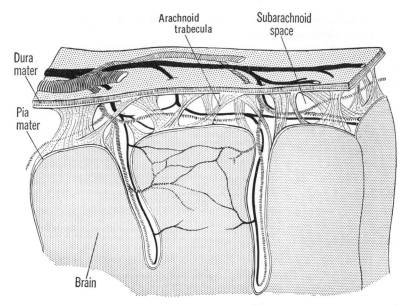

Figure 29. Schematic representation of meninges, blood vessels and nervous tissue. Arteries (black) and veins are shown as they pierce the dura mater and run in the subarachnoid space, which is filled with cerebrospinal fluid. Blood vessels that enter the brain are ensheathed by a prolongation of the pia mater. The subarachnoid space is prolonged for a short distance along the larger vessels.

arachnoid space and eventually empty chiefly into the dural sinuses. These in turn empty into the internal jugular veins by which the blood returns to the heart.

The brain stem receives its blood supply from the basilar artery as that vessel ascends on its ventral surface. The cerebellum receives branches from the vertebral arteries as well as from the basilar.

Blood Supply of the Meninges (Dura Mater). The main blood supply of the dura mater is by the middle meningeal branches of the external carotid arteries. Each ascends through a foramen in the base of the skull and then lies between the dura mater and the skull. Their special importance is that they may be torn or otherwise damaged in skull injuries. In such cases there is severe bleeding which, because it occurs between the dura mater and the skull, is known as extradural or epidural hemorrhage, and which may cause severe symptoms because of pressure on the brain.

Blood Supply of the Spinal Cord, Spinal Roots, and Spinal Nerves. An anterior spinal artery arises from each vertebral artery (Fig. 27). The two arteries join and form a single artery that descends in the anterior median fissure of the spinal cord. It is reinforced by medullary branches, which join it at irregular intervals, and it gives branches to the anterior part of the spinal cord (Fig. 30).

A posterior spinal artery arises from each vertebral artery (Fig. 30). Each descends along the posterior aspect of the spinal cord, and each usually breaks up into plexiform channels in the lower part of the spinal cord.

The various arteries also give rise to small branches that form a plexus on the surface of the spinal cord.

The spinal branches (Fig. 30) that traverse the intervertebral foramina and give rise to radicular and medullary branches are derived from the vertebral and other arteries in the neck, from the posterior intercostal arteries in the thorax, and from the lumbar and lateral sacral arteries in the abdomen and pelvis.

Blood is returned by veins that tend to follow the same course as do the arteries.

Blood Supply of the Peripheral Nerves. This involves more detail than can be given here. In general, each nerve receives branches from the arteries in each of the different regions through which the nerve runs. For example, the sciatic nerve with its branches extends from the sacrum to the toes. In so doing it receives blood from an artery in the pelvis, in the thigh, in the back of the knee, in the calf of the leg, and in the ankle and foot.

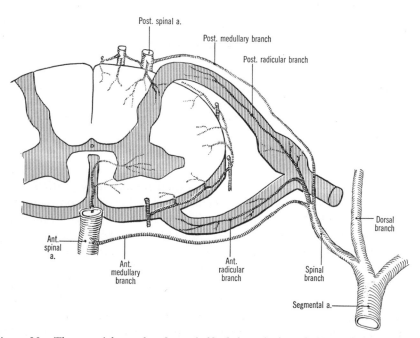

Figure 30. The arterial supply of one half of the spinal cord. Most of the extensive branching within the substance of the cord has been omitted. Note that two posterior spinal arteries are present (only one is labeled).

Cerebral Blood Flow.   There are many ways to study blood flow to the brain, but few of those that can be used on human beings give any direct information. Among techniques that have proved useful, however, are direct observation of the retina, comparison of gas tensions in the venous blood with those in the arterial blood, and measurement of the concentration of inhaled nitrous oxide in arterial and venous blood, the difference being inversely related to blood flow. Dye dilution techniques can be used, as can electromagnetic flowmeters. However, oxygen uptake is not necessarily directly related to blood flow, and to an increasing degree investigators are devising ways of measuring events on and within the brain, even in man. These include, for example, determinations of pH, oxygen tension, and concentrations of certain electrolytes.

In general, the factors that affect and control the systemic circulation also affect and control the circulation to the brain. What is of clinical importance is the degree to which local changes may occur. Experimental studies of blood vessels on the surface of the brain indicate that they are relatively unaffected by vasomotor impulses from the autonomic system. Rather, they respond more to changes in gas tensions, increasing in diameter as carbon dioxide tension increases, and decreasing in diameter as oxygen tension increases. The magnitude of these changes is not known with certainty.

CLINICAL IMPORTANCE OF BLOOD SUPPLY

The nervous system is frequently affected by derangements of its blood supply. The results are more or less familiar to all under the lay terms "stroke" or "apoplexy." These terms, however, cover a multitude of events.

Arteries larger than about half a millimeter in diameter may be affected by *atherosclerosis,* a degenerative process affecting the inner lining of the vessels. The thickening which results may partially close the lumen of a vessel, and this occlusion may become complete by a clotting of blood. This is known as a *thrombosis.* In such instances the area of the nervous system deprived of its blood supply degenerates and softens. If the portion of the nervous system so affected is an important one, the results may be severe and even fatal.

Arteries smaller than half a millimeter in diameter, that is to say, arterioles, are not affected by atherosclerosis, but instead by *arteriolosclerosis,* which is a diffuse thickening of the entire vessel wall. If, as a result, the vessels become partially occluded, resistance to blood flow increases and blood pressure rises (hypertension). Vessels damaged by various disorders may rupture, and the consequence is an *intracerebral hemorrhage.*

There is a significant body of evidence which shows that local spasm or changes in intracranial vessels may produce temporary anoxia of a part of the brain. Furthermore, it is well known that movements of the neck may temporarily occlude the carotid or vertebral arteries, if these vessels are already narrowed by atherosclerotic changes. Such occlusion may cause temporary neurological symptoms.

Angiography. Among the procedures used to diagnose neurological disorders such as strokes and tumors, *angiography* is an increasingly important one. Blood vessels are visualized by injecting a radiopaque compound into an artery in the neck or arm and x-raying the head as the material circulates through the cranial vessels. The method can detect abnormalities in vascular patterns, interruptions or blocks of

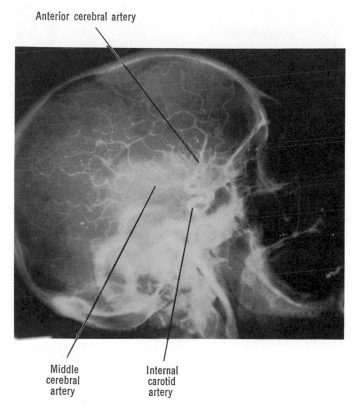

Anterior cerebral artery

Middle cerebral artery

Internal carotid artery

Figure 31. Angiogram taken by injecting a radiopaque material into the common carotid artery, and x-ray photograph taken as the material circulated through the arterial system. The internal carotid, middle cerebral and anterior cerebral arteries are visualized. (Courtesy of Drs. E. S. Gurdjian and J. E. Webster.)

Basilar artery   Posterior cerebral artery

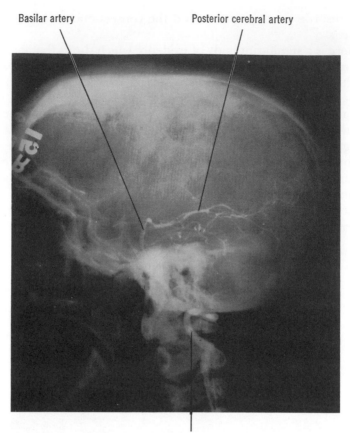

Vertebral artery

Figure 32. Angiogram taken by injecting a radiopaque material into a vertebral artery. One of the vertebral arteries is visible, as is the basilar artery and several of its branches, including superior cerebellar and posterior cerebral. (Courtesy of Drs. E. S. Gurdjian and J. E. Webster.)

blood flow, and shifts in position of blood vessels. Figures 31 and 32 illustrate some angiograms.

FORMATION AND CIRCULATION OF CEREBROSPINAL FLUID

Cerebrospinal fluid is a clear, colorless fluid, only slightly heavier than water, which fills the ventricles and subarachnoid space. Plasma, by comparison, is viscous and opalescent. The differences result from the relatively high concentration of proteins in the plasma. In recent years, particularly with the aid of radioisotopes, precise studies have been made of the distribution of a number of ions and nonelectrolytes between cerebrospinal fluid and plasma. The studies clearly show that cerebrospinal fluid is not a simple filtrate or dialysate of blood plasma. The fluid has higher sodium, chloride and magnesium ion concentrations, whereas the concentrations of potassium, calcium, urea, and glucose are lower. Thus cerebrospinal fluid is a secretion, and the question then is to discover what is responsible for the secretion.

The ventricles are lined by a thin, epithelial membrane, the *ependyma*. In certain regions of the lateral, third, and fourth ventricles, the ependymal cells, together with blood vessels and pia mater, form the choroid plexuses (Fig. 33). These may be considered as consisting of a sheet of epithelial cells separating the blood vessels from the ventricular cavity. Many studies, in particular those involving perfusion between ventricles and the subarachnoid space, have shown that cerebrospinal fluid is produced in the lateral ventricles. The bulk of evidence indicates that it is secreted by the choroid plexuses of the ventricle, although there may be some contribution by diffusion across the remaining ventricular ependyma.

When a substance such as glucose is injected into the blood, it escapes rapidly into the surrounding tissues. However, it is much longer before it appears in the cerebrospinal fluid, and equilibration may take hours. Hence it seems that there is a barrier—the *blood–cerebrospinal fluid barrier*—between the blood and the cerebrospinal fluid. This barrier is probably chiefly in the choroid plexuses, and its presence supports the secretory theory.

It is also important that a *blood-brain barrier* exists. For example, material injected into the blood may fail to pass into the brain, whereas when injected into the cerebrospinal fluid it may enter the brain readily. This barrier is at the capillary in the brain, either its endothelium or the surrounding glial end-feet, or both. The ready entrances of substances into the brain from cerebrospinal fluid indicates the presence of an extracellular space (see p. 68).

Cerebrospinal fluid circulates through the ventricles, from lateral to third to fourth. It enters the subarachnoid space through the median and lateral apertures of the fourth ventricle. It then circulates around the brain and spinal cord and is absorbed into the venous blood. This occurs chiefly through small tufts or villi of arachnoid tissue which project into the dural venous sinuses (Fig. 33). Villi are also found with the veins just external to the spinal dura mater, and absorption may occur here. It is also possible that some fluid may seep along cranial and spinal nerves to be absorbed by tissue lymphatics.

The rate of formation and flow of cerebrospinal fluid are influenced by the metabolism of the brain, the hydrodynamics of blood flow, and blood osmotic pressure. The effect of blood hydrodynamics may be shown by a maneuver during the measurement of fluid pressure at *lumbar puncture*. If both internal jugular veins are compressed manually in the neck, there is shortly a prompt rise in the pressure of cerebro-spinal fluid, because the venous occlusion prevents blood from leaving the cranial cavity. Venous pressure promptly rises, and the gradient decreases. Since arterial blood continues to enter the cranial cavity, the only result can be a general increase in cerebrospinal fluid pressure.

By thrusting a lumbar puncture needle between the third and fourth lumbar vertebrae into the subarachnoid space, the pressure of the cerebrospinal fluid can be measured by an attached manometer. Figure 33 shows that, since the spinal cord ends above this level, there is no danger of injuring it by such a lumbar puncture. In the horizontal or recumbent position, cerebrospinal fluid pressure ordinarily amounts to 10 to 20 mm. of mercury (approximately 100 to 200 mm. of water) at the level of the lumbar puncture. The lumbar pressure is higher in the erect position. Abnormal conditions, such as the growth of a tu-mor, by obstructing circulation, may cause the total intracranial pres-sure to rise to 400 or more mm. of water. Cerebrospinal fluid may also be withdrawn through the needle and examined for bacteria, cells, or chemical compounds not normally present. The fluid may be tested for various serological reactions, such as tests for syphilis. Fluid that is with-drawn may be replaced by air, or by an opaque oil. Since the air or oil may be detected by x-ray photography, the position of a mass, such as a tumor, that may interfere with normal cerebrospinal fluid dynamics may be determined. Anesthetics, such as procaine, may also be intro-duced for spinal anesthesia.

Air may also be introduced into ventricles by means of a needle thrust through the brain into the ventricles after a small hole is drilled in the skull cap. A *ventriculogram* is a radiogram of ventricles filled with air. The subarachnoid space of the cranial cavity may be visualized by air introduced at lumbar puncture (*pneumoencephalography*). Such air as-cends and enters the ventricular system through the fourth ventricle.

The final question relates to the function of cerebrospinal fluid. The brain and spinal cord are surrounded by the fluid, which cushions them and minimizes damage that might otherwise result from blows to the head and spine. Whether the fluid has a significant role in nutri-tion of the brain or in the transfer of substances resulting from metabolic activity of the brain and spinal cord remains an unsettled question.

CLINICAL IMPORTANCE OF CEREBROSPINAL FLUID

The composition and hydrodynamics of cerebrospinal fluid are important from a clinical standpoint. Infections and metabolic dis-

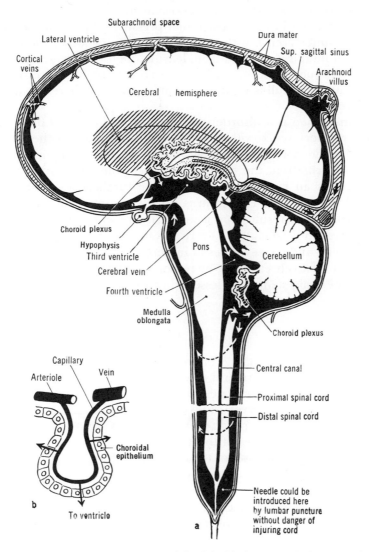

Cerebral hemisphere

Subarachnoid space
Lateral ventricle
Dura mater
Sup. sagittal sinus
Cortical veins
Arachnoid villus
Choroid plexus
Hypophysis
Third ventricle
Pons
Cerebellum
Cerebral vein
Fourth ventricle
Medulla oblongata
Choroid plexus
Capillary
Vein
Arteriole
Central canal
Proximal spinal cord
Distal spinal cord
Choroidal epithelium
b
To ventricle
a
Needle could be introduced here by lumbar puncture without danger of injuring cord

Figure 33. *a,* Circulation of cerebrospinal fluid (in black); arrows indicate the direction of circulation. The drawing represents a median section of the nervous system and therefore shows third ventricle, cerebral aqueduct, fourth ventricle, and central canal, with the approximate size and location of one of the lateral ventricles indicated by oblique lines. Note the aperture in the fourth ventricle by which fluid reaches the subarachnoid space. Note also one of the arachnoid villi through which fluid enters venous blood in a dural sinus. *b,* Fundamental plan of choroid plexuses. Cerebrospinal fluid is formed from blood plasma and passes through choroidal epithelium into the ventricular space. (Modified from A. T. Rasmussen: The Principal Nervous Pathways, 3rd ed. Macmillan Company, 1945.)

orders, for example, may cause significant changes in content and composition. As mentioned above, abnormal masses such as tumors may cause an increase in total intracranial pressure. When this occurs, it is because of interference with circulation or absorption of the fluid. For instance, if fluid is prevented from leaving the fourth ventricle, it nevertheless continues to be formed and cerebrospinal fluid pressure rises. In the adult the skull is rigid and cannot give way; therefore the brain is compressed.

Hydrocephalus is a disorder with excess cerebrospinal fluid, usually caused by interference with circulation or absorption of the fluid. The skull bones do not unite for many years after birth, hence in hydrocephalus in children, the excess fluid forces the bones apart until the head reaches an enormous size, with the forehead overhanging and the skull thinned out. The brain is usually compressed, but not to the extent which may result from a severe hydrocephalus in the adult. In many cases, the damage is severe enough to interfere with normal development, and may even result in idiocy. In such cases, death usually occurs at a relatively early age by reason of interference with important areas in the brain stem or of lessened resistance to infectious processes.

SUMMARY

The blood supply of the brain and meninges is derived from the common carotid and vertebral arteries; that of the spinal cord and its roots is derived from the vertebral, intercostal, lumbar, and sacral vessels. The peripheral nerves receive their blood supply from the main arteries in the regions through which they pass.

Some of the branches of the arterial circle at the base of the brain supply the choroid plexuses of the lateral and third ventricles; branches of the vertebral arteries supply those in the fourth ventricle. Cerebrospinal fluid formed in the plexuses enters the ventricles and circulates through them. Fluid then enters the subarachnoid space and is eventually absorbed into the blood through the arachnoid villi in the dural sinuses. The pressure of this fluid may be measured in the spinal subarachnoid space by introducing a lumbar puncture needle with a manometer attached.

Names in Neurology

THOMAS WILLIS (1621-1675)

An English physician, Thomas Willis probably holds first place among the seventeenth century neuroanatomists. In 1664 he published his famous *Cerebri Anatome,* which classified the cranial nerves and was the most complete description of the anatomy of the nervous system of its day. In this work he described the circle of arteries which is now named after him.

REFERENCES

Descriptions of and references on the blood supply of the nervous system and the structures concerned with cerebrospinal fluid are available in the textbooks cited on p. 6.

Davson, H.: Physiology of the Cerebrospinal Fluid. Boston, Little, Brown and Company, 1967. (A well-written, analytical account; an extremely valuable source book.)

Millen, J. W., and Woollam, D. H. M.: The Anatomy of the Cerebrospinal Fluid. London, Oxford University Press, 1962. (A timely volume on the anatomy and certain functional aspects of the ventricles, choroid plexuses, and meninges.)

Pease, D. C., and Schultz, R. L.: Circulation to the brain and spinal cord. C, Submicroscopic anatomy. *In* Abramson, D. I. (ed.): Blood Vessels and Lymphatics. New York, Academic Press, 1962. (A brief but excellent account of the ultrastructure of blood vessels, neuroglial cells, "spaces," and "blood-brain barrier.")

CHAPTER 5

FORMATION AND
DEVELOPMENT OF
THE NERVOUS SYSTEM

In the study of the structure of the adult nervous system, questions arise that may be answered more easily by reference to the conditions found in the embryo and fetus. For instance, how does it happen that the adult nervous system is cavitated? How do nerves and ganglia form? The answers to these questions may be had by examination of the embryonic nervous system and the correlation of its subsequent development with the adult arrangement.

EMBRYONIC AND FETAL PERIODS

The entire body develops from two highly specialized cells: one the *ovum* or egg of the female, and the other the *spermatozoon* or sperm of the male. Development begins with the penetration of an ovum by a sperm cell, thus initiating a process known as fertilization. A series of cell divisions follows the union of ovum and sperm, resulting in the formation of two cells, then four, eight, sixteen, and so on, a process which eventuates in the billions of cells which make up the infant at birth. The stimulation of cell division in the process of fertilization is equaled in importance by the combining of the factors representing maternal and paternal characteristics.

The human embryonic period is the first seven or eight weeks after fertilization. At the end of this time, most embryos are usually 28 to 30 mm. in crown-rump length. Differentiation is nearly completed and the embryo in many respects is like a miniature adult. For purposes of more precise description and comparison, investigators have divided the human embryonic period into 23 age groups or stages.

The human fetal period, normally about seven months, is from the end of the embryonic period until birth.

Germ Layer Formation and Differentiation. Early in embryonic life, as the mass of cells increases, certain areas grow at different rates, so that metabolic or physiological gradients are said to exist. For example, surface-interior gradients are evidenced by the formation of sheets or layers of cells. There is also a difference in growth rate between the head and the tail regions, the head region growing and differentiating more rapidly. Local patterns develop within this general axial gradient which are important in later developmental changes.

The sequence of development, then, is an increasing number of cells which are at first arranged in two layers. Within a short time, a third layer makes its appearance. Figure 34 illustrates this by schematic cross sections through young embryos.

Those cells on the back or dorsal portion of the embryo form a layer called *ectoderm.* The ventral layer of cells is referred to as *entoderm,* and the more diffuse collection of cells between the ectoderm and entoderm is termed *mesoderm.* Such structures as the outer skin and the nervous system develop from the ectoderm; the skeleton, muscles, connective tissue, heart, and blood vessels are derived from mesoderm. From the entoderm come the digestive and respiratory tracts and their glandular derivatives. This early arrangement of yet unspecialized cells into a pattern of three germ layers is characteristic of all vertebrates.

DEVELOPMENT OF THE NERVOUS SYSTEM

Formation of the Neural Tube. The dorsal sheet of cells, the ectoderm, shows a higher metabolic rate in the midline. As a result, differentiation proceeds much more rapidly here, and there is soon evident a thickened plate extending from head to tail. This pattern is fundamentally the same for all vertebrates.

The cells at the edge of the plate grow faster than those in the mid-

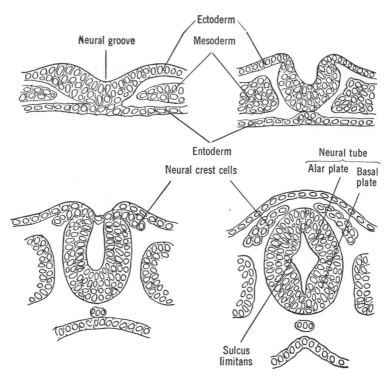

Figure 34. Transverse sections through embryos of increasing age, illustrating the formation of the neural tube and associated structures.

dle, so that a *neural groove* is formed. This deepens to form a tubular structure as the cells increase in number. This process is schematically represented in Figure 34. When the tube separates from the overlying ectoderm, the ectodermal cells at the junction become separated from both and come to lie along the dorsal side of the detached *neural tube.* These cells are known as *neural crest cells* because of their early position over the neural tube. The entire adult nervous system, except for its blood vessels and certain neuroglial cells, is formed from the neural tube and the neural crest cells. In spite of subsequent complex morphological changes, the central nervous system remains a tube throughout the lifetime of an individual.

Figure 34 also illustrates the delimitation of the neural tube into *alar* and *basal plates.* Cells derived from the basal plate become associated with motor systems, whereas those from the alar plate align themselves with afferent (so-called sensory) mechanisms.

Subdivisions of the Neural Tube. The portion of the neural tube in the head region forms the brain, whereas that within the vertebral canal becomes the spinal cord.

With the more rapid growth and differentiation in the cranial end of the neural tube, three primary enlargements or vesicles are formed. The most cranial of these is the *forebrain* or *prosencephalon*. The middle is the *midbrain* or *mesencephalon*, and the caudal, the *hindbrain* or *rhombencephalon*. These are illustrated in Figure 35. These subdivisions and their boundaries, including the cranial flexure and the primordia of the optic vesicles, can be recognized as early as three weeks after fertilization. Secondary enlargements or subdivisions shortly become evident in the prosencephalon, forming the *endbrain* or *telencephalon* and *interbrain* or *diencephalon*, and also in the rhombencephalon, forming the *afterbrain* or *metencephalon* and the *marrowbrain* or *myelencephalon*. Figure 36 shows the changes in form throughout embryonic and fetal life. All these vesicles contribute to the brain, the adult derivatives being indicated in Table 1. The neurocele or cavity of the embryonic neural tube forms, in the adult, the ventricles of the brain and the central canal of the medulla oblongata and spinal cord.

Cellular Changes in the Neural Tube. The portion of the neural tube which forms the spinal cord changes less, so that the differentiation of its primitive cells into nerve cells is more easily studied. The neural tube at first consists of a layer of elongated cells, but continuous cell division results in an expansion of the lateral walls (Fig. 37) and the formation of three layers, an inner *ependymal* or *germinal* layer, an inter-

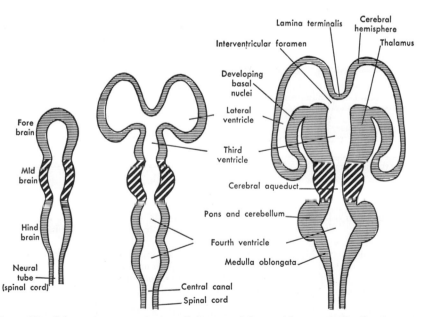

Figure 35. Schematic representation of three- and five-vesicle stage in the development of the brain, with early development of the cerebral hemispheres. The lamina terminalis of the adult brain represents the anterior end of the brain in the embryo.

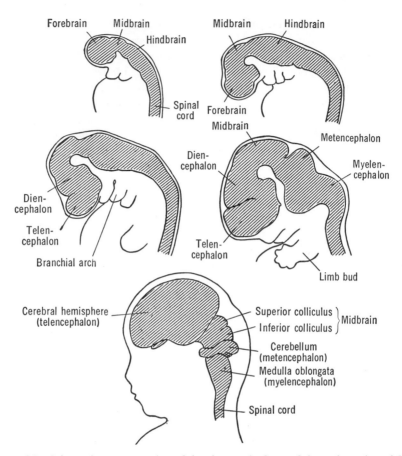

Figure 36. Schematic representation of the changes in form of the embryonic and fetal brain. (Modified after Patten.)

Table 1. Derivatives of the Primary Vesicles

PRIMARY VESICLE	SUBDIVISION	DERIVATIVES	LUMEN
Prosencephalon	Telencephalon	Cerebral cortex, corpus striatum and rhinencephalon	Lateral ventricle and part of third ventricle
	Diencephalon	Thalamus and hypothalamus	Most of third ventricle
Mesencephalon	Mesencephalon	Collicular region and cerebral peduncles	Cerebral aqueduct
Rhombencephalon	Metencephalon	Pons and cerebellum	Fourth ventricle
	Myelencephalon	Medulla oblongata	Fourth ventricle and part of central canal
Remainder of neural tube		Spinal cord	Most of central canal

mediate *nuclear* or *mantle* layer, and an outer *marginal* layer (Fig. 38). Each of the germinal cells divides, one of the daughter cells migrating to the mantle layer and the other remaining behind as a germinal cell.

Some of the cells which remain behind become *spongioblasts*, which are the forerunners of *neuroglial cells* (p. 83). Still others develop into the adult ependymal cells which line the central canal and ventricles.

The cells which migrate to the mantle layer may become *neuroblasts* and form nerve cells. In so doing, each develops an outgrowth or process, the *axon*, which extends peripherally, contributing to and forming with numbers of other axons the marginal layer. This becomes the white matter of the spinal cord. Neuroblasts develop other processes (Fig. 39), called *dendrites*, which extend peripherally for a short distance, but do not reach the marginal layer. The cells are now *multipolar*.

The neuroblasts which lie in the ventral portion of the mantle layer or basal plate send their axons through the marginal layer or white matter and out of the cord. Here, at regular intervals, larger numbers

Alar plate of neural tube   Sulcus limitans

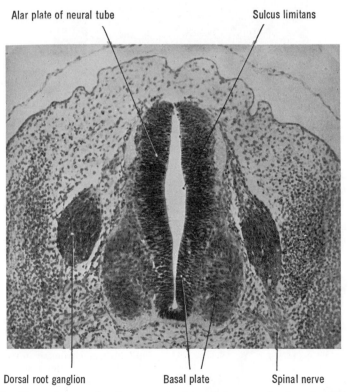

Dorsal root ganglion   Basal plate   Spinal nerve

Figure 37. Photomicrograph of a cross section of the neural tube of a 10-mm. pig embryo.

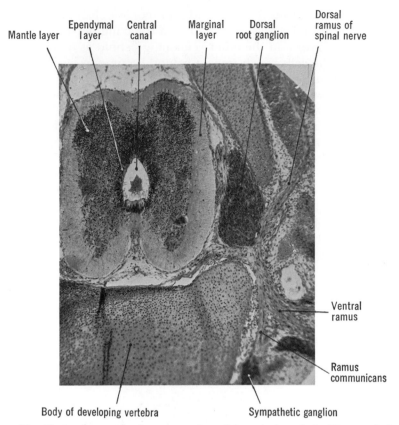

Mantle layer   Ependymal layer   Central canal   Marginal layer   Dorsal root ganglion   Dorsal ramus of spinal nerve

Ventral ramus

Ramus communicans

Body of developing vertebra   Sympathetic ganglion

Figure 38.   Photomicrograph of a cross section of the spinal cord of a 25-mm. pig fetus. Note the spinal nerve leaving through an intervertebral foramen.

of axons are collected into ventral roots of spinal nerves. Each ventral root supplies a body area which may be thought of as a transversely oriented "embryo segment." The muscles which the ventral root fibers will supply develop from tissue which at first lies but a millimeter or less from the neural tube. The first axons traversing this distance estab-

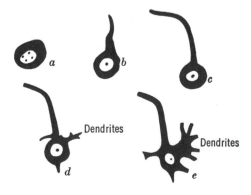

Dendrites

Dendrites

Figure 39.   Simplified representation of neuroblast differentiation. *a*, Germinal cell. In *b* and *c* an axon appears and nuclear chromatin forms a nucleolus. In *d* and *e* dendrites appear and increase in number.

lish a path which fibers developing later seem to follow. The factors which determine the growth and termination of fibers may be termed *preneural influences* in that they are operative before the nervous system assumes its functions as a conducting mechanism.

For instance, there is a general relationship between the region in which a limb bud is developing and the spinal cord at that level such that nerves from this portion of the cord grow into the region. But there is no specific relationship between the axons of the spinal nerves and the muscle fibers developing within the limb bud. It may be predetermined that a certain axon enters a given embryo segment, but within that segment the axon may vary in the exact site of its termination. This is because the direction of its growing tip is influenced by the physical nature of the non-nervous environment, such as obstructions, changes in consistency, or stresses and strains. These are prominent in regions of attachment of limb buds, where they probably influence the formation of plexuses. Once a path is established by the first fibers, however, growth of later axons is much less haphazard. Although growth is nonspecific, variation is not so marked as it might be, because of the short distances traversed and the pattern formed by the earliest fibers. It cannot be denied, however, that there is some specificity which determines that motor and sensory fibers form their proper endings once they have grown into their region of supply. This is an unsolved problem.

Cranial nerves, so far as their efferent portions are concerned, likewise arise as outgrowths of neuroblasts, but the segmental arrangement is not apparent. Furthermore, in the brain the early lateral migration of the neuroblasts is such that many come to lie at the surface. Their axons grow inward, so that the white matter thus formed is internal to the gray matter. This accounts for the fact that the surface or cortex of the cerebral hemispheres and of the cerebellum consists of gray matter.

Migration and Differentiation of Neural Crest Cells.   Growth and differentiation of the neural crest cells accompany neural tube changes. The crest divides longitudinally and then becomes segmented. Many of the cells in each neural crest segment develop two processes which grow in opposite directions (*bipolar cells*) (Fig. 40). Later, an eccentric growth of the cell body occurs and the two processes become fused at

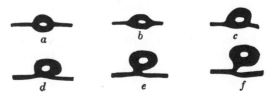

Figure 40. Illustration of the manner in which eccentric growth (more rapid growth on one side of the cell) transforms a primitive bipolar cell into a unipolar one.

their point of origin from the cell body. A *unipolar cell* is thus formed, the single process of which divides into two branches. The peripheral processes (dendrites) of the unipolar cells in each segment of the neural crest accompany corresponding ventral root fibers to form a spinal nerve (Fig. 38). The central processes (axons) of the cells grow into the spinal cord, toward the dorsal portion of the mantle layer (alar plate), thereby forming a dorsal root. The cell bodies in each neural crest segment are collected into an enlargement, the spinal ganglion. With respect to the spinal cord, the dorsal root fibers are afferent in nature.

Afferent fibers in most cranial nerves arise by a similar process, but again the regular sequence is not apparent. Furthermore, the ganglion cells associated with the olfactory and acoustic nerves remain as bipolar cells.

Many of the cells in the neural crest and in the ventral part of the mantle layer migrate peripherally and take up positions along the vertebral column and in the abdominal cavity. Here they differentiate into multipolar cells and collect into groups of cells, the ganglia of the sympathetic trunk and the prevertebral ganglia (celiac, mesenteric, and so forth). Some axons of these sympathetic ganglion cells go to viscera, others by way of rami communicantes to spinal nerves. Some investigators consider that the sympathetic ganglion cells develop entirely from neural crest cells. It is of considerable importance that developing sympathetic nerve cells in birds and mammals are sensitive to the growth-promoting effects of a protein termed the *nerve growth factor.* This protein is a normal constituent of sympathetic cells and blood and body fluids. Its presence suggests the possibility that there may be other growth factors for other cells of the developing nervous system.

The medullae of the adrenal glands are formed by cells migrating from neural crest and mantle layer. Thus, from early stages, the adrenal medullae are intimately associated with the sympathetic part of the autonomic nervous system.

Parasympathetic ganglion cells are probably similarly formed after migration from the central nervous system and neural crest.

Not all the cells in the neural crest and in the mantle layer become neurons. Peripheral nerves contain *neurilemmal cells,* which are comparable to neuroglial cells. Neurilemmal cells are of ectodermal origin and probably develop from cells that have migrated from the neural crest and the ventral part of the mantle layer.

With the definitive formation of the vascular system in the embryo, blood vessels soon invade the central nervous system and, in so doing, carry with them a small amount of connective tissue, some of the cells of which apparently form a type of neuroglial cell known as microglia (see Chapter 6). These are said to be the only mesodermal elements of the central nervous system.

Growth and Differentiation after Birth and in the Adult. At or shortly after birth, cell division in the nervous system stops. Apparently all the cells of the adult are present at this time. This means that when a nerve cell is destroyed, a new one cannot be formed to replace it. Individual cells and their processes, however, continue to grow and enlarge until after puberty.

The spinal cord in the embryo occupies the whole extent of the vertebral canal. The vertebrae, however, grow at a much more rapid rate and for a longer time, so that the vertebral column soon surpasses the spinal cord in length. Consequently, the spinal cord ends at an increasingly higher level until, in the adult, it extends only to the level of the first or second lumbar vertebra. Since the spinal nerves leave the canal between the vertebrae, they are "dragged down," as it were, as the disproportion between vertebral and cord levels increases. Thus the vertebral canal below the end of the spinal cord is filled with the roots of spinal nerves.

CONGENITAL DEFECTS OF THE NERVOUS SYSTEM

Congenital malformations of the human nervous system are common. These may be as severe as the complete absence of cerebral hemispheres, or even of the head, or they may be as mild as the ordinary variations in the usual neuroanatomical pattern. They cause much fetal death as well as infant mortality and morbidity.

An example of a common defect is *spina bifida,* caused by an interference with the normal process of formation and closure of the neural tube. The spinal cord may be affected, and usually there is also an incomplete development or absence of some of the vertebral arches. In severe cases, either the meninges or spinal cord or both protrude to the surface, separated from the exterior only by skin and connective tissue. Most spinae bifidae are mild, without accompanying symptoms, and consist in a defect or absence of a vertebral arch, usually the fifth lumbar.

SUMMARY

The structural unit in the body is the cell. Union of two specialized cells, the ovum and the spermatozoon, initiates the development of the embryo. Repetitive cell division leads to the formation of three cellular germ layers — ectoderm, mesoderm, and entoderm. The nervous system arises from ectoderm. A dorsal invagination of the ectoderm forms first a neural groove and then a neural tube. Rapid unequal growth of the cranial end of the neural tube forms three primary vesicles which give rise to five secondary vesicles from which the adult brain is derived. The remainder of the neural tube forms the spinal cord.

Cells in the neural tube form two types of cells: the spongioblasts, which give rise to the neuroglial cells, and the neuroblasts, which form nerve cells. Processes of the neuroblasts form the white matter. Some of the processes leave the brain and spinal cord to form fibers of cranial nerves and ventral roots of spinal nerves.

Most neural crest cells form unipolar cells which compose the spinal ganglia. The central processes form dorsal roots, and the peripheral ones enter spinal nerves. Some neural crest cells and cells from the mantle layer also migrate peripherally to form neurilemmal cells, sympathetic ganglion cells, and cells of the adrenal medullae.

REFERENCES

Arey, L. B.: Developmental Anatomy. 7th ed. Philadelphia, W. B. Saunders Company, 1965.

Balinsky, B. I.: An Introduction to Embryology. 2nd ed. Philadelphia, W. B. Saunders Company, 1965.

Bartelmez, G. W., and Dekaban, A. S.: The early development of the human brain. Contrib. Embryol., Carnegie Inst. 37:13-32, 1962. (A first-rate scientific paper.)

Child, C. M.: Origin and Development of the Nervous System. Chicago, University of Chicago Press, 1921. (In spite of the lapse of time since it was written, this volume is valuable because of its discussion of the physiological factors in development.)

Hamilton, W. J., Boyd, J. D., and Mossman, H. W.: Human Embryology. 3rd ed. Baltimore, Williams & Wilkins Company, 1963.

Langman, J.: Medical Embryology. Baltimore, Williams & Wilkins Company, 1963.

Straus, W. L., Jr.: The concept of nerve-muscle specificity. Biol. Rev., 21:75-91, 1946. (An outstanding review of the relations of nerve and muscle, and of factors in early development.)

CHAPTER 6

MICROSCOPIC ANATOMY
OF THE NERVOUS SYSTEM

GENERAL CHARACTERISTICS OF CELLS

The tissues of the body are composed of cells, plus intercellular material, including formed elements such as fibers, and an amorphous "ground substance" or matrix. Cells vary in structure and appearance according to the tissues they compose. Muscle cells, for example, differ considerably from nerve cells. Nevertheless, cells have certain common characteristics. Each consists of a living, complex substance known as *protoplasm,* which is usually organized into a *nucleus, cytoplasm,* and other structures. The last include *organelles* and *inclusions.*

Organelles are particles of organized living substance such as those shown in Figure 41, and which are discussed further on page 79. Inclusions are lifeless, often temporary constituents of cells. Examples are pigments, secretory granules, and crystals.

Cells vary in size and shape and are usually specialized to perform a particular function, such as secretion, contraction, or conduction.

THE NEURON

The adult nervous system consists of nerve cells and neuroglial cells which are so closely packed together that there is scarcely any

67

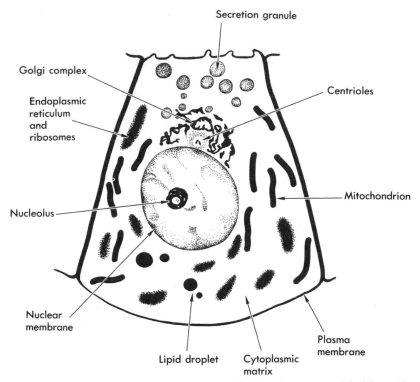

Figure 41. Schematic representation of a cell and its constituents. (Modified from Bloom and Fawcett.)

intercellular space. What space there is, and therefore what ground substance there is, occurs chiefly in the white matter.

Nerve cells, also called neurons, contain the characteristic organelles in their cytoplasm (Fig. 42), but are specialized in that they exhibit to a great degree the phenomena of irritability and conductivity. They also have long protoplasmic processes (Figs. 43 and 44). Microscopic and physiological studies show that these processes make possible the functional connections between different nerve cells. The nervous system is composed of billions of neurons, which are linked together to form conduction pathways and which are supported or held together by a framework of specialized, nonconducting cells known collectively as neuroglia.

STRUCTURE OF THE CELL BODY

The bodies of nerve cells vary in diameter from 4 to 5 microns up to 50 or even 100 microns. Their processes, on the other hand, range

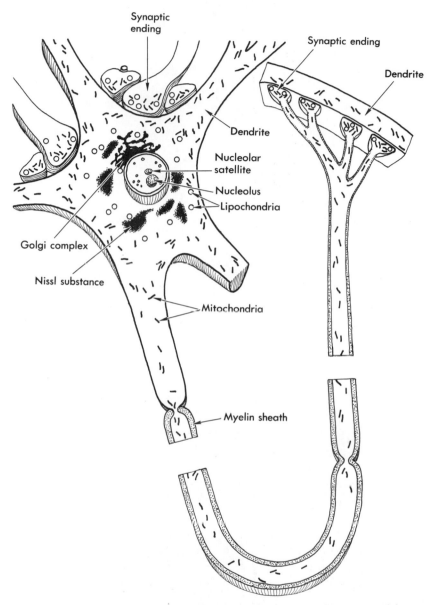

Figure 42. Schematic representation of a nerve cell with some of its structural features. (Modified from J. Z. Young: Endeavour, *15*:5-19, 1956.)

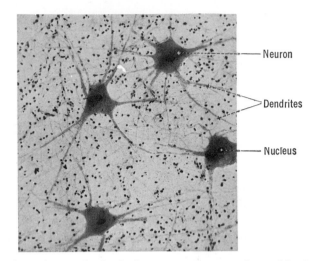

Figure 43. Photomicrograph of spinal motor neurons teased out of fresh material and stained. Note the extent of neural processes. The numerous small dots are nuclei of neuroglial cells.

from a few microns up to several feet in length. Neurons with long processes are frequently called Golgi type 1 (Fig. 45), whereas those whose processes are all short are Golgi type 2 (Fig. 46).

Cell Membrane. The cell membrane, or *plasmalemma,* is a triple-layered membrane about 75 to 100 Å thick which consists of two elec-

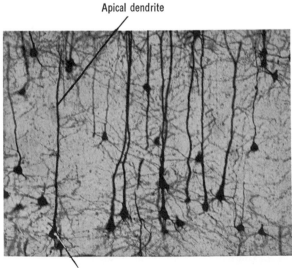

Figure 44. Photomicrograph of a section of cerebral cortex (rabbit) showing neurons and their processes. Cox-Golgi stain.

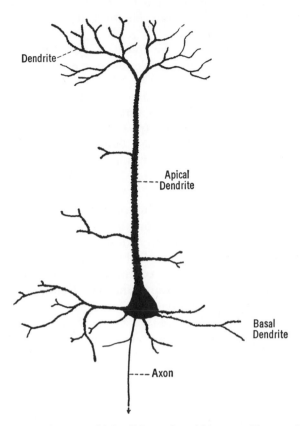

Figure 45. Drawing of a pyramidal cell from the rabbit cortex illustrated in Figure 44. This is a Golgi type 1 neuron. Note the surface irregularities of the dendrites. The axon of this type of cell in man may be several feet long.

Figure 46. A spindle-shaped neuron from rabbit cortex (Fig. 44). This is a Golgi type 2 neuron. Only the first part of the axon is shown.

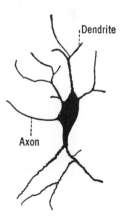

tron-dense layers separated by a structureless interzone (see Figure 53). The interchange of materials between the cell and its environment is regulated by the cell membrane.

Cytoplasmic and Nuclear Constituents. The chief constituents of the cytoplasm are *mitochondria, Golgi substance, endoplasmic reticulum, ribosomes, fibrils,* and *microvesicles.*

Mitochondria are small, double-layered membrane structures which occur throughout the cytoplasm and cell processes. They are concerned with enzymatic activities (p. 119).

The Golgi substance, also called Golgi complex, is a system of closely packed double-layered membranes and vesicles and, not infrequently, lipid spheres termed *lipochondria.* The Golgi complex occurs near or around the nucleus.

Nerve cells are characterized by masses of basophilic material in the cytoplasm (Fig. 47). This chromatin-like material is called *Nissl substance,* after Franz Nissl, who first described it (p. 93). The larger the cell, the more abundant is the Nissl substance. Electron microscopy has shown that Nissl substance is composed of the endoplasmic reticulum and ribosomes, and consists of masses of tubes and vesicles on the surfaces of which are the small ribosomes. The latter consist chiefly of a nucleoprotein, *ribonucleic acid* or *RNA* (p. 118).

Also characteristic of neurons are long, thin fibrils that extend throughout both the cytoplasm and the processes. These neurofibrils

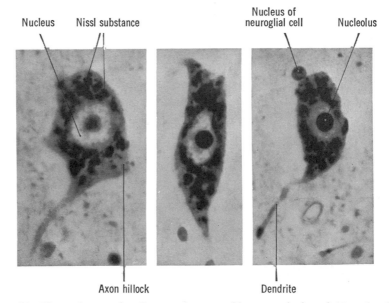

Nucleus   Nissl substance   Nucleus of
neuroglial cell   Nucleolus

Axon hillock   Dendrite

Figure 47. Photomicrographs of motor neurons of human spinal cord. Note the abundant Nissl substance, prominent nucleoli, and relative clearness of the nuclei. The sections do not show axons, and include the axon hillock in but one of the cells. Cresyl violet stain.

can be demonstrated only by a special staining process in which solutions of a silver salt are used. When the silver salt is absorbed by the tissue and then reduced in a manner similar to the development of a photographic plate, metallic silver is deposited in or on the neurofibrils.

Some nerve cells, especially certain ones in the hypothalamus, are secretory cells. Their secretory granules are, in the example given, related to the hormones of the posterior pituitary.

Pigment granules are frequently found in the cytoplasm. In certain areas of the brain, such as the substantia nigra, the cells normally contain large amounts of melanin pigment, thus accounting for the dark appearance of the region. Many neurons contain a yellow, lipochrome pigment which increases in amount with age. No pathological significance can be attached to such an increase.

The nuclear membrane is layered in much the same way as the cell membrane. Within the nucleus, RNA is present as a spherical, basophilic body termed the *nucleolus.* This has a diffuse coating of *deoxyribonucleic acid (DNA).* The nucleus has additional DNA which, however, is so dispersed that the nucleus is pale-staining with basic dyes.

In some large neurons, and in other cells of the body, chromatin DNA is condensed into a small mass which lies near or on the nucleolus. This *nucleolar satellite* is especially common and prominent in neurons of female animals.

STRUCTURE OF THE CELL PROCESS

The processes of nerve cells differ according to the direction in which they conduct nerve impulses. Some are afferent in nature, conducting impulses toward the cell bodies; processes of this type are known as dendrites. Others are efferent, conducting impulses away from the cell bodies, and are known as axons or axis cylinders. This direction of conduction is determined, not by structural characteristics of the processes, but by a polarity set up at the points of functional connection between neurons.

Nerve cells usually have a single axon and at least one or more dendrites. The cells in cranial and spinal ganglia are exceptions to this rule. It was pointed out in Chapter 5 that the single processes of the unipolar cells in dorsal root ganglia divide into two branches, one projecting toward the central nervous system and the other toward the periphery (Figs. 48, 49). The cells of most of the cranial ganglia, such as the semilunar ganglia of the trigeminal nerves, are also unipolar. However, in the spiral and vestibular ganglia, in the olfactory mucous membrane, and in one of the layers of the retina, nerve cells retain their bipolar characteristics. Except for these unipolar and bipolar varieties, all the cells in the nervous system are multipolar. Multipolar cells of the cerebral cortex are shown in Figures 45 and 46, and one from the anterior gray matter of the cord in Figure 49.

Unipolar   Cell
process   body

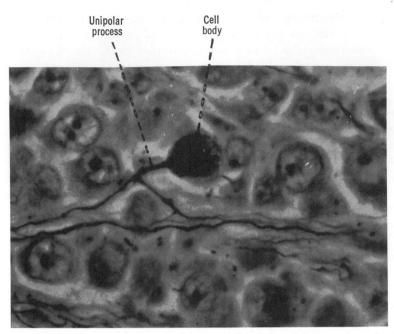

Figure 48. Photomicrograph of a unipolar nerve cell in a dorsal root ganglion of a three month human fetus. Silver stain. The nucleus of this cell was not included in the section. Note how the single process divides a short distance from the cell body.

It should be pointed out that the general structure of vertebrate neurons may also be categorized according to impulse origin, as illustrated in Figure 50.

Structure of Dendrites.   Dendrites usually extend but a short distance from the cell body, branch profusely, and contain Nissl substance. This arrangement increases the surface area of a neuron, so that large numbers of other neurons may be associated or linked with it.

Structure of Axons.   Axons differ from dendrites in that they lack Nissl substance, often extend for long distances, and have relatively few branches until near their terminations. The area of the cell body from which they arise may also lack Nissl substance and is known as the *axon hillock* (Fig. 47).

Axons end by forming synaptic junctions with nerve cells (p. 82) or by forming motor endings with non-nervous tissues, such as muscle (p. 146). Mitochondria are present in considerable numbers in synaptic and motor endings, and a few are scattered throughout the remainder of the axon.

The axon is surrounded by the *myelin sheath* which is the cytoplasm of neurilemmal cells in peripheral nerve fibers, and of glial cells in central nervous system fibers. The myelin sheath is lipid in nature and

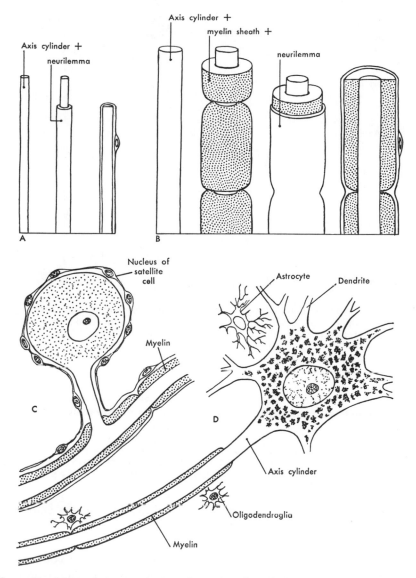

Figure 49. Schematic representation of a nonmyelinated fiber. *A*, the right hand figure of the group showing the fiber cut longitudinally. This figure shows a single nonmyelinated fiber, but such fibers tend to occur in groups, with a common neurilemma (see Fig. 54). *B* shows components of a myelinated fiber. The various layers of the nerve fiber are exaggerated in certain respects. For details, as shown by electron microscopy, see Figure 53. *C* is a dorsal root ganglion cell with its unipolar process dividing into peripheral and central branches. *D* is a multipolar cell of the spinal cord, with associated neuroglial cells.

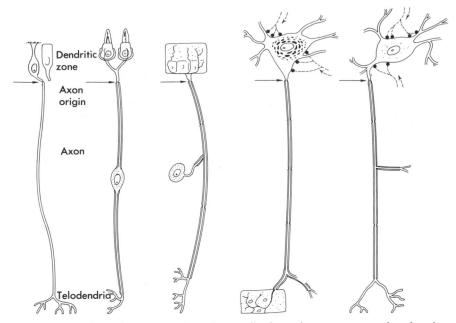

Figure 50. Schematic representation of generalized vertebrate neurons to show how impulse origin, rather than location of cell body, may be taken as the focal point in defining dendrites and axons. From left to right, olfactory receptor neuron, auditory receptor neuron, cutaneous receptor neuron, motor neuron, and interneuron. (Modified from D. Bodian: Science, *137*:323-326, 1962.)

is arranged in layers that are formed as illustrated in Figure 53. The largest axons, with their myelin sheaths, may be 20 microns in diameter. Osmic acid, when used as a stain, colors the myelin black, leaving the axon unstained. Accordingly, osmicated fibers seen in cross section look like black rings. Osmic acid penetrates poorly, however, so that for large pieces of nerve tissue a different technique must be used to give the same result. After treatment with a chemical compound such as potassium dichromate or iron alum, the myelin sheaths stain blue or black with the dye hematoxylin. Fibers stained by such a method are shown in Figure 51. This is the Weigert method of staining (p. 94), and its use shows that the white matter of the central nervous system contains large numbers of myelinated fibers. Gray matter is gray by contrast because it is composed mainly of cell bodies and fibers which, for the most part, lack myelin. The same method also reveals that ventral and dorsal roots, cranial and other peripheral nerves contain large numbers of myelinated axons. In peripheral nerves and in the central nervous system the term "nerve fiber" is often used to specify a process and its covering sheaths. Peripheral myelinated fibers are also known as A fibers if they are somatic, or B fibers if they are auto-

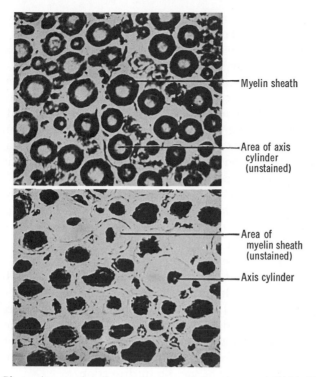

Myelin sheath

Area of axis cylinder (unstained)

Area of myelin sheath (unstained)

Axis cylinder

Figure 51. Photomicrographs of cross sections of dorsal roots (rabbit). The fibers in the upper half of the figure are stained by the Weigert method to show myelin sheaths; those in the lower half by a silver method to demonstrate axis cylinders.

nomic (p. 103). A fibers are associated with many sensory and motor functions.

Silver stains color axons rather than myelin sheaths; by using such methods, one can show that gray matter contains many fibers which are 1 micron or less in diameter and are, therefore, nonmyelinated. The white matter also contains many nonmyelinated fibers. This is also true of dorsal roots (but not ventral roots) and peripheral nerves. Peripheral nonmyelinated fibers, whether somatic or autonomic, are also known as C fibers (p. 175). Like A fibers, they are associated with many functions. It should be emphasized that, while one of the two divisions of a unipolar process of a dorsal root ganglion cell is functionally an axon and the other functionally a dendrite, both are structurally like axons.

All myelin sheaths are interrupted at regular intervals. These interruptions, which are termed the *nodes of Ranvier* (Fig. 52; also see Fig. 49), may be several hundred microns or more apart.

Axons Outside the Central Nervous System. All axons outside the central nervous system, whether myelinated or not, are closely related to neurilemmal cells. The cytoplasm of these cells forms the myelin sheath of the larger axons (Fig. 53). Nonmyelinated fibers are embedded in neurilemmal cells in the manner shown in Figure 54. Neurilemmal cells are also called *cells of Schwann*, p. 93, and usually but one cell occurs between two successive nodes of Ranvier. The neurilemma of spinal ganglion cell processes is continuous with the layer of "satellite" cells that surrounds the ganglion cells (Fig. 49). Neurilemma is comparable to the neuroglia of the central nervous system. In addition to its role in the formation of myelin, it has important functions in the regeneration of nerve fibers (p. 90).

Axons in the Central Nervous System.   These axons may be either myelinated or nonmyelinated. The myelinated axons of the central nervous system have nodes of Ranvier, although they are difficult to demonstrate. In neither case, however, is a neurilemma present. Instead, neuroglial cells are found in comparable positions.

Spinal Roots, Spinal Nerves, and Peripheral Nerves.   These structures are composed of large numbers of nerve fibers bound together by a type of connective tissue, which is present in the central nervous system only around blood vessels (Figs. 55, 56). The connective tissue contains small blood vessels that supply the nerves. The connective tissue of peripheral nerves is abundant enough to make them firm, tough, and relatively easy to handle in dissection.

The dorsal roots are composed of central processes of spinal ganglion cells and contain thousands of myelinated and nonmyelinated fibers (Fig. 55). These range in diameter from less than 1 to about 20 microns. The nonmyelinated fibers are by far the most numerous.

Node of Ranvier

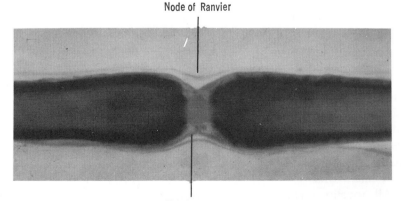

Neurilemma

Figure 52.   Photomicrograph of a single myelinated fiber from frog sciatic nerve, stained with osmic acid. The myelin stains black and is interrupted at the node. The thin membrane external to the neurilemma represents endoneurium. The axis cylinder (stained grayish) continues through the node.

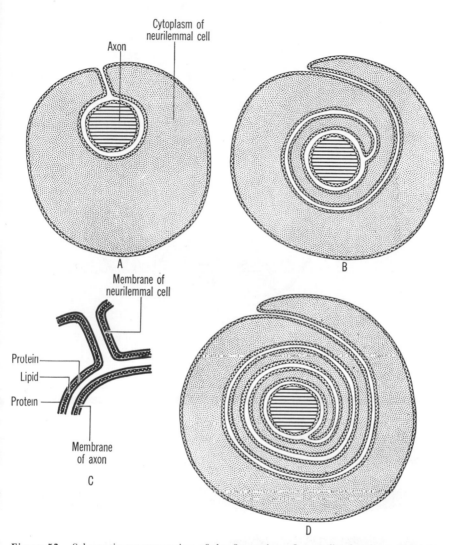

Figure 53. Schematic representation of the formation of a myelin sheath, as shown by electron microscopy. *A,* a single axon indenting or invaginating a neurilemmal cell. *B,* the neurilemmal cell begins to spiral around the axon. *C,* high magnification of the region of invagination in *A,* showing the protein-lipid-protein layers in the cell membranes. *D,* an adult myelinated fiber in which the myelin consists of spiral, double layers of neuri-lemma cell membrane, with alternating neurilemmal cytoplasm and extracellular area. (Based on Robertson, J. D., Sci. Amer., *206*:64-72, 1962.)

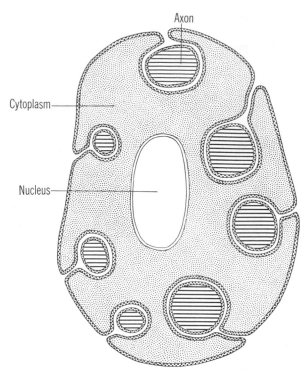

Figure 54. Nonmyelinated fibers in peripheral nerves occur in groups. Each group is related to a single neurilemmal cell as schematically represented here.

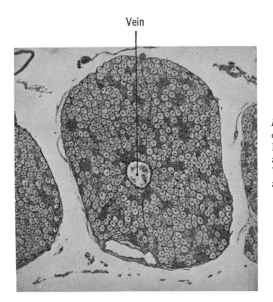

Figure 55. Photomicrograph of a cross section of a human dorsal root. Each fiber is seen as a round, clear area, in the center of which is a dot. The clear area is myelin; the dot, an axis cylinder.

The fibers in the ventral roots, that is, the axons of cells in the anterior gray matter of the spinal cord, are all myelinated. There is not, however, a continuous variation in size. If the fibers are grouped according to their diameters, there will be found one group of fibers which averages two to eight microns (with a peak of two to three microns), and another group which averages 12 to 20 microns.

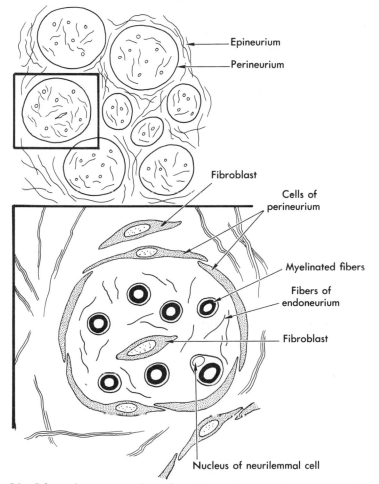

Figure 56. Schematic representation of peripheral nerve to show its general arrangement. The upper figure represents the connective tissue of a nerve. The square indicates the portion represented at a higher magnification in the lower figure. Epineurium is the irregularly arranged connective tissue which surrounds the nerve. Perineurium, the middle coat, is a thin sleeve of flattened cells which surrounds fascicles, that is, groups of nerve fibers. Perineurium is a barrier to diffusion. The innermost coat, endoneurium, is the connective tissue between and surrounding individual fibers, external to neurilemma. (See Burkel, W. E.: The histological fine structure of perineurium. Anat. Rec., *158*:177-189, 1967.)

Spinal nerves are mixed nerves, since they contain fibers of both ventral and dorsal roots. The small myelinated fibers of the ventral roots contribute to the formation of rami communicantes that extend to the paravertebral sympathetic trunks. Here they usually make functional connections with multipolar sympathetic ganglion cells. The axons of these cells are nonmyelinated. Many supply the thoracic, abdominal, and pelvic viscera. Others return to the spinal nerves by way of rami communicantes and thence are distributed to smooth muscle and glands by way of peripheral nerves.

The rami also contain afferent myelinated fibers derived from viscera. The cell bodies of these fibers are in spinal ganglia, and the central processes proceed to the cord by way of dorsal roots.

A major peripheral nerve, such as the sciatic, may contain over a million fibers of all types. The branches of such a nerve may contain fibers in which a group of one average diameter predominates. Branches to muscle, for instance, contain many large myelinated fibers, while those to skin and to subcutaneous tissues contain more of the smaller fibers and many nonmyelinated ones.

SYNAPSES

Within the central nervous system and in autonomic ganglia, nerve cells make functional contacts termed *synapses* (Fig. 57). Transmission of impulses occurs at synapses. Their structure is as follows:

As an axon approaches another cell, it decreases in diameter and divides repeatedly, forming *telodendria.* Each small branch or telodendron ends by making contact with the surface of a dendrite *(axodendritic contact)* or of the body *(axosomatic contact)* of the succeeding cell, or of the terminal axon of another cell *(axo-axonal contact).* There may also be dendrodendritic functions. In general, synapses are small swellings, often with a ring-like appearance. Such endings are called *boutons terminaux* (end-feet or terminal buttons). The telodendron may, however, make synaptic contact (by a *bouton de passage*) and then continue to another part of the same cell or to another cell. Thus, an axon may have synaptic junctions with many cells (frequently hundreds with each cell). Conversely, any one cell may have hundreds or thousands of synaptic contacts on its surface, derived from many axons.

In spite of the diversity of size, shape, and arrangement, all synapses are similar in structure. The details of this structure have been shown by electron microscopy and are represented schematically in Figure 58. At the point of contact, the fiber or the bouton makes a slight indentation in the cell. The two membranes are separated by a space of about

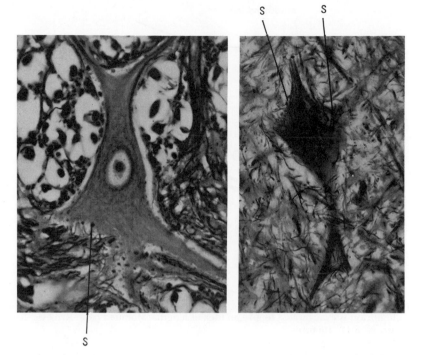

Figure 57. Photomicrographs of nerve cells stained with silver. That at the left is from medulla oblongata and shows synaptic endings, S, at the edge of the cell body and dendrites. The cell on the right, from spinal cord, is cut through the edge so that the nucleus is not included. Synaptic endings, S, occur on its surface. The left-hand leader ends between two synaptic endings.

100 Å. Mitochondria are very numerous in the bouton, as are round structures called *synaptic vesicles*. These are probably related to the formation and release of transmitter substances. The electrical and chemical changes at synapses during conduction are discussed on p. 110.

NEUROGLIA

The supporting cells of the central nervous system are known collectively as *neuroglia*. Although glial cells vary in size and shape, they all have processes which weave around nerve cells and fibers and frequently attach to the walls of blood vessels (Fig. 59). In gray matter, the end-feet of glial cells attach to and completely surround blood vessels to the extent that there is little, if any, extracellular space. Special stains are necessary to demonstrate neuroglial cells. Some have

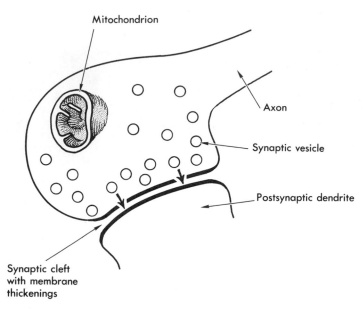

Figure 58. Schematic representation of a synaptic ending and its constituents. The mitochondrion is exaggerated to give an idea of length. (Modified from Krnjević, K.: Endeavour, 25:8-12, 1966.)

many processes and, because of their star shape, are called *astrocytes.* Other neuroglial cells with fewer and shorter processes occur along axons and near cell bodies. These are called *oligodendroglia.* Both types are derived originally from ectodermal cells of the neural tube. Still others, the *microglial* cells, are much smaller and probably originate from connective tissue of mesodermal origin that grows in with blood vessels. Our knowledge of the function of neuroglial cells is limited. It is known that microglial cells can enlarge and become *phagocytes,* capable of removing degenerating nervous tissue after injury or destruction. Astrocytes proliferate in response to many types of infections and disorders of the nervous system. Neuroglial cells can divide mitotically and are particularly important because they are the most common source of primary tumors of the nervous system. Glial cells are involved in the formation of myelin, and therefore are of considerable importance in diseases involving myelin. The usual methods of studying neuroglial cells fail to reveal the extent of their delicate protoplasmic extensions, the intimate relationship of these extensions to blood vessels and nerve cells, and the fact that these cells have motility. The assumption that the chief function of these cells is a supporting one is probably wrong. These cells undoubtedly have an important role in the metabolic activity of the nervous system.

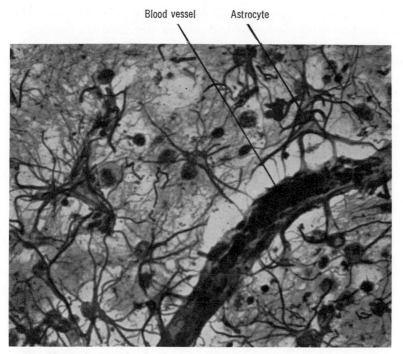

Figure 59. Photomicrograph of a section of human cerebral cortex stained for astrocytes. The cortex had been involved by an infection which had caused astrocytes to increase in number. The leader to the indicated astrocyte ends on the nucleus. Note how the extensions of this cell attach to the adjacent blood vessel.

DEGENERATION AND REGENERATION IN THE NERVOUS SYSTEM

Adult nerve cells cannot divide mitotically and cannot, therefore, replace any that happen to be destroyed. For reasons that are not known, some nerve cells die during the normal lifetime of an individual. It has been estimated that up to a fourth of all the nerve cells in the brain, spinal cord and peripheral ganglia may be lost by the eighth or ninth decade. This loss is a major factor in the sensory changes that are common with advancing age—diminishing sensitivity to touch, taste, and vision, for example.

If the axon of a nerve cell is destroyed, the cell body may survive, although it usually undergoes characteristic changes. For example, if an axon of an anterior horn cell is severed by cutting a peripheral nerve, cytoplasmic nucleoproteins are depleted, as evidenced by *chromatolysis,* that is, the gradual disappearance of Nissl substance (Fig. 60). The cell body, nucleus, and nucleolus increase in size, and the nucleus shifts toward the periphery of the cell. After several days or weeks the cell gradually reconstitutes itself. The chromatolysis and changes in volume probably represent redistribution of nucleoproteins and also the synthesis of new axonal material. The various changes are more noticeable in large cells with abundant Nissl substance, and their severity is related to the distance of axonal section from the cell body, being more severe as the division is closer.

Recovery is not invariable. Some cells die when axons are severed, and this is more likely to happen if the injury is near the cell body. Cells confined entirely to the central nervous system generally do not survive axonal section.

Cellular changes after axonal injury may be used to locate the cells of origin of axons in a peripheral nerve or in a pathway of the central nervous system. If a nerve or pathway is cut, and an appropriate interval allowed, the nervous system can be studied microscopically. Cells whose axons contribute to the nerve or tract that was sectioned undergo

Nissl substance

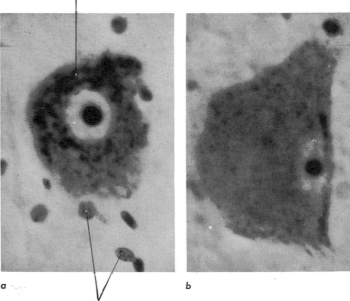

a   b

Nuclei of neuroglial cells

Figure 60. Photomicrographs of giant pyramidal cells of human cerebral cortex. The cell on the left is normal. That on the right is undergoing chromatolysis. Note the swelling, the shifting of the nucleus, and the loss of Nissl substance. The magnification is the same as that of Figure 47 (p. 72), which allows a comparison of relative sizes.

chromatolysis. Such experiments must be carefully controlled by examination of similar areas in normal material because, in certain regions
of the brain and spinal cord, there are cells that normally appear as if
they were undergoing chromatolysis. Furthermore, if the tissues being
examined are not fixed promptly after death, postmortem disintegration causes cellular changes that may, in their early stages, resemble
chromatolysis.

An axon that has been severed from its cell body undergoes changes
that collectively constitute *wallerian degeneration* (Fig. 61). The terminal
parts of the axis cylinder (at the end organ or at synaptic junctions)
begin to swell (within a day or so after section). The terminal axis
cylinder then begins to disintegrate. The process of swelling and disintegration proceeds proximally, toward the cell body. If the axon is myelinated, the myelin lamellae quickly begin to loosen and within a few
days begin to break down. This is accompanied by an increase in the
cytoplasm of the nonmyelin parts of neurilemmal cells. By about the
fourth day, the neurilemmal cells begin to divide and thereby form a
syncytial nucleated band. Some of the cells also become phagocytic and
ingest disintegrating axons and myelin. Proliferating connective tissue
cells may also aid in the phagocytosis. Eventually, all remains of axis
cylinder and myelin are removed and only cords of neurilemmal cells
are left. Similar changes may extend for a short distance proximal to
the point of axon section *(retrograde degeneration)*.

Similar axonal changes are found in the central nervous system
except that neuroglial cells proliferate (gliosis) and act as phagocytes
(Fig. 62). Also, if the affected neuron is located entirely within the central nervous system, the cell body often dies after axonal section. The
subsequent breakdown and phagocytosis extend toward the cell body
from the point of section, as well as away, and the entire nerve cell disappears. In man, phagocytosis may not be completed for several months
or longer. If many nerve fibers are severed, the proliferating glial cells
that replace the nerve fibers and cells form a dense glial scar.

Degenerating myelin differs chemically from normal myelin. Degenerating myelin, after chemical treatment with a compound such as
potassium dichromate, will stain black with osmic acid (Fig. 100), normal myelin will not stain in this way if similarly pretreated. This reaction
forms the basis of the *Marchi* method (p. 92) for staining degenerating
myelinated fibers, and enables one to trace such fibers in microscopic
sections.

In the peripheral nervous system, very shortly after an axon has
been severed, the severed axon tip begins to grow distally, through the
neurilemmal cord, by ameboid extension. There is a marked tendency
for each such tip to branch or sprout, but generally only one of these
branches continues distally for any distance. Such distal growth does

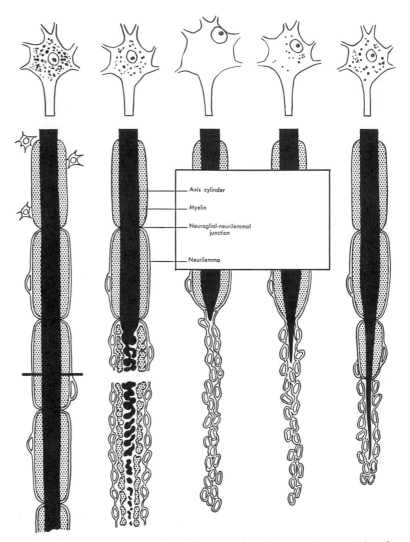

Axis cylinder

Myelin

Neuroglial-neurilemmal
junction

Neurilemma

Figure 61. Schematic representation of degeneration of an axon in a peripheral nerve. The upper row shows the cell body, the normal one being at the left. After section, Nissl substance disappears and the nucleus shifts peripherally. The Nissl substance then reappears and the nucleus regains its central position. The lower row shows the axon (at a higher magnification), the line representing the level of section outside the spinal cord. The axis cylinder and myelin begin to disintegrate and are removed by phagocytosis. A cord of proliferating neurilemmal cells remains, into which the axis cylinder begins to grow. The growing axon may have multiple sprouts (not shown).

Axis cylinder

Myelin

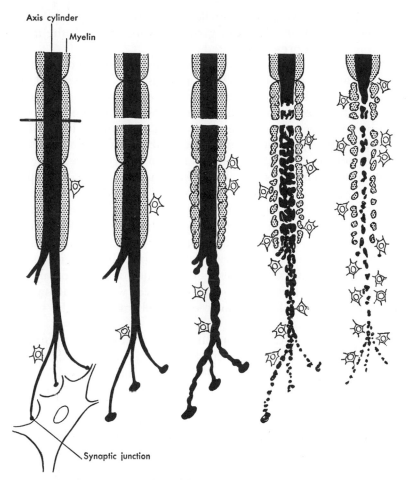

Synaptic junction

Figure 62. Schematic representation of degeneration of an axon in the central nervous system (cell body not shown). After section at the level indicated on the left, the synaptic junctions begin to swell, then the axis cylinder, these degenerative processes extending toward the cell body. Neuroglial cells proliferate and phagocytize the fragmenting axis cylinder and myelin.

not occur unless the cell body survives and begins to reverse the chromatolytic process. The axon regenerates at the rate of a few millimeters a day, at least initially. The rate of growth later becomes considerably less. With regeneration, myelin is formed by neurilemmal cells. Eventually, the axon establishes contact with whatever structure it comes in contact with. The contact may not be normal at first, or the axon may be misdirected during its growth, and functional recovery may be delayed.

Practically speaking, the neurilemmal cords might be regarded as tubes that conduct or direct the growing axon, although the interrelationship is much more complicated.

Regeneration does not occur in the brain and spinal cord, at least to any significant degree. In very young animals, however, neuroblasts may still be present and these may enable some regeneration to occur. Abortive attempts at regeneration have been observed in the adult (axonal sprouting in the vicinity of the injury), but without evidence of significant regrowth. Apparently the dense glial and collagenous scars that are characteristic of central nervous system injuries are major factors that prevent regeneration. Other, unknown factors are also important, related to differences between warm- and cold-blooded animals. The amazing capacity for regeneration in lower forms of life is familiar to all. Such capacity is retained to a considerable extent in fishes and amphibians, but is less evident in reptiles, and, so far as the nervous system is concerned, is practically restricted to the peripheral nervous system in birds and mammals. If recovery of function in the central nervous system does occur, it is either because the cells were not actually killed or their fibers severed, or because other cells or areas take over their functions.

Figure 61 illustrates the various changes in degeneration and regeneration of a single fiber. Widely different agents may produce almost identical changes in nerve cells and fibers. Chromatolysis, which was discussed as a consequence of axonal injury, may follow a direct attack on nerve cells by poisons, bacterial toxins, viruses, and the like, although in such cases, recovery is certainly less common. With such direct attacks, chromatolysis is more likely to be followed by cellular disintegration and phagocytosis. Metabolic disorders, or diminution or loss of blood supply, may cause chromatolysis followed by cell shrinkage and disappearance. Some diseases and poisons affect only the axonal processes, either axis cylinder or myelin sheath, or both, and may produce swelling, demyelination or disintegration. Any injurious change may be initially irritative and later destructive, so that the functions of involved neurons may be at first enhanced or exaggerated, and later lost.

The degeneration of an axon usually does not involve the succeeding cell with which that axon may be functionally connected. This is another example of data supporting the theory that functional units or cells of the nervous system are entities that are not morphologically continuous.

When a peripheral nerve is cut, hundreds or thousands of fibers are separated from their cell bodies. Function is immediately lost, and degenerative changes go on almost simultaneously in each fiber of that nerve. When recovery begins, however, it proceeds at different rates for nonmyelinated (faster rate of regeneration) and myelinated fibers. Recovery is also affected by the manner in which the cut ends of the nerve are united. A close union, without scar formation, favors recovery. Scar tissue prevents proper growth and as a consequence the multiple growing tips often form a swelling or *neuroma* above the scar. Similarly, the loss of a long stretch of nerve prevents recovery unless the gap is bridged in some way.

Growth is not limited to regenerating nerve fibers. For example, when an area of skin is deprived of its nerve supply, branches of the fibers that supply adjacent normal skin may grow into the denervated area and will, of course, reach it before the severed axons can regenerate. Consequently, some return of sensory function may occur long before that calculated on the basis of rate of regeneration.

THE NEURON THEORY

Even today there are remnants of the great debate of past years on the existence of functional entities of the nervous system, the neurons. The crux of the debate was the question of protoplasmic continuity at the synapse. The facts which support the neuron theory are as follows: It was established in the latter part of the last century that each neuroblast in the embryo formed a single adult nerve cell. Later, synaptic junctions were demonstrated and it was shown that neurofibrils did not pass from one cell to another. If cells were continuous, it would be difficult to explain how nerve impulses subserving a particular function could be conducted within a chain of neurons without spreading haphazardly to other chains.

Studies of degeneration and regeneration offered further substantiation. In most cases, neither chromatolysis nor degeneration involves other neurons. There is no evidence that any structures other than neurons are concerned in the actual transmission of nerve impulses.

Additional evidence was provided by the experimental method. In tissue cultures of neuroblasts it was observed that nerve processes arose by direct growth from cells and not by differentiation from intercellular material. Furthermore, electron microscopic studies have provided clear confirmation of discontinuity at synaptic junctions. The evidence is overwhelmingly in favor of the neuron as a cellular entity and of conduction as occurring over chains of such neurons.

SUMMARY

The adult nervous system is composed of specialized cellular units called neurons that are linked together by synaptic junctions to form conduction pathways for nerve impulses. Dendrites are usually proto-plasmic extensions of the neuron; they conduct toward the cell body. Axons lack Nissl substance, have fewer branches, are usually longer, and conduct away from the cell body. They may be either nonmye-linated or myelinated, the myelin being interrupted by nodes of Ranvier. Axons in the peripheral nervous system have a protoplasmic layer, the neurilemma, which is responsible for the formation of myelin. The white matter of the nervous system contains myelinated and nonmye-linated fibers; the gray matter has cell bodies and nonmyelinated and a few myelinated fibers. Dorsal roots, spinal nerves, and peripheral nerves contain both types of fibers; the ventral roots contain only mye-linated fibers. Axons end by forming synapses with other nerve cells or motor endings with non-nervous tissue.

In the central nervous system there is a supporting framework formed by a system of neuroglial cells.

New nerve cells cannot be formed in the adult nervous system. If axons are destroyed, the cells of origin undergo chromatolysis. If the axonal injury has occurred outside the central nervous system, regen-eration is possible, seemingly because of the presence of neurilemmal cells which form cords along which the regenerating fibers grow.

Names in Neurology

CAMILLO GOLGI (1844-1926)

Golgi was an Italian anatomist who, in 1883, used silver chromate to stain multipolar cells and all their processes. His studies and his stain, which was modified by later investigators, formed the basis for many important investigations of the nervous system. He was awarded the Nobel Prize in Physiology and Medicine in 1906, which he shared with S. Ramón y Cajal of Madrid. His research was not confined to neuro-anatomy. He made important studies in malaria, especially the relation of fever to the development of parasites within the blood. It was by his staining method that the structures in cytoplasm which now bear his name were first demonstrated.

VITTORIO MARCHI (1851-1908)

Marchi was an Italian physician who contributed to the establish-ment of the neuron theory by developing a method for staining de-generating fibers and applying it to experimentally produced lesions.

FRANZ NISSL (1860-1919)

Nissl was a German neuropathologist and psychiatrist who developed a method of staining nerve cells with aniline dyes. He discovered the chromidial substance in the cytoplasm of nerve cells. He also studied pathological lesions of the nervous system resulting from syphilis.

SANTIAGO RAMÓN Y CAJAL (1852-1934)

Ramón y Cajal was the greatest of all neuroanatomists. He did so much that is fundamental to present day knowledge that it is difficult to list his accomplishments. When he was professor of anatomy at the University of Valencia, he learned of Golgi's method for staining nerve tissue. The stain, however, was capricious and undependable. After two years of vain attempts to use it, he conceived the use of embryos in which myelin sheaths are not fully developed and, therefore, less liable to interfere with the impregnation of processes by silver. Because of this, and because of certain modifications of the stain, he demonstrated nerve cells in their entirety, their relationships to other neurons and the presence of synaptic junctions. With this method and with others which he subsequently developed he studied almost every portion of the nervous system. He described the fundamental structures of cerebral cortex, cerebellum, retina, spinal cord, and peripheral nerves. His account of degeneration and regeneration is a masterpiece. He demonstrated neuroglial cells in all their detail. In 1906 he shared the Nobel Prize for the Section on Physiology and Medicine with Camillo Golgi. During the latter part of his life, he was professor of normal histology and pathological anatomy at the University of Madrid.

LOUIS ANTOINE RANVIER (1835-1922)

Ranvier was a French histologist, best known for his description in 1878 of the interruptions of peripheral myelin sheaths which now bear his name.

THEODORE SCHWANN (1810-1882)

Schwann, a German physician, is best known for the studies by which he concluded that fundamental units in animal and vegetable tissues are cells. He also demonstrated the influence of organisms and lower fungi on fermentation and putrefaction; he investigated muscular contractions and first described neurilemma.

AUGUSTUS WALLER (1816-1870)

Waller, an English physician, contributed to the neuron theory through his studies of degenerating nerve fibers. He traced the degeneration which resulted from section of various cranial nerves and spinal roots. He established the direction and, thereby, the source of the process which is now frequently termed wallerian degeneration.

CARL WEIGERT (1845-1904)

Weigert was a German pathologist who contributed immensely to our knowledge of the nervous system by his development of various staining methods. The one applied to myelin sheaths, somewhat modified today, is still the most important single stain for nervous tissue. He also stained neuroglia. He was the first to stain bacteria, and he studied the pathological anatomy of smallpox and of Bright's disease.

REFERENCES

The neuroanatomy textbooks cited on p. 6 discuss the microscopic anatomy of the nervous system. The following textbooks contain similar discussions, as well as illustrations of ultrastructure.

Bloom, W., and Fawcett, D. W.: A Textbook of Histology. 9th ed. Philadelphia, W. B. Saunders Company, 1968.
Fawcett, D. W.: An Atlas of Fine Structure. The Cell. Philadelphia, W. B. Saunders Company, 1966.
Ham, A. W.: Histology. 5th ed. Philadelphia, J. B. Lippincott Co., 1965.
Schadé, J. P., and Ford, D. H.: Basic Neurology. Elsevier Publishing Company, Amsterdam, 1965.

The following references deal with neuroglia.

Bunge, R. P.: Glial cells and the central myelin sheath. Physiol. Rev., 48:197-251, 1968.
Causy, G.: The Cell of Schwann. Edinburgh, E. & S. Livingstone Ltd., 1960.
Glees, P.: Neuroglia. Oxford, Blackwell, 1955.
Kuffler, S. W., and Nicholls, J. G.: The physiology of neuroglial cells. Ergebn. Physiol. Biol. Chem. u. Exper. Pharm., 57:1-90, 1966.

The following references deal with experimental aspects of degeneration and regeneration.

Guth, L.: Regeneration in the Mammalian Peripheral Nervous System. Physiol. Rev., 36:441-478, 1956.
Windle, W. F.: Regeneration of axons in the vertebrate central nervous system. Physiol. Rev., 36:427-440, 1956.

Chapter 7

EXCITATION, CONDUCTION, AND TRANSMISSION

A fundamental property of living organisms is excitability, the ability to respond or react to a *stimulus,* that is, to some change in external surroundings or internal medium. The response is a change in state of activity of the organism. Excitability is also a property of cellular units of organisms. The reactions of such units are often specific. For example, gland cells may secrete (or a secreting cell may stop secreting), muscles may contract. In many, if not all, cells the change initiated by the stimulus spreads throughout the cell. Nerve cells are peculiarly adapted for controlling and directing such spread of activity. The reactions are accompanied by such phenomena as the utilization of oxygen, the formation of carbon dioxide, the production of heat, ion transfer across the cell membrane, and the appearance of certain electrical changes. Furthermore, nerve cells are usually dynamically polarized in such a way that a nerve impulse can only be transmitted from the axon of one nerve cell to the dendrites or cell body of the next nerve cell. Also, within a nerve cell, excitation normally spreads in the direction of from dendrites to axon. Finally, excitation may become independent of the stimulus and be conducted (see nerve impulse, farther on). However, conducted impulses are chiefly characteristic of the axon. Changes in many parts of a nerve cell often do not become nerve impulses, but remain local and help to determine the firing of impulses in certain critical regions.

95

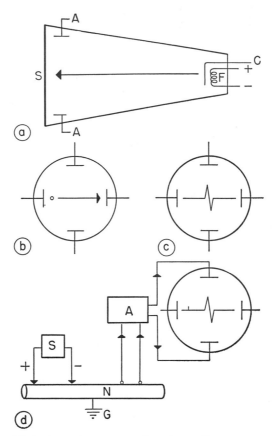

Figure 63. Simplified schematic representation of recording arrangement with cathode-ray oscillograph. In *a*, the cathode ray tube is shown in side view. A current heats the filament, *F*, and this in turn heats a cathode, *C*. Electrons from the heated cathode stream to the front of the tube, attracted by anodes, *A*, with a positive voltage. Negatively charged plates (not shown) are placed between cathode and anode. They repel electrons and are arranged so that electrons are concentrated into a narrow beam. The front of the tube (screen, *S*) has a material that fluoresces wherever electrons strike it. When viewed from the front *(b)* a single glowing spot is seen. There are four plates at the front of the tube. If a positive voltage is placed on the right-hand plate, and if this voltage is increased, the electrons will move across the screen toward the right-hand plate. If, on reaching the right-hand side, the voltage abruptly stops and is applied to the left-hand plate, the spot returns to the left. If, while the spot is moving across the screen, voltages are applied to upper or lower plates, the spot will move up or down according to the rate and amount of voltage change, *c*. If the electron spot moves fast enough, fluorescence persists so as to give the impression of a line. In actual recording, an oscillating voltage is applied to right- and left-hand plates. In *d*, a nerve, *N*, is stimulated by a brief shock from a stimulator, *S*. The nerve impulse is picked up by electrodes and led into the amplifier, *A*. Amplifiers are necessary because high voltages are needed to operate the cathode-ray tube. The output of the amplifier feeds to upper and lower plates of the tube, producing the vertical deflection characteristic of the nerve impulse as the spot moves across. The initial small deflection after the spot starts moving is the shock artifact, which signals the moment of stimulation. Some of the stimulating current leaks down the nerve to pick-up electrodes, most, however, leaking off to ground at *G*. The recorded deflection of the tube can be photographed for permanent records.

METHODS OF STUDY

One of the problems in studying excitation, conduction, and transmission is how to detect and record such activity. One method is to use the end result, such as muscular contraction or glandular secretion. Another is to estimate activity by measuring the uptake of oxygen during conduction. A common method is to gauge activity by measuring the electrical changes during conduction (Fig. 63). Electrical currents applied to nerve are effective stimuli and, since they are easily measured and controlled, are the most commonly used artificial stimuli. Physiological stimuli may also be used and, in some instances, may be precisely applied and controlled, as for example, the stimulation of the retina by light and of the ear by sound.

STEADY OR RESTING POTENTIAL

Nutrient materials and waste products readily enter and leave a cell, but a variety of mechanisms prevent the movement or loss of substances that are specifically essential to the activity of cells. These mechanisms account for the fact that the concentration of potassium (K^+) in the cytoplasm is much higher (by 20 to 50 times) than that in the fluid which surrounds the cell. The cytoplasm also has a high concentration of organic anions (A^-). On the other hand, the concentration of sodium (Na^+) and of chloride (Cl^-) is much higher in the extracellular fluid. Furthermore, the interior of the cell is electrically negative to the exterior, and in resting (nonconducting) nerve cells this potential difference, which is termed the *steady* or *resting potential,* may amount to 50 to 90 millivolts (mv.), depending upon the method of recording (Fig. 64). The cell membrane of the cell in the resting phase is said to be in a state of *polarization.* Any change which modifies the resting level of polarization produces important changes in the excitability of the cell. Thus, if the internal concentration of K^+ is increased, a condition of *hyperpolarization* will result, which lessens the excitability of the cell. Conversely, a diminution of K^+ produces a partial *depolarization* and an increased excitability.

The most widely accepted theory holds that the steady potential is a *membrane potential,* resulting from differences in concentration of ions in the cell and in the extracellular fluid, differences for which the cell membrane is chiefly responsible. These differences arise because of *passive factors,* which result in a slow diffusion of ions, and *active transport* (sodium-potassium pump), in which energy is used to transport ions.

Passive Factors.   The passive factors include (1) the nature of the cell membrane, (2) charges of the ions, and (3) concentrations of ions. For example, the lipid-protein nature of the membrane resists diffusion, but it does not resist the diffusion of all ions equally, being much more permeable to potassium than it is to sodium. The potassium ions, which have a positive charge, move inward, attracted by the negative charge of the organic ions. These factors nearly balance the tendency for potassium to diffuse outward to the lower external concentration. The net result of the various passive factors is a slight but steady diffusion of Na^+ into the cell, and a slight but steady diffusion of K^+ out of the cell. Nevertheless, the ionic concentrations on each side of the membrane remain steady, owing to the mechanisms of active transport.

Active Transport.   Energy derived from metabolic activities of the cell is used to carry Na^+ from a region of lower concentration (inside the cell) to a region of higher concentration (outside the cell). Energy is likewise necessary for the transport of K^+ in the opposite direction. This metabolically driven mechanism, which extrudes sodium ions and takes up potassium ions, is termed a *sodium-potassium pump*, or, more simply, a *sodium pump*. The exact nature of the pump is not yet known.

Some investigators believe that the steady potential cannot be explained on the basis of the mechanisms outlined. They hold that there is no correlation between the steady potential and the cytoplasmic concentration of potassium, and that the steady potential is caused by fixed charges on each surface of the membrane, these fixed charges being due, in part, to ions which are either disassociated or adsorbed. The explanation of the steady potential is still one of the major problems in cellular physiology.

CHANGES IN POTENTIAL

If an adequate stimulus, physiological or artificial, is applied to a nerve fiber, the steady potential is reversed (see Figure 64). The nerve fiber thereafter recovers, although somewhat more slowly. This reversal of potential is termed a *spike potential* and one of its characteristic features is that it travels, or is conducted, along the nerve fiber, away from the point of stimulation. The spike potential travels along the fiber independently of the stimulus, much as a bullet travels independently of the pull on the trigger.

During the reversal of potential, in which the interior of the fiber becomes positive to the exterior, the membrane is said to be *depolarized*. In terms of ion concentrations, the depolarization resulting from the

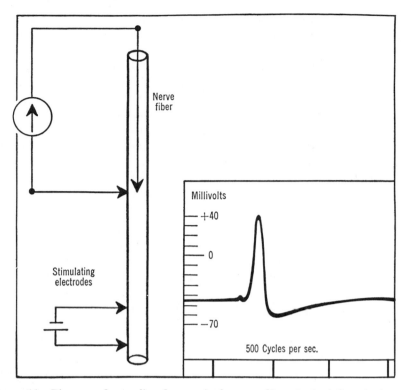

Figure 64. Diagram of recording from a single nerve fiber. At the left, a single nerve fiber is represented as a tube. One electrode is placed inside the fiber and the other on the surface so that the electrodes are across the membrane. These two electrodes are connected to a recording instrument. The two stimulating electrodes are indicated on the lower part of the fiber. The recording electrodes are so connected that when the internal electrode becomes more positive, the recording instrument gives an upward deflection. To the right is a figure indicating that when the electrodes are placed as indicated, the interior of the fiber is negative to the exterior. When a nerve impulse is initiated (the small initial deflection is the shock artifact), the steady potential is not only abolished, but is reversed, so that the interior of the fiber becomes momentarily positive to the exterior. Measurements like this have usually been made on giant nerve fibers from invertebrates, but similar results have been obtained from vertebrate cells and fibers. (Modified from Hodgkin and Huxley.)

stimulus is accompanied by a sudden increase in permeability to sodium which moves into the cytoplasm to the extent that the cytoplasm becomes positive. Soon thereafter, the permeability to potassium increases, and potassium moves outward, so that the steady potential begins to be restored. This outward movement is coupled with sodium inactivation, a sudden stoppage of inward sodium movement. Next, the membrane is gradually *repolarized* as the sodium pump transports sodium out and potassium in.

The explanation of the action potential as outlined is termed the *membrane* or *core theory.* Although it satisfactorily explains many phases of nerve activity, our knowledge of nerve activity is still elementary.

As mentioned above, the depolarization and the reversal of potential spread along the fiber independently of the stimulus. The spike potential is followed by certain changes termed *after-potentials.* Together with the spike, they constitute the *action potential* or nerve impulse. The various potential changes are accompanied by the uptake of a very small amount of oxygen, the formation of carbon dioxide, and the production of a small amount of heat.

When ions move inward (ionic movement is often spoken of as *current flow*) through the depolarized membrane at the point of stimulation, they flow longitudinally inside the fiber. They reach intact (polarized) regions ahead of and behind the depolarized zone. In these intact regions, they flow out through the membrane to the extracellular fluid, through which they return to the depolarized region and thereby complete the circuit. The region where current flows inward (the depolarized region) is spoken of as a *sink.* Where current flows out constitutes a *source.* Just what part the *axoplasm* (the interior of a fiber) plays is uncertain. Giant nerve fibers from which axoplasm is removed continue to behave like a core conductor.

It is believed that the current flow out through the membrane acts as a stimulus (just as the current of the artificial stimulating circuit does) and that when the density of such flow is great enough, resistance breaks down and the membrane potential reverses. In other words, an impulse, once started, is self-propagating because the current flow created by the membrane reversal acts as a stimulus for preceding portions of the fiber; when these break down, the process is repeated.

One can consider conduction as if two whirlpools were moving down a fiber (Fig. 65). Each whirlpool or *dipole* consists of lines of current flow inside a fiber, out through the membrane (source), back through extracellular fluid and into the fiber through the membrane. The convergence of the entering lines of both dipoles is the sink. The leading dipole is associated with propagation, since its current, on flowing outward, acts as a stimulus. The trailing dipole is associated with recovery processes.

If a whole nerve is being studied, the recorded response is very complicated. Its form is determined by the time relationships of the changes in each fiber of the nerve. If the fibers are conducting together, that is, have the same time relationships, then the form of the recorded change may approach the theoretical triphasic type. This, however, is to be expected only when dealing with parallel elements, such as nerve fibers lying side by side. Otherwise, it may be difficult, if not impossible, to interpret the electrical changes which occur in many elements. This is

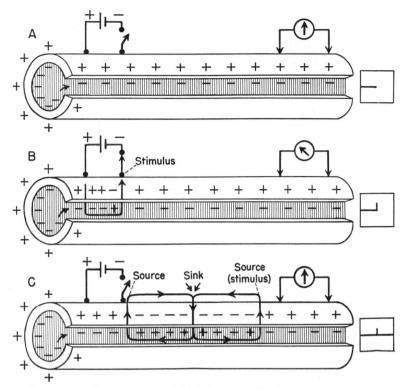

Figure 65. Diagram illustrating the initial changes following application of a stimulus to a nerve fiber. *A*, The fiber is represented as a tube with a strip cut away so as to expose the interior. The stimulating electrodes, indicated by + and −, are at one end and the recording electrodes at the other. The electrical charges internal and external to the membrane are also indicated. *B*, When the switch is closed, a current flows from the positive electrode into the fiber and out through the membrane back to the negative electrode (cathode). This current is derived entirely from the battery. Some of it leaks down the nerve, instantaneously for all practical purposes, and is recorded as a small deflection (inset at right). This is the shock artifact and indicates the moment of stimulation. *C*, The effect of current flow out through the membrane is to initiate the conduction of a nerve impulse. The impulse is represented as two dipoles, each consisting of current flow (not the stimulating current from the battery) within a region indicated by the reversal of electrical charges. The current flow out through the membrane in the leading dipole acts as a stimulus, just as did the artificial current from the battery. According to conventional methods, the recording instrument will not show a deflection until the region of negativity passes under the first electrode.

true in the central nervous system, where, in a given area, great numbers of fibers and cell bodies are crowded together.

One might ask, if current flows through extracellular fluid, could it not flow through adjacent nerve fibers and affect them? Experimental evidence indicates that it does and that it probably produces a local response (p. 109) in the inactive fiber; that is, makes it more susceptible to a stimulus. One may block conduction in a nerve, for example with cold, and yet the current flow can spread beyond the block. On flowing out through the membrane beyond the block it may actually stimulate (and in effect cause the nerve impulse to jump the block), or it may simply render the nerve beyond the block more susceptible to stimulation.

Rates of Conduction.   Rates of conduction in nerve fibers vary according to fiber diameter. That is, a large fiber conducts at a faster rate than a small one. The ratio is such that for myelinated fibers in warm-blooded animals, multiplying the diameter by 6 gives the approximate conduction rate in meters per second. An axon 20 microns in diameter conducts about 120 meters per second. These figures are for cats; available evidence indicates that fibers of comparable size in man conduct more slowly. Nonmyelinated fibers conduct much more slowly, 2 meters per second or less (Fig. 66). Nerve fibers conduct without decrement, that is, the impulses travel without decreasing in magnitude.

Not all of the factors responsible for differences in conduction rates are known, although the presence of myelin is important. Myelin, by virtue of its lipid nature, prevents an outward flow of current, so that only at breaks in the myelin, such as at nodes of Ranvier, can current flow out. During conduction, therefore, current flows out at each node. Its outward flow is prevented between nodes. Hence, the concentration of flow becomes very great at nodes, and this increases the effectiveness of stimulation. By, in effect, skipping from one node to the next, the rate of conduction is greatly increased. The impulse is said to proceed in a *saltatory fashion,* from node to node.

Refractory Periods.   In shooting a rifle, another shot will not result until another bullet is in place and the firing pin drops again. In the same fashion there is a short period following the initiation of a nerve impulse in which another one cannot be set off, no matter how strong the stimulus. This is the *absolute refractory period.* In larger fibers, it lasts about 0.5 millisecond and probably corresponds to most of the time that a given region is depolarized. This continues into the *relative refractory period,* in which nerve impulses can be initiated, but the stimuli have to be stronger than usual; that is to say, the threshold is higher. The total refractory period corresponds approximately to the duration of the spike potential. The threshold returns to normal in 0.5 to 2 milliseconds, depending upon fiber size, but then is lowered as fibers enter a *supernormal phase* (corresponding in time to the negative after-potential). Finally, the threshold increases during a *subnormal phase* (corresponding in time to the positive after-potential). Threshold variations cease after about 80 milliseconds.

The fact that during the passage of a spike potential a fiber is refractory to stimuli limits the number of impulses per unit time in any one

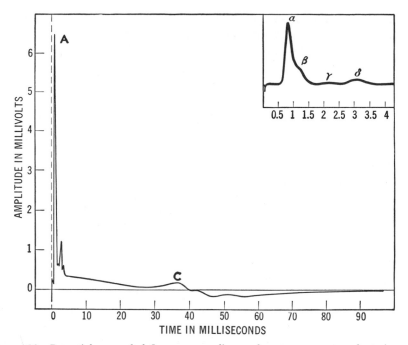

Figure 66. Potentials recorded from mammalian saphenous nerve several centimeters from the point of stimulation. Rapidly traveling nerve impulses reach the electrodes first and are recorded as the *A* elevation. Following the *A* elevation by a considerable interval is the *C* elevation, representing nonmyelinated fibers. The inset shows the *A* elevation recorded from the cat saphenous nerve 6 cm. from the point of stimulation. Since the recording rate is faster, the *A* components, *alpha, beta, gamma* and *delta*, are dispersed to a greater degree and represent the algebraic summation of potentials recorded from fibers varying from 2 to 16 microns in diameter. An intermediate or *B* elevation is recorded only from nerves containing preganglionic autonomic fibers, which are myelinated, but differ considerably from *A* fibers in duration of spike potential and type of after-potential. (From Gasser, H. S., Ohio J. Sci., *41*:145-159, 1941; and Gasser, H. S., Proc. A. Res. Nerv. & Ment. Dis., *23*:44-62, 1943.)

fiber. Nerve impulses, then, are not like a stream of water, but are more like a succession of shots from a machine gun.

After-Potentials. The action potential consists of the spike and the negative and positive after-potentials, the last two being of relatively low amplitude. The *negative after-potential* begins before the spike is through and is a relatively prolonged negative electrical change which may last 15 milliseconds. It is related in time to the supernormal phase of nerve. The *positive after-potential* is a positive electrical change succeeding the negative. It is of longer duration and is associated in time with the subnormal phase of nerve. These after-potentials are probably associated with processes of recovery following the passage of nerve impulses. The total time of all the changes produced by a stimulus may amount to as much as 80 milliseconds. The spike potential accounts for less than 1 millisecond.

The after-potentials are very variable, and are easily affected by changes in ionic environment. Certain drugs also have profound effects. Veratrine, for example, increases and prolongs the negative after-potential.

RECORDING OF POTENTIAL CHANGES

Action potentials may be recorded from a nerve that is removed, suspended on electrodes in a moist atmosphere, and stimulated electrically, according to the method shown in Figure 63. Initiation of an action potential by an artificial stimulus, the application of a brief electrical shock, is illustrated in Figure 65 (p. 101). When the switch is closed, current flows from positive to negative. The region where the current flows out of the membrane to the negative electrode *(cathode)* is the region where depolarization begins and the action potential starts. Figure 67 indicates the conventional method of indicating the recorded response. With two electrodes on a nerve fiber (or on a nerve with many fibers), a diphasic response is recorded. If one electrode is on the killed end, the potential charge cannot travel past that electrode, and a monophasic response is recorded.

One might suppose that if the surface of the depolarized membrane, through which current is flowing inward, is negative, then the surface of the membrane through which current is flowing outward should be relatively positive. Accordingly, in Figure 68 the first change to be detected by the nearest electrode should really be positive, representing current flow outward through the membrane, ahead of the nerve impulse. This should be followed by what is usually thought of as the action potential, represented by a negative change at the depolarized region. This should in turn be succeeded by positivity, representing outward current flow behind the impulse. With both electrodes relatively near the tissue under study, one should record this triphasic process twice. With one electrode relatively far away, only a single triphasic response would be detected.

Such changes are not readily demonstrable in isolated conducting tissue, because the fluid surrounding nerve fibers is less in amount than normal, with the result that the longitudinal flow of current is altered or impeded. This can be demonstrated by replacing this fluid with a nonconducting medium, such as mineral oil. The external resistance is thereby so increased that the rate of conduction decreases.

These complicated electrical changes are more easily demonstrated when the conducting tissue is in its normal situation, that is, in the body

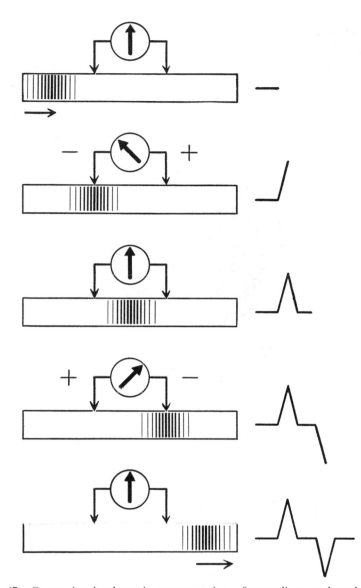

Figure 67. Conventional schematic representation of recording conducted activity. The long rectangle is a nerve on the surface of which are two electrodes (arrows) connected to a galvanometer in which the direction of conduction is indicated by an arrow. As an excitatory or negative change (vertical lines) comes under the first electrode, current flows from positive to negative, as indicated. When the impulse is between the electrodes, no current flows and the record returns to the base line. When it reaches the second electrode, current again flows from positive to negative, but in a direction opposite to that recorded first. When the impulse is past the electrode, no current flows. Thus a diphasic record is obtained.

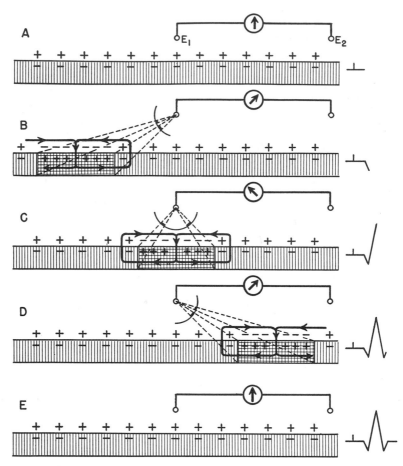

Figure 68. Diagram indicating recording from a volume conductor. *A,* Nerve fiber with electrical charges. At some distance from the nerve, separated by body fluid and tissue, are two electrodes, E_1 and E_2, connected to a recording instrument. E_2 is considered to be far enough away so that it can be neglected in this discussion. At some distance away a stimulus has been applied (not shown), and the shock artifact is shown at the right. *B,* The nerve impulse is conducting toward E_1, and the leading dipole is indicated completely. In order to determine the sign of any recorded potential, lines are drawn from E_1 to each end of the planes separating depolarized from polarized regions. With E_1 as a center, part of a circle is drawn. The length of arc included between each pair of lines is an indication of sign, in the following manner: The pair of lines to the right occupies a longer arc than does the other pair, and the surface of the fiber included by these two lines is positive, whereas that included between the other two is negative. Therefore, E_1 is "looking at more positivity than negativity," and a small positive deflection will be recorded. *C,* Both dipoles are under E_1, and the surfaces included by the lines are both negative; therefore a large negative deflection is recorded. *D,* Both dipoles are past E_1, which is again "looking" at positivity, and a small positive change is again recorded. *E,* The dipoles are relatively far away, and the triphasic change is completed. If E_2 were now represented as being affected, another triphasic change would be recorded, but with opposite signs.

and surrounded by electrolytic fluid or other conducting tissue. Since these electrical changes spread in all directions and since their interpretation involves geometry in three dimensions, the conduction is often called *volume conduction.* The contraction of a muscle is preceded by electrical activity which can easily be detected by electrodes on the overlying skin. The spread of excitation through the heart muscle is accompanied by characteristic electrical changes, the recorded form of which constitutes the *electrocardiogram.* This can be detected by electrodes placed in many positions, a few of which are usually selected as standard leads. An electrode on each wrist, for example, can, when connected with the proper recording equipment, detect the electrical activity of the heart. Electrodes on the scalp can detect the *electroencephalogram,* which is the complex electrical activity of the brain (p. 296).

NERVE IMPULSES AND STIMULI

A nerve impulse derives no energy from an initiating stimulus. If the stimulus reaches a threshold value, one just strong enough to initiate activity, then the nerve fiber responds to the maximum of its ability. A stronger stimulus to the same fiber can accomplish no more. The magnitude of the impulse remains the same. This is known as the *all-or-none law,* and the process may be compared to the firing of a gun. If the pull on the trigger is just strong enough to drop the firing pin (threshold value), the gun will be fired. Pulling harder on the trigger will not change subsequent events. It is the powder charge of the bullet and not the pull on the trigger which determines the response. Nerve fibers, however, differ in their excitability, and any one fiber may change in excitability. Larger and faster conducting fibers are more easily stimulated. An impulse may be initiated in them by a stimulus many times weaker than that necessary to stimulate a nonmyelinated fiber. Furthermore, the spike potentials of larger fibers rise to higher momentary values than do those of smaller fibers. An analogous condition would be the difference between a high-powered rifle with a hair trigger and a .22 caliber rifle in which the trigger pull was great.

Ideally, in studying the events characterizing stimulation, one would use normal physiological stimuli. Light falling on the retina can be controlled in wavelength, intensity and duration. Other stimuli, such as sound, can likewise be controlled. But for nerves coming from regions containing a variety of endings, each sensitive to different types of stimuli, it is difficult to control or measure physiological stimuli. Consequently, artificial stimuli such as electric currents are used. Nerve fibers are long, many times longer than their diameter, and they are cylindrical. Both the axoplasm and the membrane offer resistance to current flow, and the membrane also has the properties of a capacitor. These represent the cable properties of a nerve fiber.

If the electric current applied to a nerve is strong enough, the outward current flow at the cathode will depolarize the membrane to the point that the steady potential is reversed, and the action potential initiated. The cathode, therefore, is the stimulating electrode.

Stimulation takes place primarily during the rate of change. That is, if the current is turned on and left on, so that a constant current is said to flow, then stimulation takes place at the make, when the current is turned on, and at the break, when the current is turned off.

Current has to flow for a certain finite period of time in order to be effective. For example, if one uses brief shocks, that is, currents turned on and off rapidly, then it is found that if the time each stimulus lasts is made shorter and shorter, there is produced a current which lasts such a short time that it will not stimulate, no matter how strong it is. This accounts for the fact that high frequency currents, even though they may be thousands (or millions) of volts, may not stimulate. Conversely, a subthreshold current may not stimulate, no matter how long it is allowed to flow.

The curve illustrated in Figure 69 is a *strength-duration curve*, show-

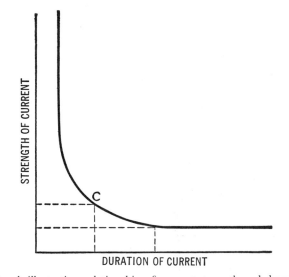

Figure 69. Graph illustrating relationship of current strength and duration. The horizontal portion of the curve indicates the rheobase, the least strength of current which, if flowing an infinite time, is just sufficient to stimulate. A current of less strength will never stimulate, no matter how long it flows. A current of twice rheobase strength reaches threshold after a time interval known as chronaxie, *C*. The vertical portion of the curve indicates that the stronger a current, the shorter its excitation time. Currents of high frequency act over such short times that they may never stimulate, no matter what their intensity.

ing the relationship of the strength of the stimulus to the time during which it acts. That strength of current which, when acting over an infinite time, is just sufficient to stimulate is known as the *rheobase*. If a current of twice the rheobase is chosen and the shortest time during which this can flow and still stimulate is measured, then this time is known as the *chronaxie* or *excitation time*. Chronaxie is an arbitrary but useful measure of excitability which has rather characteristic values for different tissues. More useful, however, are strength-duration curves, whose applications are discussed on p. 151.

Subthreshold Stimuli. It should not be supposed that a stimulus too weak to produce a nerve impulse has no effect on a fiber. On the contrary, a weak (subthreshold) stimulus causes a local response. At the stimulating electrode (the cathode), there is a momentary increase in excitability, that is to say, a decrease in threshold, which can be recorded as a momentary increase in negativity of the surface. This change is not propagated; that is, no such change can be recorded elsewhere than under the cathode. But if another subthreshold stimulus is applied to the same area before the local change dies away, the second local response summates with the first, and the combined effect may result in an excitation of threshold magnitude. In this event it becomes propagated and can be recorded elsewhere as it traverses the fiber. In other words, the first stimulus has facilitated the fiber. It is as if in using a gun one had pulled the trigger halfway back. This is a subthreshold stimulus, and the addition of another one causes the trigger to reach the point at which the firing pin falls and detonates the cartridge.

When a constant current of subthreshold strength is applied, the part of the nerve under the cathode becomes more excitable, but this excitability then slowly decreases, even though the current is still flowing. The converse occurs at the anode. This decline from maximum excitability during the period of constant current is known as *accommodation*, and the various changes are summarized in Figure 70.

Electrical Activity of Cell Bodies. The evidence is that when the cell body is activated, the propagated spike discharge originates in the axon hillock and from the short segment of bare axon. The remainder of the cell body has a higher threshold to a superimposed electrical stimulus than does the axon. After the spike discharge has occurred, the depolarization, which began at the initial segment, also sweeps backward into the cell body and dendrites. This depolarization is then followed by a prolonged hyperpolarization and lowered excitability.

Dendrites also have a higher membrane resistance than do axons. Conduction is slow, it may be decremental, and there is evidence that the depolarization may persist for long periods of time. There is also evidence that local current flow from depolarized dendrites may depolarize cell bodies and cause them to discharge. Maintained dendritic

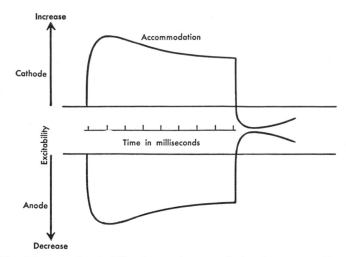

Figure 70. Diagram of excitability changes in nerve during the passage of a current for a short period of time. Note that the nerve under the negative electrode (cathode) increases in excitability very quickly, but that this excitability slowly decreases (accommodation) as the current continues to flow, and drops very abruptly when the current is turned off. In fact, the nerve momentarily becomes less sensitive to stimuli than it was before the current was applied. Converse changes occur in that part of the nerve under the positive electrode (anode). (Based on Erlanger and Blair, Am. J. Physiol., vol. 99, 1931, and Lloyd, in Ruch and Fulton: Physiology, cited on p. 6.)

depolarization may, therefore, serve as a constant stimulus to the cell body and be a factor in repetitive activity in the nervous system. The apical dendrites of cortical neurons have been most extensively studied with regard to these phenomena.

Unipolar and bipolar cells pose some puzzling questions. Their processes are structurally like axons, and there is some question as to the functions of the cell bodies in transmission of nerve impulses. Furthermore, there is some evidence that these cells may conduct in either direction under normal conditions.

SYNAPTIC TRANSMISSION

The arrival of an action potential or of a volley of action potentials at a synapse may be followed by one of a variety of changes, depending upon the origin of the nerve fibers, the distribution and function of the nerve cell, the existing excitability of the nerve cell, and a host of other factors. The following is a simplified account of synaptic mechanisms.

Synaptic transmission can be either chemical or electrical. Chemical synapses are the most common and function as follows. A specific transmitter is synthesized and stored in synaptic vesicles. It is liberated when the nerve impulse arrives at the terminal. It then diffuses across the synaptic cleft and reacts with a chemical receptor in the postsynaptic area. This reaction results in a change in ionic permeability and a change in potential. The synaptic changes may be excitatory or inhibitory, and the synapses involved may be distinguished microscopically.

In neuromuscular junctions, which are a type of excitatory synapse (p. 146), transmitter substance is continually being released in multimolecular packets or quanta. Each packet released causes a local depolarization of the membrane and a tiny, transient fluctuation in potential called a *miniature end-plate potential*. Such changes are now known to occur at central synaptic junctions. The known excitatory transmitters are norepinephrine and acetylcholine (p. 233), in the autonomic system and in certain central nervous system synapses. However, the nature of the transmitter for most central synapses has not yet been determined.

When a nerve impulse arrives at an excitatory synapse, a greater number of packets of transmitter is released. The local depolarization which occurs is greater in magnitude and is known as the *excitatory postsynaptic potential* (EPSP). This local change declines slowly and it is not conducted. It may be enough (about 10 mv.) and may involve enough of the cell surface (by summation with other local changes) to activate the axon hillock and initial segment. The cell is said to "fire off" and the propagated impulse appears.

The total delay in the passage of an impulse across a synaptic junction probably occupies no more than a fraction of a millisecond. When a cell discharges, it undergoes refractory periods as do the axons, and the time relationships may be approximately the same.

The size of EPSP is dependent upon the incoming action potentials. In other words, it does not follow the all-or-none law. Furthermore, the EPSP is capable of summation. If two subthreshold volleys are delivered, one following the other very closely, the second EPSP may summate with the latter part of the first, and thereby cause enough depolarization to fire the cell *(temporal summation)*.

The numbers and locations of synapses on a cell are important factors in synaptic transmission. If subthreshold impulses over several different fibers arrive at widely separated synapses, the EPSP's may not summate (because they conduct decrementally and the depolarized regions may not meet). However, if subthreshold impulses arrive at synapses which are close together, summation may result *(spatial summation)*.

In the case of inhibitory impulses, the transmitter which is released changes permeability and the postsynaptic membrane is hyperpolarized, so that it becomes more stable and less excitable. The result is to decrease or stop existing activity and to prevent future activity for a variable period of time. The potential change is known as the *inhibitory postsynaptic potential* (IPSP). Like the EPSP, it is a graded local response.

The nature of the inhibitory transmitter is unknown, although a number of substances have been implicated. There is inconclusive evidence that amino acids, in particular, γ-aminobutyric acid (GABA) may be involved.

Presynaptic inhibition is another way of preventing activity, and occurs at axo-axonal synapses. The nerve impulse depolarizes the postsynaptic axon so that nerve impulses along the latter will reach the depolarized region and not be conducted.

Electrical synapses also occur, especially in invertebrates. Here, the current flow from the axon terminal is sufficient to depolarize the postsynaptic membrane without the necessity of a chemical transmitter. The current flow can be large enough only when the presynaptic element is large. In most vertebrate synapses, the presynaptic terminals are small relative to the postsynaptic cell, and chemical transmission is therefore a must. It is likely, however, that chemical synapses may depend in part upon, or have properties of, electrical transmission.

SUMMARY

The interior of a nerve fiber or nerve cell is negative to the exterior, the potential difference being known as the steady or resting potential. A threshold stimulus results in a reversal of the steady potential, the interior becoming positive to the exterior. This potential reversal spreads along the cell or fiber. Self-propagation or spread is possible because the current flows inside the fiber, and on flowing out through the membrane ahead of the altered membrane, acts as a stimulus. The conducted potential changes constitute the action potential, the form of which depends upon methods of recording, and is complicated when recorded from intact conducting tissue.

Nerves conduct at rates which depend upon fiber diameter. After the passage of a nerve impulse there are absolute and relative refractory periods as well as negative and positive after-potentials. There are changes in excitability of the nerve, the supernormal and subnormal periods, which correspond to the after-potentials and are associated with recovery processes in the nerve.

A subthreshold stimulus produces a local excitatory state in a fiber; as a result, another subthreshold stimulus may raise the local excitation to a threshold value and thereby set off a nerve impulse. The time during which the stimulus current flows is important. If it is too short, the current will not stimulate. A measure of excitability is chronaxie, the shortest time during which a current of twice rheobase strength must flow in order to stimulate.

Nerve impulses arriving at synaptic junctions may activate the post-synaptic element either electrically or chemically; chemical transmission is the most common and may be excitatory or inhibitory. At excitatory synapses, the known transmitters are norepinephrine and acetylcholine; both depolarize the postsynaptic membrane. The inhibitory transmitter is unknown; it hyperpolarizes the membrane.

REFERENCES

See the references to physiology books cited on p. 6.

Brazier, Mary A. B.: The Electrical Activity of the Nervous System. 2nd ed. New York, Macmillan Company, 1961. (This is an excellent, generalized account of the subject. Both peripheral and central nervous systems are treated, and the conciseness and clearness of the text make it suitable for both beginning and advanced students.)

The following are reviews, monographs and books of an advanced nature, also containing valuable bibliographies.

Bishop, G. H.: Natural history of the nerve impulse. Physiol. Rev., 36:376-399, 1956.
Douglas, W. W., and Ritchie, J. M.: Mammalian nonmyelinated nerve fibers. Physiol. Rev., 42:297-334, 1962.
Eccles, J. C.: The Physiology of Synapses. New York, Academic Press, Inc., 1964.
Hodgkin, A. L.: The Conduction of the Nervous Impulse. Liverpool, Liverpool University Press, 1964.
Ochs, S.: Elements of Neurophysiology. New York, John Wiley and Sons, Inc., 1965.
Tauc, L.: Transmission in invertebrate and vertebrate ganglia. Physiol. Rev., 47:521-593, 1967.

The following two works are clearly written, concise accounts of some of the early studies of nerve conduction and function. All three men were awarded the Nobel Prize in recognition of their work in neurophysiology.

Adrian, E. D.: Mechanism of Nervous Action. Philadelphia, University of Pennsylvania Press, 1932.
Erlanger, J., and Gasser, H. S.: Electrical Signs of Nervous Activity. Philadelphia, University of Pennsylvania Press, 1937.

CHAPTER 8

CHEMISTRY OF THE
NERVOUS SYSTEM

The following is a brief summary of some major trends and problems in a field of major importance. Chemical studies of the nervous system were pioneered primarily by J. L. W. Thudichum. Following his death in 1901, however, anatomical and physiological aspects dominated investigations of the brain. Research in neurochemistry lagged behind biochemical studies of other regions of the body. In recent years, however, biochemistry of the nervous system has become a field of major importance, and developments in this field are of extraordinary significance to our understanding of the nervous system.

GENERAL METABOLISM

The metabolism of the nervous system in general is high. Although the rate of respiration, that is, oxygen consumption, is about the same in resting peripheral nerve as it is in resting muscle, that in the central nervous system is about thirty times as great.

Central Nervous System. Respiratory quotients calculated from cerebral arterial and venous differences and a variety of flow and uptake measurements clearly show that glucose is the prime source of metabolic energy for the brain. Lactate and pyruvate can contribute at times, and substances such as butyrate may be additional sources of energy in long-term starvation. In a person at rest, about 20 per cent of inspired

114

oxgen is removed from the blood by the brain (a significant part of the general circulation is to the brain). Sleep does not decrease overall cerebral metabolism, but surgical anesthesia, diabetic coma, uremia, and hepatic coma are accompanied by decreased cerebral oxygen consumption. In tissue slice studies, changes in electrolyte composition which necessitate active transport of ions cause a marked increase in metabolism.

Peripheral Nervous System. Information about the metabolism of the nervous system has also been obtained by studying isolated peripheral nerves. Such studies show that peripheral nerves differ from the central nervous system in that their respiratory quotient is 0.8 instead of 1, indicating that they utilize noncarbohydrate as well as carbohydrate. For example, if a peripheral nerve is removed and placed in a moist chamber, oxygen consumption may continue at the usual rate, and the ability to conduct may persist for hours, even after the utilization of carbohydrate has stopped. An active peripheral nerve is not metabolically restricted to glucose, but may derive energy from some as yet unknown metabolite.

Exogenous glucose likewise seems to be the main substrate for resting metabolism in sympathetic ganglion cells. However, although glucose utilization is accelerated during activity, the substrate for activity metabolism is not glucose. The significance of increased glucose utilization during activity is uncertain.

INTERMEDIARY METABOLISM

Carbohydrate Metabolism. All the enzymic components of the classic Embden-Meyerhof glycolytic pathway have been found in brain tissue. The elegant studies of Lowry and his coworkers on the dynamics of all the substrates of the pathway have clearly shown the roles of phosphocreatine and glycogen as energy stores maintaining adenosine triphosphate homeostasis (Fig. 71). The regulatory role of phosphofructokinase can be seen in stresses such as anoxia, in which the intermediates beyond this point in the pathway increase and those preceding decrease. Phosphofructokinase is an allosteric enzyme affected by a number of small molecules involved in glycolysis. Mental retardation is frequent in galactosemia associated with galactose-1-phosphate uridyl transferase deficiency. The hypoglycemia seen after galactose injection may be causally related to the mental deficiency.

The pentose monophosphate pathway also makes a contribution to cerebral carbohydrate metabolism but there is disagreement as to

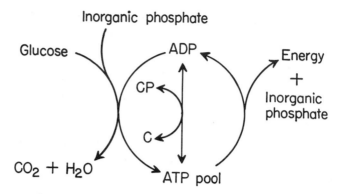

Figure 71. A schematic representation of the transfer of energy from glucose metabolism. Energy latent in the glucose molecule is evolved in the form of a high energy phosphate group. The hydrolysis of most common organic phosphate esters evolves 2000 to 4000 calories per mole, while certain of the organic phosphates produced in glucose metabolism yield 10,000 to 16,000 calories per mole. These high energy phosphate groups are used by the cell in the form of the nucleotide, adenosine triphosphate (ATP), which is synthesized by the cell from adenosine diphosphate (ADP), inorganic phosphate and energy. Although a pool or reserve supply of ATP is available, the cell calls upon a secondary energy carrier, creatine phosphate (CP), during sudden bursts of activity. In the resting state some ATP is used to synthesize CP, which is then reconvertible to ATP at the appropriate time. Thus, slices of guinea pig cerebral tissue show a loss of CP following electrical stimulation, and a concomitant rise of inorganic phosphate, while ATP remains normal. When stimulation stops, CP and inorganic phosphate return to their normal levels.

the extent of its contribution. Careful studies with calf brains in which the perfusion fluid was not recirculated and the fates of glucose-6-^{14}C and glucose-6-^{3}H were parallel indicated that the pentose pathway was major. Others appraise the pathway at one fifth the level of the Embden-Meyerhof contribution.

The dynamics of citric acid cycle intermediates have also been studied. The anesthetic agents studied caused a marked decrease in α-ketoglutarate, fumarate and malate, whereas insulin hypoglycemia was associated with a general decrease of all the intermediates in the cycle.

Lipid Metabolism. Lipids comprise almost half of the dry weight of the brain. About one fourth of the cholesterol of the body is found in the nervous system, and isotope incorporation studies and the presence of cholesterol intermediates suggest that most cerebral cholesterol is synthesized *in situ.* The turnover of cholesterol is small. Modest amounts of unesterified fatty acids are found, but major amounts are found in esterified form. Although brain tissue slices can metabolize C-8 and C-10 fatty acids, these are normally not an important energy source *in vivo.* Phospholipids represent a major group of lipids, of which phosphatidyl ethanolamine (cephalin), phosphatidyl choline (lecithin), phosphatidyl serine, phosphatidyl inositol and plasmalogens are major components. Certain phospholipids, e.g., phosphatidyl inositol, undergo fairly rapid metabolic turnover, suggesting an important as yet undefined metabolic role. Sphingomyelin containing lipids, or sphingolipids, comprise a complex group of substances with wide-ranging properties. The biosynthesis and degradation of these substances are under careful study because of the accumulation of these substances in the brain in certain hereditary diseases. Generally speaking, these diseases — sphingomyelin lipidosis (Niemann-Pick disease), sulfatide lipidosis (metachromatic leukodystrophy), ganglioside lipidosis (Tay-Sachs' disease), cerebroside lipidosis (Gaucher's disease) and glycolipid lipidosis (Fabry's disease) — represent failure of normal sphingolipid degradation subsequent to deficiency of specific enzymes.

Amino Acid Metabolism. Amino acid metabolism is also a prominent feature of nervous tissue, as would be expected from the number of amino acid derivatives (epinephrine, norepinephrine, γ-aminobutyrate, serotonin and melatonin) and peptide hormones found. The biosynthesis of these substances has been well studied and much current work is concerned with control of their synthesis and release. Pineal melatonin plays an important role in circadian rhythm. Many psychic energizers and depressants act by displacing active molecules from receptors or by inhibiting their breakdown (e.g., monoamine oxidase inhibitors). Many drugs bear a close chemical resemblance to active molecules (e.g., lysergic acid diethylamide and serotonin).

Hereditary disorders of amino acid metabolism secondary to enzyme deficiency are often accompanied by mental and neurological symptomatology. Mental retardation is frequent. Phenylketonuria (hereditary phenylalanine hydroxylase deficiency) is the most publicized of this class of disorders, but branched chain ketonuria (maple syrup urine disease), histidinemia (histidase deficiency), hypervalinemia (valine transaminase deficiency), hyperlysinemia, hydroxyprolinemia ("hydroxyproline oxidase" deficiency), hyperprolinemia (proline oxidase deficiency), hyperammonemia (ornithine transcarbamylase deficiency), citrullinemia, argininosuccinaciduria (argininosuccinase deficiency), cystathioninuria (cystathionase deficiency) and homocystinuria (cystathionine synthetase deficiency) are all frequently associated with mental retardation. The existence of this group of diseases implies that the concentration of each free amino acid must be carefully controlled, especially in early life. Although serotonin deficiency secondary to tryptophan metabolism inhibition by phenylalanine derivatives has been proposed for the chemical pathogenesis of phenylketonuria, it seems likely that some more general phenomena is involved, such as interference with protein synthesis or with membrane transport of a group of amino acids. Familial goiter is often associated with mental retardation. Various metabolic defects may be found in different family groups.

Protein and Ribonucleic Acid Metabolism.   Nerve cells have the highest content of ribonucleic acid (RNA) of any somatic cell of the body and a correspondingly high rate of protein turnover. This has spurred some elegant experimental work on the synthesis and characterization of RNA during the learning process in single cells and considerable speculation about the role of proteins or RNA as memory molecules. Agranoff has clearly shown that puromycin, an inhibitor of protein synthesis, inhibits the development of long term but not short term memory in goldfish.

Vitamins.   Vitamins (or derivatives formed from them in the body) usually function as cofactors for enzymes. Accordingly, deficiency may cause neurological symptoms. Deficiencies of thiamin, which plays a role in the oxidative decarboxylation of α-keto acids; nicotinamide, which is a frequent acceptor for hydrogens removed by dehydrogenases; pyridoxine, which functions in transamination and many other reactions of amino acids; and cobalamin (vitamin B_{12}), which is a carrier of single carbon fragments, are often associated with neurological symptoms.

Clinical Importance.   A better understanding of metabolic reactions in nervous tissue and their relation to nervous activity can lead to such practical matters as diagnosis and therapy, as well as the advancement of ancillary fields such as anesthesiology. At present, anesthetics are used on an empiric basis so far as their effects on the nervous system are concerned. Their modes of action remain unknown, although it is highly probable that they affect the permeability of nerve membranes, or alter or inhibit the chemical reactions at synaptic junctions. Ether, for example, produces surgical anesthesia by acting mainly on higher centers. Barbiturate compounds, of which there are a variety, may have more general effects, and their use is often accompanied by a more profound depression of vital centers in the medulla oblongata and spinal cord. Local anesthetics such as *procaine* block conduction of impulses at the site of application.

INORGANIC CONSTITUENTS

In general, cerebral tissue has a fairly constant water content; water forms 85 per cent of the gray matter and 70 per cent of the white matter. Potassium and sodium are among the most important cations and are discussed elsewhere (p. 97). Other minerals are present, but their functions are largely unknown. Iron is present in nerve cells, and there are regional differences in its concentration. Copper is also present, and there are indications that it has an important function. There is a degenerative disease of the liver and the basal ganglia (Wilson's hepatolenticular degeneration), in which there is abnormal excretion of amino acids, and in which copper is found in especially high concentrations in the liver and the basal ganglia. There is also evidence that an abnormality of copper metabolism may be concerned in certain demyelinating diseases affecting sheep. Copper is usually associated with a particular protein in the blood, ceruloplasmin, the level of which is markedly decreased in Wilson's disease.

CHEMISTRY OF CELL CONSTITUENTS

Myelin.   Myelin is composed of alternating layers of lipid and protein (Fig. 53, p. 79). The chief lipids in myelin are *cholesterol, cerebrosides,* and *sphingosides.* The last two are complex esters of fatty acids, phosphoric acid, and the unsaturated amino alcohol, sphingosine. Cerebrosides are complicated by the presence of a molecule of hexose in their structure. Also present in the lipoproteins of myelin are a number of the simpler *phospholipids.* There is little or no triglyceride in the brain.

The nature of proteins in myelin is largely unknown. Perhaps they are *neurokeratins,* the proteins in myelin having solubility properties similar to those of the keratins of the skin and hair, although their amino acid content is different.

Golgi Apparatus.   The Golgi apparatus, which includes the Golgi bodies or *lipochondria,* is chemically very complex. The lipochondria contain phosphatides (phospholipids), as well as the class of carbohydrate-containing lipids known as *glycolipids.* The Golgi apparatus may be associated with certain enzymatic processes. After an axon is cut, many small spheres (lipochondria?) are seen near the nucleus.

Nucleoproteins of Nucleus and Cytoplasm.   Nucleoproteins are conjugated proteins associated with the nucleic acids, *ribonucleic acid* (RNA) and *deoxyribonucleic acid* (DNA). RNA is present in the nucleolus, small quantities are found in chromosomes, and it is present in large amounts in the Nissl substance. DNA is found only in the nucleus, where it forms the sex chromatin. Nucleic acids in general are large polymers of subunits or nucleotides, which in turn are composed of a pentose unit, a purine or pyrimidine base, and phosphoric acid. Nucleoproteins are apparently depleted during intense activity of the nerve cell, are depleted or altered during chromatolysis, and are involved in some way in regenerative processes. Possibly they are associated with protein synthesis, because cytological evidence indicates a local increase in nucleic acid during regeneration. For example, nucleoli enlarge when regeneration begins after section of an axon.

Mitochondria.   Mitochondria are distributed throughout the cytoplasm. Often called the powerhouse of the cell, they are the sites of the

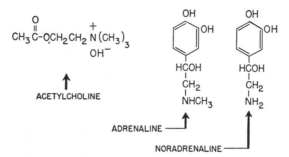

Figure 72. Formulae of certain transmitters and of adrenaline.

citric acid cycle and oxidative phosphorylation, and accordingly are the major site of ATP synthesis. Mitochondria have been shown by electron microscopy to be surrounded by double membranes that consist of two protein layers separated by a double layer of lipids.

Hormones. Special hormones may also be important constituents of certain nerve cells. Thus, there are neurosecretory cells in the hypothalamus (p. 228). These cells form a substance that passes down their axons to the neurohypophysis and is there released as posterior pituitary hormones.

Transmitters. Transmitters are released at the synaptic and motor endings of nerve fibers (p. 110). These substances, acetylcholine, adrenaline, and noradrenaline (Fig. 72), are probably closely related to the general metabolism of carbohydrates and amino acids. Adrenaline and noradrenaline are related in structure to the amino acid tyrosine, whereas acetylcholine probably derives its component structures from both amino acid and carbohydrate metabolism.

CHEMISTRY AND BEHAVIOR

Recent work relating chemical to behavioral processes is of special interest. Particular attention has been paid to the biogenic amines, the distribution of which has been studied by histochemical fluorescent methods. These include the catecholamines, norepinephrine and dopamine, and the indole amine, *serotonin.* Norepinephrine is a transmitter (p. 150); it is also found in high concentrations in certain parts of the brain such as the hypothalamus. However, its role in the brain is still uncertain. It is synthesized from the amino acid tyrosine through intermediates, one of which is dopamine.

Serotonin is synthesized from the precursor amino acid 5-hydroxytryptophan. It is found in various peripheral tissues, and is present in the brain in roughly the same areas where norepinephrine is found.

There seems to be a fairly consistent relationship between the biogenic amines and affective or behavioral states in that drugs which depress or inactivate norepinephrine centrally cause sedation or depression, whereas the converse is generally associated with stimulation or excitement. One such drug is *reserpine*, which interferes with the intraneuronal binding of catecholamines and serotonin. Its resultant depressant action is the basis of its use as a "tranquilizer." An example of a drug used as a psychic stimulant is *amphetamine*, which may both release physiologically active norepinephrine from nerve cells and block its inactivation.

Many compounds have the capability of producing profound mental disturbances, including hallucinations and psychotic episodes. *Lysergic acid diethylamide* (LSD) is one such drug. When given even in the most minute quantities, it causes severe, often long-lasting disturbances and may also cause marked chromosomal damage. Its mode of action is still uncertain.

Names in Neurology

J. L. W. THUDICHUM (1828-1901)

Generally called father of the chemistry of the brain, Thudichum, a London physician of German birth, first practiced medicine and then, in 1864, began the study of what are now called lipochromes or carotinoids. He and his assistants then carried out the first systematic attempts to isolate and characterize the chemical composition of the brain. The results of their work were published in 1884 as "A Treatise on the Chemical Constitution of the Brain," revised in 1901. Thudichum clearly recognized the importance of his contributions, but decades were to elapse before extensive study in the field began again. Thudichum actively practiced medicine, mainly in ear, nose, and throat work, he studied gallstones and later in life he wrote two books, one on cookery and one on wines.

REFERENCES

Agranoff, B. N.: Memory and protein synthesis. Sci. Amer., *216*:115-122, 1967.

McIlwain, H.: Biochemistry and the Central Nervous System. 3rd ed. Boston, Little, Brown and Company, 1966. (A treatise of an advanced nature, with considerable factual data.)

Quastel, J. H., and Quastel, D. M. J.: The Chemistry of Brain Metabolism in Health and Disease. Springfield, Ill., Charles C Thomas, 1961. (A monograph by outstanding investigators.)

Schildkraut, J. J., and Kety, S. S.: Biogenic amines and emotion. Science, *156*:21-30, 1967. (An excellent review.)

Stanbury, J. B., Wyngaarden, J. B., and Fredrickson, D. S.: The Metabolic Basis of Inherited Disease. 2nd ed. New York, McGraw-Hill Book Co., 1966. (An excellent volume on an important aspect of neurological disorders.)

CHAPTER 9

GENERAL PROPERTIES
OF THE REFLEX ARC

A reflex act may be defined as a relatively fixed pattern of response or behavior that is similar for any given stimulus. The pupil of the eye gets smaller when a light is flashed in the eye. A hand inadvertently set on a hot object is immediately jerked away; the withdrawal is partially completed before pain is felt. A few drops of a weak acid may be placed on the skin of a frog that has had its brain destroyed. The animal attempts to get rid of the irritating agent by making active, coordinated limb movements. These movements do not take place if the spinal cord is destroyed or if the nerves between the cord and the leg have been cut. The pathway consists of afferent nerves by which impulses initiated by the stimulus reach the spinal cord; synaptic connections are made within the cord so that impulses leave by way of efferent nerves which transmit them to the proper skeletal muscles. The total pathway is termed a *reflex path* or *reflex arc* and can function independently of higher centers. This independence, however, is rarely characteristic of normal activity.

Receptors, Neuroeffector Junctions and Effectors. These are the structures that receive stimuli and produce responses. They are discussed in more detail in Chapter 10. *Receptors* are either specialized terminations of the peripheral processes of unipolar cells, or they are nerve endings associated with special sense organs. *Neuroeffector junctions* are specialized terminals of efferent fibers arising from cells in the central nervous system or from cells in autonomic ganglia. *Effectors* are structures which carry out the actual responses. In the higher animals, including man, they are muscle fibers and gland cells.

TYPES OF REFLEXES

Reflexes are often classified according to the smallest number of neurons by which their pathways can be represented. Such paths are abstractions only; functionally, they rarely, if ever, operate in such isolated form.

Three-Neuron Reflex Arcs. There are a variety of such reflexes, perhaps best exemplified by the reflex withdrawal of a limb in response to a painful stimulus. The impulses travel centrally and are widely distributed within the spinal cord so that, after passage through *interneurons (intercalated* or *internuncial neurons),* they activate many motor cells. Thus, reflex flexion at several joints may follow a painful stimulus to a relatively small area of skin. Figure 73 illustrates the simplest abstraction of such a reflex. Three-neuron reflexes may also be initiated by stimulation of receptors in deep tissues (in reflex components of walking) and are the most common type of reflex involving skeletal muscle.

Two-Neuron Reflex Arcs. Certain reflexes may be represented by a pathway of two neurons (Fig. 74). Nearly everyone is familiar with the knee jerk, which is elicited by tapping the tendon of the quadriceps

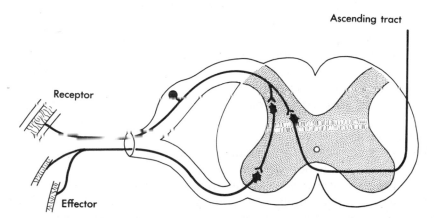

Figure 73. Diagram illustrating how impulses from a cutaneous receptor reach an effector (skeletal muscle), by a three-neuron arc at the level of entrance. Impulses also reach the cerebral hemisphere by way of an ascending tract.

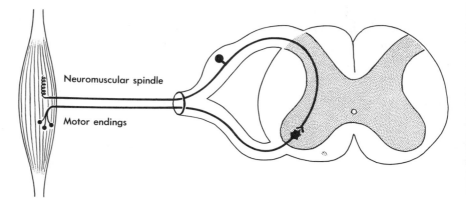

Figure 74. Diagram of a two-neuron reflex, from a spindle in a muscle back to other fibers of the same muscle.

femoris muscle just below the patella (knee cap). This stretches the muscle, and the receptors stimulated include *neuromuscular spindles* (described on p. 138). The resulting nerve impulses reach the spinal cord over fibers which synapse with cells in the ventral gray matter. These are large multipolar cells called ventral horn cells, or *motor neurons*. The axons of these cells transmit impulses to the muscle originally lengthened, which then contracts and regains its former length.

This *stretch* or *myotatic reflex* is a rather restricted or local type of response. In its simplest form, it involves two neurons and, therefore, one area of synaptic junctions. The nerve fibers concerned are large and conduct rapidly. Since there is also a minimum of synaptic delay, the resulting reflexes are among the fastest known. Myotatic reflexes are further characterized by the fact that the motor discharge is mainly restricted to the muscle which was stretched.

The knee jerk is also called a *phasic* type of stretch reflex. The muscle is stretched quickly, and the spindles within it are stimulated at the same time. Consequently, the resulting nerve impulses travel centrally as a synchronous volley, much like a volley from a rifle squad when the rifles are fired simultaneously. The reflex discharges from the spinal cord are likewise in phase, so that muscle fibers are activated at the same time. The result is a quick, reflex muscular contraction, lasting but a short time; hence the term "jerk."

There are also *static* types of stretch reflexes. If a muscle is slowly stretched, varying numbers of spindles are stimulated, some at first and some later as the stretch increases or is maintained. The result is an irregular, or asynchronous, discharge from these endings, much as if the members of a rifle squad were firing in sequence or at random. The reflex motor discharge is likewise asynchronous, and muscle fibers are activated at different times. The result is a more sustained contraction, but one in which at any one time only a relatively few muscle fibers may be in action.

Muscles are stretched when their antagonists contract, and also when joints are flexed as a result of the effect of gravity upon a limb. It is ordinarily held that antigravity muscles are so sensitive to the latter situation that they always exhibit static stretch reflexes, to the extent that they have what is called *tone* or *postural contraction*. It is also held that tone may be present in muscles which are not strictly postural. Although tone is undoubtedly present in lower animals, its presence in man under all postural conditions is debatable. A muscle can be so relaxed that no electrical or mechanical activity can be detected. What tone it now possesses is a result of its inherent elasticity and not of neurological mechanisms. Furthermore, in an upright, comfortable position, with feet fairly well apart, there is little if any electrical or mechanical activity in the antigravity muscles until there is a fairly considerable deviation or flexion. In other words, the structure and arrangement of human joints are such that in an upright static position they provide maximum stability. Little if any muscular effort is needed. In other types of positions tone is undoubtedly present, and reflex mechanisms are of course easily demonstrated upon deviation from the mechanically stable situation. It should be emphasized that most experimental work on stretch reflexes has been carried out on lower animals, such as cats.

COORDINATION OF REFLEX ARCS

Reflex arcs are not limited to the spinal cord, but occur over brain stem areas as well. In an intact organism, the initiating impulses may also traverse fibers which reach the cerebral cortex, where they may be interpreted as sensations. But reflexes are not dependent upon this. A painful stimulus may be followed by a reflex response before the subject experiences pain or even without the knowledge of pain. Responses may occur after the spinal cord has been severed above the level over which the reflex takes place. Although a subject under general anesthesia feels no pain, reflexes can be elicited by appropriate stimuli.

To the casual observer a reflex is an apparently simple and relatively isolated mechanism of which the knee jerk is a splendid example. The response is an extension of the leg. But is it so simple? In order for this to happen, the opposing muscles (flexors of the leg) must give way to a degree corresponding to the extension. The muscles are said to relax, and the production of this relaxation is an inhibitory function of the gray matter of the cord. Impulses from the receptors in the muscle are

carried by dorsal root fibers into the cord. Here the fibers reach the
motor neurons supplying the extensors. But branches also reach inhibitory interneurons (Fig. 75) whose axons in turn reach the motor
cells supplying flexor muscles. This *reciprocal inhibition* is frequently
termed *Sherrington's inhibition* (p. 134). Motor cells may also be inhibited
by interneurons termed Renshaw cells which are activated by recurrent
collaterals of other motor cells (Fig. 75). The transmitter released by
the recurrent collaterals is known to be acetylcholine. Inhibition may be
inhibited, and it may be presynaptic (Fig. 76).

Let us return to the protective reflex, cited on p. 122, brought about
in a frog by placing a few drops of a weak acid on the skin of its leg. The
reflex is complex because a number of muscles are involved in the withdrawal movement. These are supplied by efferent fibers from more than
one segment of the cord. Therefore, the cells with which the entering
dorsal root fibers synapse connect with motor neurons at the same level
and also send axons up and down the cord to motor neurons at other
levels (Fig. 77). These *ipsilateral* connections provide for widespread
reciprocal responses.

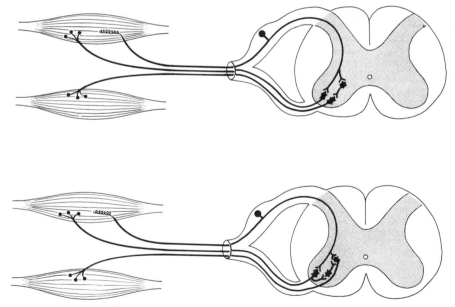

Figure 75. Upper, schematic representation of a two-neuron reflex with a collateral given
to an interneuron which is inhibitory to the motor neuron supplying the antagonistic
muscle. *Lower,* schematic representation of another mechanism of inhibition, namely, the
Renshaw cell which is activated by collaterals of motor cells and which in turn is inhibitory
to adjacent motor cells. (Modified from Wilson, V. J., Sci. Amer., *214*:102-110, 1966.)

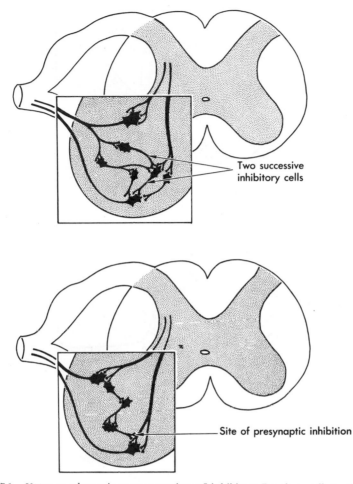

Two successive inhibitory cells

Site of presynaptic inhibition

Figure 76. *Upper,* a schematic representation of inhibitory Renshaw cells (activated by collaterals of axons of motor neurons) acting upon a second inhibitory cell, thus allowing excitation of another motor cell. *Lower,* a schematic representation showing that pre-synaptic inhibition (p. 112) depends upon events occurring at axo-axonal synapses. (Modified from Wilson, V. J., Sci. Amer., *214*:102-110, 1966.)

These responses are further complicated by the necessity, in many cases, of *contralateral responses.* Suppose that a painful stimulus is applied to the bottom of the foot. The entire lower limb may be withdrawn or jerked away. The weight of the body must then be supported by the opposite lower limb whose muscles, therefore, contract strongly. There is an anatomic basis for such a response. In addition to the connections of internuncial neurons cited earlier, axons cross the midline of the spinal cord and reach motor neurons at many levels (Fig. 78). Motor

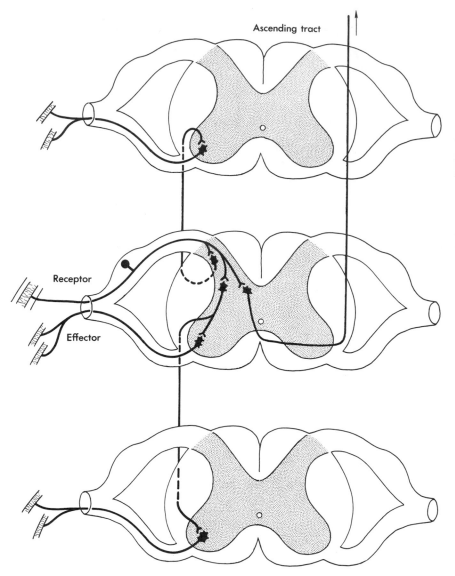

Figure 77. Diagram of the connections by which impulses from a receptor reach motor neurons at different cord levels. This accounts for multisegmental, ipsilateral responses.

impulses thus reach muscles in the opposite extremity; this again is accompanied by the necessary reciprocal inhibition.

These examples illustrate admirably the remarkable degree of co-ordination of two equally significant interacting mechanisms, namely, excitation and inhibition. When one group of muscles contracts, certain other muscles must either contract or relax to a like degree. This may

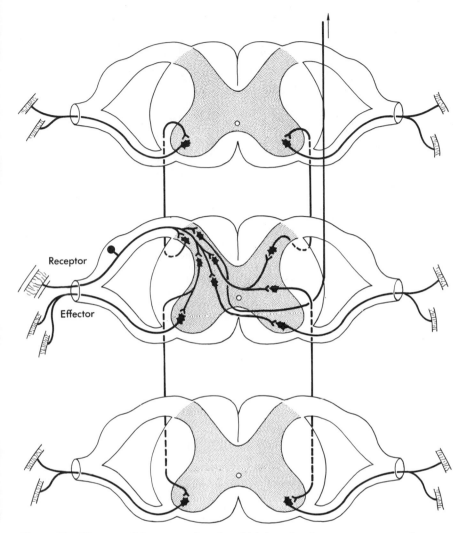

Figure 78. Diagram of the connections by which impulses from a receptor reach motor neurons at various levels of both sides of the spinal cord. This accounts for multisegmental, ipsilateral and contralateral responses.

be a reflex activity or, as will be shown later, a result of voluntary mechanisms.

Reflexes are not so invariable as the definition of a reflex would indicate. For instance, an afferent nerve may be stimulated and a muscle reflexly contracts. But when the stimulation stops and impulses can no longer be recorded from the afferent nerve, the muscle may continue to contract for many milliseconds during which time impulses can be recorded from the efferent nerve. This is an *after-discharge*. The branch-

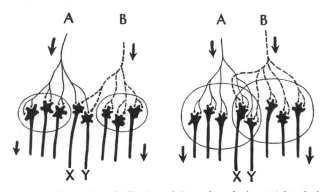

Figure 79. Diagram illustrating facilitation *(left)* and occlusion *(right)*. It is arbitrarily assumed that impulses at two synaptic junctions are necessary to stimulate a motor neuron. *Left:* Afferent fiber *A* forms two junctions with each motor neuron in the encircled field, but only one each with motor neurons *X* and *Y*. An impulse over *A* therefore causes three neurons to discharge. The same situation obtains for *B*. But if impulses arrive over *A* and *B* simultaneously, not only will the six encircled neurons discharge, but also *X* and *Y*, since these will have two active junctions each. The reflex response will be greater than could be postulated from the result of stimulating *A* and *B* separately. *Right:* Afferent fiber *A* forms two junctions with each of five motor neurons, as does *B*. But *X* and *Y* are common to both, so that impulses over *A* and *B* simultaneously cause eight, and not ten, neurons to discharge. The reflex response is less than could be postulated from the result of stimulating *A* or *B* separately.

ing of an entering fiber allows an impulse to traverse paths containing varying numbers of interneurons and thus to reach a motor neuron at different times, providing for a succession of discharges from it. Furthermore, some of the interneurons in the gray matter form closed circuits which can continue to excite a motor neuron after impulses have ceased entering the cord (see Fig. 107, p. 184). The multiple and closed circuits may be characteristic of gray matter throughout the central nervous system.

The degree to which afferent fibers overlap in making functional connections with interneurons and motor neurons provides another basis for variability. Figure 79 illustrates how reflexes elicited by stimulation of different afferent fibers may either summate or become occluded.

REFLEXES AND BEHAVIOR

It would seem justified to consider the reflex arc a basic unit of the nervous system. The isolation and study of clear-cut reflexes would support the conception of a nervous system composed of a series of such arcs, integrated and controlled by higher centers. Indeed, such a conception is commonly encountered. But is such the case? Do the facts support it? Can we really conceive of the nervous system as a mass of such stereotyped patterns? No, we cannot. The reflex should be regarded as a local, highly differentiated mechanism the study of which affords little insight into those higher functions which are characterized by extreme variability.

The concept that the reflex arc is the basic unit of the nervous system implies that it is the first recognizable pattern to appear in the embryo. There are, however, no anatomic or physiologic data which adequately support this hypothesis. In taking motility, that is, muscle activity, as an index of behavior, one can distinguish two general modes of origin of motility: spontaneous (resulting from the activity of motor nerve supply) and reflex (resulting from the stimulation of sensory elements). In the embryo, motor nerve supply develops first, as described below. Hence, spontaneous and not reflex activity is usually the first kind of motility to be present.

The admirable work of Coghill on the spotted salamander, *Ambystoma punctatum,* established that in amphibians motility and behavior show integrated patterns from the beginning. As the larva develops, the longitudinal motor chains are formed, from brain to muscle. In the early but nonmobile stage, muscles are contractile, but the animal cannot respond to the stimulus of light touch on the skin, even though nerve fibers supply the skin. There are no interneurons in the cord, and reflexes do not appear until interneurons do.

In birds and mammals, early spontaneous motility is even more marked, and appears before reflexes do. The spontaneity is evidence of activity generated within the central nervous system. It is both random and rhythmic, and yet shows no evidence of pattern. One of the major problems concerns the way in which patterned, integrative, adaptive behavior emerges from this generalized, spontaneous motility of embryos. In any event, it is evident that the pattern of skin and muscle innervation is laid down *before* animals can reflexly respond to changes in the external environment. Therefore, experience with such changes cannot influence the initial development of structural foundations of response.

CLINICAL VALUE OF REFLEXES

Reflexes are important, because an examination of them may yield information about the nature and location of neurological disorders. Clinically, reflexes may be classified as superficial, deep, special, and abnormal.

Superficial reflexes are those elicited by cutaneous stimulation. If the skin of the abdominal wall is scratched, the abdominal muscles contract.

The toes flex if the sole of the foot is scratched. These responses are of the three-neuron or flexor type.

Deep reflexes are those elicited by tapping a tendon and are of the stretch or myotatic type. Those commonly tested are the *ankle jerk*, by tapping the tendo calcaneus (Achilles tendon, p. 133), with resulting plantar flexion of the foot; the *knee jerk*, by tapping the quadriceps femoris tendon just below the patella, the leg extending; the *biceps jerk*, by tapping the biceps brachii tendon and obtaining a flexion of the forearm; and the *triceps jerk*, by tapping the tendon of the triceps brachii muscle, the forearm extending.

Special reflexes involve structures other than skeletal muscles. When a light is flashed upon the eye, the diameter of the pupil lessens, thus restricting the amount of light which can enter the organ. Some of the more important special reflexes will be discussed in Chapters 14 and 16.

Abnormal or *pathological reflexes* are those not present normally or are exaggerations of normal ones. Disorders of the spinal cord or higher centers are the common causes, and the reasons for them are discussed in Chapter 11. The most important pathological reflex is the *Babinski response* (p. 133). This is a dorsiflexion of the big toe and often a fanning of the other toes, rather than plantar flexion, when the sole of the foot is stimulated (Fig. 80).

The usefulness of such examinations is shown as follows: If a knee jerk is absent and cutaneous sensation is absent over the knee and thigh, but the patient can voluntarily extend his leg, an action which cannot be produced reflexly, then dorsal roots must be involved. This interrupts

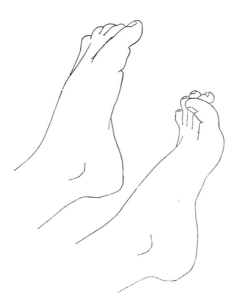

Figure 80. *Upper:* The normal response to scratching the sole of the foot. *Lower:* Pathological or Babinski response.

afferent impulses of reflex and sensory pathways. But if cutaneous sensation is normal and leg extensions cannot be produced either reflexly or voluntarily, the involvement is of ventral horn cells or ventral roots, that is, the efferent pathway. If the first two instances are combined, however, the disorder must affect spinal or peripheral nerves in which both efferent and afferent fibers are present.

SUMMARY

In reflex mechanisms, nerve impulses from the periphery reach the central nervous system and are then relayed back to the periphery, where a response occurs. Receptors, central connections, neuroeffector junctions, and effectors are parts of reflex arcs.

The simplest of these are two-neuron arcs for stretch or myotatic reflexes, and three-neuron arcs for flexor or superficial reflexes.

Reflex responses involve not only contractions, but also relaxations, of opposing muscles. A number of muscles may be involved in or be subsidiary to a reflex. Ipsilateral and contralateral connections within the cord provide for these.

Reflexes are to be regarded as highly differentiated mechanisms which arise secondarily from a total response pattern. They are not to be regarded as the basic units of the nervous system.

The clinical examination of reflexes may enable one to determine the nature and location of neurological disorders.

Names in Neurology

ACHILLES, SON OF PELEUS AND THETIS

After Thetis dipped the child in the waters of the River Styx, he became invulnerable except in that part of the heel by which she held him. From this arises the proverbial term, "heel of Achilles." It was here he later received a mortal wound. The tendon by which the calf muscles attach to the calcaneus or heel bone is termed the Achilles tendon, and the reflex elicited by tapping this tendon is the Achilles reflex.

JOSEF BABINSKI (1857-1932)

Babinski, a Parisian of Polish parentage, made great contributions to clinical neurology. In 1896, he began a series of short publications in which he described one of the most significant signs in clinical neurology—the pathological cutaneous plantar reflex which now bears his name.

SIR CHARLES SCOTT SHERRINGTON (1859-1952)

There is scarcely a phase of neurophysiology in which this noted English physiologist was not a pioneer or a leading investigator. A few of his most important contributions are studies of muscular rigidity, reciprocal innervation, physiology of synapses, many types of reflexes, the activity of the cerebral cortex, and functions of the inner ear. In all his work, he stressed the integrative actions and coordinating mechanisms of the nervous system. It is difficult to do justice to the extent of his contributions to our understanding of the nervous system. So much that is known today can be traced to an original work by Sir Charles that one can do more than state that this is the situation. He was as pre-eminent in neurophysiology as Jackson was in clinical neurology and Ramón y Cajal in neuroanatomy.

REFERENCES

For discussions of structure and function of reflex arcs, refer to the neuroanatomy and physiology textbooks cited on p. 6.

Coghill, G. E.: Anatomy and the Problems of Behavior. Cambridge, Cambridge University Press, 1929. (A summary of a series of classic investigations of nervous structure and behavior.)
Hamburger, V.: Some aspects of the embryology of behavior. Quart. Rev. Biol., 38:342-378, 1963. (An excellent review, relating Coghill's work to recent studies on higher animals.)
Walshe, F.: The Babinski plantar response, its forms and its physiological and pathological significance. Brain, 79:529, 1956. (A classic review. See also the reference to Clinical Examinations cited on p. 154.)

CHAPTER 10

STRUCTURES MEDIATING RECEPTION AND RESPONSE

A hand touching a hot light globe is pulled away; the patellar tendon is tapped and the leg reflexly extends; an object moves suddenly into the field of vision and the eye blinks; one is thirsty and takes a drink of water; a symphony orchestra provides a pleasurable background to a session in the easy chair. These are responses to stimuli, that is, to changes in the environment. How are such changes recorded, and how is one type of change differentiated from another? What structures carry out the responses? The environmental changes are detected by *receptors,* and the responses are carried out by *effectors.* These structures and their connections will be the subject of this and succeeding chapters.

Receptors sensitive to stimulation of the skin and underlying tissues are *exteroceptive receptors* (also called exteroceptors). The sensations with which they are associated are often termed cutaneous or superficial sensations (p. 175). A special category of receptors, sometimes termed *teleceptors,* comprises those that are sensitive to stimuli originating some distance away. These receptors are located in the ear, eye, and nose (Chapter 13); they are associated with the special senses. Changes in tension of muscles or tendons, or in the position of a limb, are stimuli arising within the body that affect *proprioceptive receptors,* which are concerned with deep sensation (p. 181). A special category of these includes certain receptors in the inner ear which are discussed in Chapter 13. *Interoceptive receptors* are sensitive to stimuli arising within the body in connection with such visceral changes as distention of the bladder, dry-

135

ing of the throat, variations in blood pressure, and so forth. The sensations that may result are termed *visceral* sensations. By contrast, the other types listed above are sometimes classified as *somatic* sensations.

Still other terms are often used, especially in connection with the type of stimulus that excites the receptor, for example, *mechanoreceptor, chemoreceptor*. A *nociceptor* is a receptor that responds to pain.

Neuroeffector junctions are specialized associations of nerve fibers and effectors. Effectors include skeletal or voluntary muscle, smooth or involuntary muscle, cardiac or heart muscle, and glands. In lower forms of life such structures as *electric organs* (electric eel) and *luminescent organs* (firefly) are also effectors.

RECEPTORS

Exteroceptive Receptors of the Skin. When the skin of a normal subject is lightly stroked with a wisp of cotton, touched with a fine hair, or lightly stroked with the fingers, the sensation perceived is *touch* (often termed *light touch*), sometimes *tickle,* depending upon the subject. The stimulus activates several types of receptors, depending upon the type of skin touched. Skin without hair contains specialized, encapsulated endings (for example, *Meissner's corpuscles,* p. 153) in the dermis, and *free endings* in dermis and epidermis (in epidermis they may be called tactile disks). Hairy skin lacks encapsulated endings (although skin with sparse hair may have a few). Free endings are found in dermis and epidermis, and relatively large fibers form complex plexuses around hair follicles (roots of hairs). The various cutaneous endings are illustrated in a combined drawing (Fig. 81). The tactile endings are derived from myelinated and nonmyelinated fibers that enter the deeper skin (dermis), where they form an extensive plexus. The fibers branch as they approach the outer skin (epidermis), and the endings arise from these branches.

Tactile endings are examples of mechanoreceptors. A deformation of these endings initiates nerve impulses which, if they reach the cerebral cortex, are interpreted as light touch. These receptors, and all others, are functionally specific in that they are more sensitive to one type of stimulus than another.

Tactile receptors are not distributed evenly throughout the skin, but occur in groups. Only by a stimulation of one of these groups (a *touch spot*) can the sensation of touch be aroused. Between the spots, tactile sensation is decreased or absent. Tactile groups are numerous in the finger tips, but relatively scarce in such areas as the skin of the back.

If the skin is damaged, *pain* may be felt. The receptors concerned are thought to be free nerve endings, derived from myelinated and non-

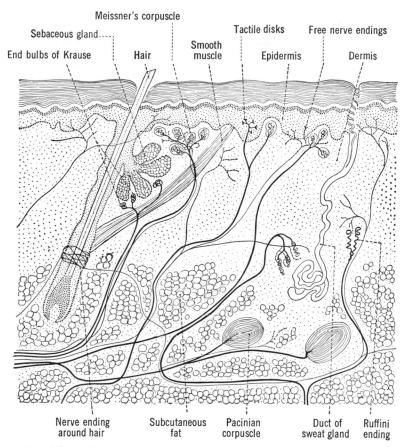

Figure 81. Schematic representation of the nerve supply of skin with sparse hair. Not all the endings shown are to be found in any one skin area. The heavy lines are myelinated fibers, the light lines, nonmyelinated fibers. (Modified after Woollard et al.: J. Anat., 74:441-458, 1940.)

myelinated fibers in the plexus of the dermis. The endings derived from myelinated fibers are found mainly within the epidermis, although the myelin is lost before the fibers end, while free nerve endings in the dermis arise mainly from nonmyelinated fibers. Free nerve endings are also found near encapsulated terminals, such as pacinian corpuscles (Fig. 82).

Changes in temperature above or below the normal body variations activate endings in the dermis near blood vessels. No specific kind of receptor can be related to temperature, however, at least with any certainty.

In spite of the fact that in skin lacking hair, as in the palm of the hand, there are various kinds of encapsulated endings, one cannot be

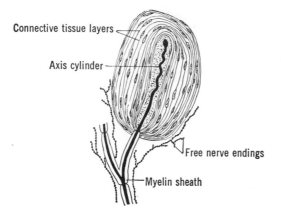

Connective tissue layers

Axis cylinder

Free nerve endings

Myelin sheath

Figure 82. Simplified representation of a pacinian corpuscle.
Note that the connective tissue
layers are separated from the axis
cylinder by a central space. Note
also the accessory fibers forming
free endings, similar to those of
Figure 81. The myelin may extend a short distance into the
central space, but usually disappears. No neurilemmal cells are
present in the central space; the
axon is directly exposed to extracellular fluid.

sure of the functional specificity of these endings. In hairy skin, where
only free endings and plexuses around hair follicles are found, all types
of skin sensations can be aroused, just as in the hand. It may be that
sensation depends more on frequency and timing of impulses than on
the type of receptor stimulated.

Exteroceptive Receptors in the Deeper Tissues. A variety of receptors are present in the subcutaneous tissues and in the connective tissue
of fascial planes, muscles and tendons. Among the types reported to be
present are free nerve endings (presumed to be sensitive to noxious
stimuli), encapsulated endings such as pacinian corpuscles (sensitive to
pressure), and Ruffini endings (sensitive to stretch).

If the skin is pressed with the finger or with a blunt instrument, the
pressure transmitted through the skin deforms pacinian corpuscles,
yielding a quality of sensation known usually as *pressure* and occasionally
as *deep touch*. Pacinian corpuscles are a type of mechanoreceptor. Many
varieties have been described, according to size, shape, and location. The
classical pacinian corpuscle is formed by numerous, thin laminae of
connective tissue arranged like the layers of onion skin which surround
the end of a large myelinated fiber (Fig. 82). These receptors are often
large enough (1 to 2 mm. long) to be seen with the naked eye during
dissections.

Proprioceptive Receptors. These occur in muscles, tendons, and
joints. There are several types in muscle. Those best known and most
widely studied are the *neuromuscular spindles* (Fig. 83), found in most
muscles, generally near musculotendinous junctions. Each spindle,
which is usually several millimeters long, consists of several specialized
muscle fibers. The spindle is fusiform in shape because it is wider in
its middle third, where its fibers are surrounded by fluid contained
within a capsule. These fibers, termed intrafusal, are of two kinds,
the nuclear-bag and the nuclear-chain. The middle of the nu-

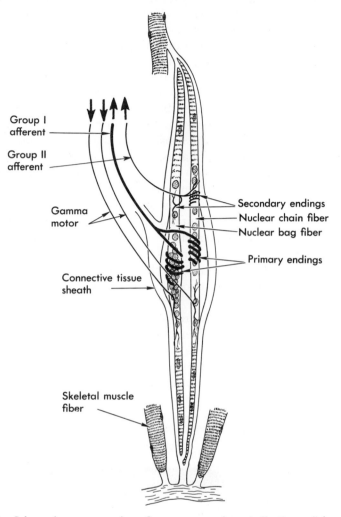

Figure 83. Schematic representation of a neuromuscular spindle. Parts of three skeletal muscle fibers are shown (cross-striated, nuclei at edge). Inside the connective tissue sheath of the spindle are three muscle fibers (thinner than regular skeletal muscle fibers, with central nuclei, and striations minimal or absent in region of sensory endings). Sensory nerve fibers form primary (annulospiral) and secondary (flower-spray) endings, the primary arising from the large fibers. (The form of primary and secondary endings varies according to species. In some, such as rabbit and man, the primary endings of the large fiber may be flower-spray in type, not winding around the muscle fiber.) Small nerve fibers (*gamma* efferents) form motor endings at each end of the spindle muscle fibers. Motor discharges over *gamma* efferents cause the spindle muscle fibers to contract at each end, thus stretching the intervening, non-contractile, sensory region and activating the sensory endings. Arrows indicate direction of conduction. (Based on Barker, D., Quart. J. Micr. Sc., *89*:143-186, 1948; Boyd, I. A., Phil. Trans. Royal Soc. Lond., Ser. B., *245*:81-136, 1962; and Matthews, P. B. C., Physiol. Rev., *44*:219-288, 1964.)

clear-bag fibers contains an aggregation of nuclei; here the striations are less marked (Fig. 84). The nuclear-chain fiber has only a single line of nuclei. Each type of fiber receives a large afferent nerve fiber which forms spiral primary endings around the middle of the muscle fiber. Smaller afferent nerve fibers form secondary endings on the chain fibers, and occasionally on the bag fibers also. Each type of intrafusal muscle fiber also has a motor supply by small nerve fibers termed *gamma* fibers. These form small motor endings which are at each pole of the bag fibers, but are scattered along the length of the chain fibers.

Neuromuscular spindles are sensitive to changes in tension caused by increase in muscle length, that is, by stretching, and are therefore often called stretch receptors. It seems that when a muscle is being stretched, the primary spindle endings signal both the instantaneous length of the muscle and the velocity of stretch, whereas the secondary endings signal mainly the instantaneous length. The sensitivity of the endings, particularly of the primary ending, may be altered by intrafusal contraction. Such contraction probably changes the mechanical properties of the intrafusal fibers. The chief functions of neuromuscular spindles are probably in the subconscious nervous control of muscular contraction.

Muscles also have other kinds of nerve endings, as shown in Figure 89. Furthermore, there are encapsulated endings in tendons called *neurotendinous spindles* or *endings* (often called Golgi tendon organs). They are stimulated by the tension produced in the tendon during either contraction or stretching of its attached muscle, and the impulses arising from them inhibit the nerve cells supplying the muscle.

Nerve fiber   Muscle fiber of spindle

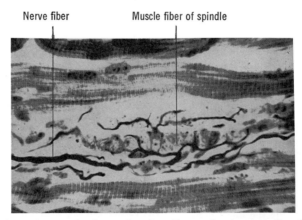

Figure 84. Photomicrograph of a nuclear-bag fiber and primary ending from a neuromuscular spindle (mouse). The lack of cross-striations in the bag region is evident. (Reproduced from Gardner: Anat. Rec., vol. 83, courtesy of Wistar Institute of Anatomy and Biology.)

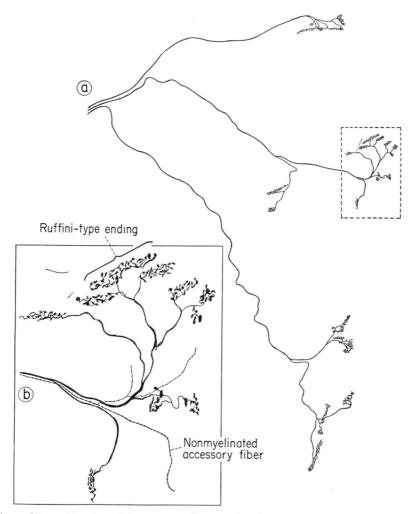

Ruffini-type ending

Nonmyelinated
accessory fiber

Figure 85. *a*, Drawing of three nerve fibers giving rise to proprioceptive receptors in the knee joint (cat), showing that many endings arise from a single fiber *b*, Drawing at higher magnification of endings in the region indicated in *a*. (Reproduced from Gardner: Nerve supply of diarthrodial joints. Stanford M. Bull., vol. 6.)

Proprioceptive endings are present in the connective tissue around muscles and bones, and in the connective tissue that forms the capsules of synovial joints. Small pacinian corpuscles occur in joints, but the most common ending is the Ruffini ending (Fig. 85). This is a slowly adapting ending that records the position of joints and movements at joints. These endings in joints are concerned with the sensation of position and movement, as well as with reflexes, whereas similar endings in other tissue may be concerned with other sensations, for example, pressure. Pain endings are present in joints also, but are classified as exteroceptive.

Interoceptive Receptors. These have been less extensively studied. Free nerve endings, which are probably excited by such stimuli as distention, are found in the walls of many of the viscera. Rather complex terminals occur in the walls of some of the larger arteries, such as the arch of the aorta and the bifurcations of the common carotids, and also in venous areas such as the right atrium of the heart. These endings appear to be particularly sensitive to changes in blood pressure (p. 238). There are nerve fibers in the lungs which branch profusely and form endings sensitive to the stretching produced by the expansion of the lungs during inspiration (p. 268). Pacinian corpuscles are found in such connective tissue areas of the abdominal cavity as the mesenteries, and are associated with the branching points of small arteries. It may be that the effective stimulus to these endings is a deformation produced by changes in diameter of these vessels with each pulse. There are other types of interoceptive receptors, but their structure and function are less well known.

Some of the interoceptive receptors are concerned with visceral sensations, for example, pain, hunger, and thirst.

Receptors for the Special Senses. These include receptors sensitive to radiant energy (rods and cones of the retina), receptors activated by chemical changes (smell and taste), and special mechanoreceptors in the ear (activated by sound waves for hearing, and fluid pressure changes in response to changes in position of the head). These receptors are discussed in Chapter 13.

PHYSIOLOGY OF RECEPTORS

When a receptor such as a pacinian corpuscle is stimulated, there results a local electrical change termed a *receptor potential,* which is confined to the region of the receptor. A receptor potential always precedes a nerve impulse from the receptor, and a nerve impulse results when the receptor potential reaches a certain magnitude. If a subthreshold stimulus is applied to a receptor, a small receptor potential is generated. If a more intense, but still subthreshold, stimulus is applied, the receptor potential will be correspondingly greater. Two subthreshold stimuli applied closely together will summate, that is, the receptor potentials they generate will summate. If the combined potential is great enough, the receptor fires off.

It is generally held that, at least in the case of mechanical stimulation, the receptor potential stimulates the nerve fiber at the first node of Ranvier.

Whatever the mechanism of receptor stimulation, the impulses are always the same. That is to say, they are of the same magnitude and rate of conduction. However, the number of impulses per unit time varies, depending upon the strength of the stimulus. A stimulus just above threshold initiates only one, or at most a few, impulses. A higher frequency of impulses results from stronger stimuli. If a stimulus is applied and maintained at a constant strength, a burst of impulses occurs initially; subsequently the frequency becomes lower and lower, until finally there are either no impulses, although the stimulus is still being maintained, or else there are impulses at a very low frequency. This phenomenon is known as *adaptation,* and it depends considerably upon the mechanical properties of the receptor. It is not a matter of fatigue, for if the stimulus is even momentarily released and then re-applied, there is again an initial burst of activity and the process is repeated. For example, an adaptation familiar to most people is experienced when one lies in bed with an arm or leg maintained in one position without moving; within a short time, one is no longer conscious of the position of that part of the body. Adaptation has occurred and the receptors are no longer active. A slight movement, however, interrupts the constant stimulus, and the consciousness of position returns.

The rate of adaptation differs for the various receptors (Fig. 86). Tactile receptors adapt in a few seconds. Neuromuscular spindles, on

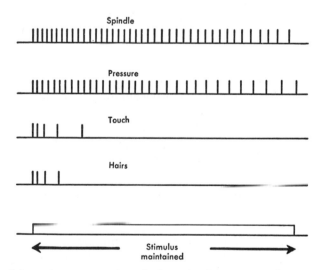

Figure 86. Schematic representation of adaptation in sensory endings. Each ending is stimulated for the same length of time, and nerve impulses are shown as if they were being recorded on moving film or paper. When a neuromuscular spindle is stimulated (by maintaining a stretch on its muscle), the spindle fires at a relatively high rate, a rate that decreases only slightly as the stimulus is maintained. A pressure receptor (pacinian corpuscle), on being touched or compressed, likewise continues to fire, but its rate of discharge decreases somewhat more. A touch receptor in skin, and receptors around hair follicles, adapt very rapidly, giving but a few impulses when the stimulus begins.

the other hand, adapt only after the stimulus has been maintained for a relatively long time, perhaps thirty minutes or more. Some receptors, such as those for pain, appear in some circumstances to have little or no adaptation.

Of special interest in receptor physiology is the mechanism whereby the excitability of neuromuscular spindles can be altered. Nerve impulses over *gamma* efferents cause the spindle muscle fibers to contract. This shortening stimulates the sensory endings and the rate of firing to the spinal cord increases. Discharge over *gamma* efferents can be affected by reflex mechanisms or by discharges reaching the spinal cord from higher centers. Thus, there are two methods of producing sensory discharge from spindles—by stretching the muscle and by contraction of spindle fibers. Both are important in the reflex regulation of the movements of the muscle.

EFFECTORS

Skeletal (Striated) Muscle.   Muscles vary greatly in size and shape, but the fundamental structural unit of any muscle is a multinucleated cell known as a muscle fiber. The variation occurs in the number and size of the constituent fibers. Skeletal muscle fibers are often many centimeters long, but only 50 to 100 microns in diameter. Each fiber or cell has many nuclei, located along its sides. The cytoplasm is known as *sarcoplasm,* and running lengthwise in it are thin structures known as *myofibrils.* Each myofibril is made up of alternating light and dark segments. Because the segments of adjacent myofibrils are aligned, the fibers appear to be cross-striated (Fig. 87). Between the skeletal muscle fibers are many blood vessels, particularly capillaries.

Muscle fibers contract rapidly, and their energy changes are accompanied by measurable electrical activity (p. 148). This is followed by refractory periods, much the same as those observed in nerve fibers. Not all skeletal muscle fibers have the same contractile characteristics. Some contract more slowly and fatigue less easily; others contract faster and fatigue more easily. A muscle may contain both types of fibers or be predominantly of one type. For instance, muscles concerned in maintenance of posture have large numbers of the more slowly contracting fibers.

Smooth (Nonstriated) Muscle.   The unit of smooth muscle is a small, spindle-shaped cell which contains but a single nucleus (Fig. 88). Myofibrils are found in the cytoplasm, but do not exhibit the alternations seen in skeletal muscle myofibrils and hence are not cross-striated, but smooth. The fibers are ordinarily arranged in sheets or bundles, within

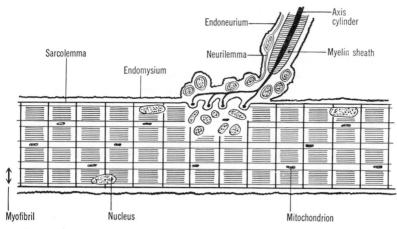

Figure 87. Schematic representation of a skeletal muscle fiber and a motor nerve ending. Note the division of the axis cylinder and the resemblance of its endings to synapses. Several kinds of cells are present around the nerve endings; some are neurilemmal cells. For further details, see Zacks, S. I.: The Motor Endplate, Philadelphia, W. B. Saunders Co., 1964.

the walls of viscera, around glands, and in the walls of blood vessels. Contractions spread from one fiber to another through the sheet or bundle; hence smooth muscle is said to be characterized by contraction waves. These are slow in comparison with the contraction rates of skeletal muscle fibers and are usually not under voluntary control.

Cardiac (Cross-striated) Muscle. As its name denotes, this type of muscle comprises the greater bulk of the heart. The fibers are apparently multinucleated, and the myofibrils have alternating segments which give the fibers a cross-striated appearance. The fibers branch,

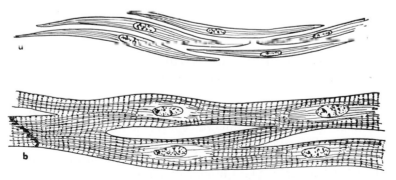

Figure 88. *a*, Smooth muscle cells. *b*, Cardiac muscle fibers.

however (Fig. 88), and appear to fuse with each other, so that a continuous net or *syncytium* seems to be formed. However, electron microscopy has shown that there is no syncytium.

Glands.   Glands are composed of epithelial cells adapted for the formation of substances other than those directly concerned in their intrinsic metabolism. Glands secrete such substances as enzymes, hormones, and mucus. They may be *unicellular,* and such single cells adapted for secretion are found in the mucous membrane of the respiratory and digestive systems. *Multicellular* glands are embryologically derived from the skin, as, for instance, a sweat gland, or from the epithelium of the respiratory and digestive systems and other hollow viscera. They frequently retain their connections with these surfaces by ducts, so that their secretions can be discharged onto these surfaces. Such glands are termed *exocrine*, or glands of external secretion. Certain glands, however, do not retain such connections, or else arise differently. The cells in such glands are arranged in groups or cords in such a relation to blood vessels that each cell can discharge its contents into the blood. These glands are termed *endocrine* glands, or glands of internal secretion.

NEUROEFFECTOR JUNCTIONS

STRUCTURE OF NEUROEFFECTOR JUNCTIONS

Neuroeffector Junctions (Myoneural Junctions or Motor Nerve Endings) in Skeletal Muscle.   Axons of motor neurons leave the spinal cord and brain stem via ventral roots or cranial nerves and eventually reach skeletal muscles. Each axon entering a muscle divides into a number of secondary branches. Each of these ends on the surface of a single muscle fiber, forming a specialized ending known as a *motor end plate* or *myoneural junction* (Figs. 87, 89). The axon loses its myelin sheath just before reaching the end plate, dividing into filaments that arborize in the end plate. The sarcolemma (p. 149) and sarcoplasm subjacent to the nerve endings are also specialized. This junctional region between nerve and muscle represents a neuromuscular synapse, having properties similar to those of chemical excitatory synapses in the central nervous system.

The axon of a single motor neuron supplies a number of skeletal muscle fibers (Fig. 89). The nerve cell, its axon, and the muscle fibers supplied by it, form a *motor unit.* A nerve impulse traversing the axon of a motor unit therefore excites the contraction of all the muscle fibers supplied by that axon. The number of motor units in any one muscle depends upon the number of muscle fibers in the muscle and upon their

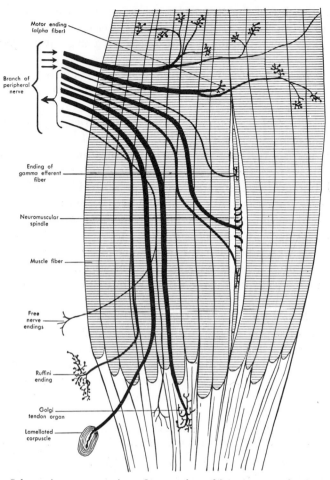

Labels (top to bottom, left side):
Motor ending (alpha fiber)
Branch of peripheral nerve
Ending of gamma efferent fiber
Neuromuscular spindle
Muscle fiber
Free nerve endings
Ruffini ending
Golgi tendon organ
Lamellated corpuscle

Figure 89. Schematic representation of a muscle and its nerve supply. Arrows indicate direction of conduction. Each muscle fiber has a motor ending from a large myelinated *(alpha)* fiber. The muscle fibers within a spindle have motor endings from small myelinated *(gamma)* fibers. Muscle nerves have many sensory fibers. Some are large myelinated fibers coming from primary sensory (annulospiral) endings in spindles, from neurotendinous spindles (Golgi tendon organs), and from lamellated corpuscles (pacinian corpuscles) in the connective tissue between muscle fibers or external to the muscle as a whole. Smaller myelinated fibers arise from proprioceptive endings (such as Ruffini endings) in the connective tissue in and around muscle, or in joints. Finally there are small myelinated and nonmyelinated fibers that form free endings (presumably for pain) in the connective tissue in and around muscle.

number in a motor unit. In man, some muscles have fewer than 100 muscle fibers per motor unit, while others may have between 1500 and 2000. It follows that a muscle with many motor units for a given number of muscle fibers is capable of more delicate and precise work than a muscle with fewer motor units for the same number of muscle fibers.

Thus the muscles of the thumb have many small units, each with only a few muscle fibers, while the antigravity muscles are characterized by relatively fewer motor units, each of which has a large number of muscle fibers.

Neuroeffector Junctions in Smooth Muscle.   Smooth muscle cells are supplied by the autonomic system, sometimes by both the parasympathetic and sympathetic divisions. The impulses originate in the central nervous system, but are interrupted before they reach the effectors. For example, an impulse from the thoracic cord reaches a sympathetic ganglion cell via a ventral root and a ramus communicans. The conducting fiber is thus a *preganglionic axon.* The *postganglionic axon* from the ganglion cell then goes to the smooth muscle fiber or fibers. This peripheral interruption is characteristic of the entire autonomic system (Chapter 14). Just how postganglionic fibers terminate in smooth muscle has not been satisfactorily determined. It is said that these nonmyelinated axons form free endings in the substance of the muscle fibers. Not every smooth muscle fiber, however, receives an ending as do all skeletal fibers, and it is uncertain how fibers without nerve endings are controlled.

Neuroeffector Junctions for Cardiac Muscle.   The heart has a specialized type of supply by the autonomic system. In the right atrium is a group of specialized muscle fibers forming the *sinoatrial node* (also called the sinus node). These cardiac muscle fibers are peculiar in being specialized for conduction rather than contraction. They are connected with other specialized muscle fibers termed *Purkinje fibers* (p. 285), which are located in the ventricles. The connections are made by way of the *atrioventricular node,* which, through its divisions, continues into the Purkinje fibers in the ventricles. The nodes thereby can activate the Purkinje fibers, which conduct the excitation to the cardiac muscle fibers. The nodes are controlled by autonomic nerve fibers, being stimulated by sympathetic fibers, and inhibited by parasympathetic fibers, in each instance by postganglionic fibers.

Neuroeffector Junctions in Glands.   Gland cells may also be supplied by the autonomic system, and in such cases the postganglionic fibers form free nerve endings near or directly in the substance of the individual cells.

PHYSIOLOGY OF NEUROEFFECTOR JUNCTIONS

Skeletal Muscle.   If a muscle is given a brief electric shock, or its nerve so stimulated, the muscle responds by a brief contraction or *twitch.* If successive stimuli are rapidly applied, the contractions may summate, producing a prolonged *tetanic contraction* or *tetanus.* If the rate of stimulation is lessened, summation may be incomplete, and the tetanus is said to be incomplete. In a muscle as a whole, gradation of activity is further aided by motor units. If all motor units act at once (in phase, or synchronously) the muscle contracts once. But if nerve impulses reach motor units at different times (out of phase, asynchronously), a certain amount of tension is maintained in the muscle.

A muscle fiber has a very thin membrane, the *sarcolemma,* which is involved in the characteristic differences in ionic concentrations in the fiber and in the extracellular fluid. The interior of resting muscle fibers is negative to the exterior by 30 to 100 mv. A reduction or reversal of the steady potential can lead to contraction of the muscle fiber.

When a nerve impulse reaches a motor end plate, *acetylcholine* is released from synaptic vesicles. It diffuses across the synaptic gap and combines with a receptor substance to form a compound that depolarizes the cell membrane of the muscle. The depolarization is accompanied by a localized negative *end plate potential* (Fig. 90). If the depolarization reaches threshold, a propagated muscle action potential results and the muscle contracts. The potential change precedes the contraction. Another receptor substance is present at the end plate, namely the enzyme *acetylcholinesterase,* which combines with and quickly inactivates the transmitter. The action of acetylcholinesterase in turn can be prevented or inhibited by *eserine,* which thereby indirectly accentuates the effect of acetylcholine.

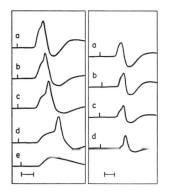

Figure 90. Records of end plate potentials of a single muscle fiber. In the left-hand column, the initial short deflections signal the stimulation of the motor nerve to the muscle fiber. In *a,* there is a compound deflection that, in *b-d,* breaks up into end plate potential and muscle action potential upon the application of curare at increasing strengths. In *e,* the preparation is deeply curarized, and only the end plate potential is left. In the right-hand column, the initial, short deflection signals the stimulation of the motor nerve to a single muscle fiber. In *a,* one electrode is on the end plate. In *b,* one electrode is on the nerve-muscle junction. In *c* and *d,* the electrode is placed at increasing distances from the end plate. Note that the end plate potential decreases in amplitude, indicating that it is not a conducted potential, but rather a local change. (Data from Kuffler: J. Neurophysiol., 5:18-26, 1942.)

Evidence relating to these effects is offered by the treatment of the disease *myasthenia gravis*. In this disease, when muscles are used they become weak and, to all intents, paralyzed. But after a variable period of rest, activity can be resumed, only to have the weakness set in again. In many cases, the use of eserine or of compounds with similar actions offers striking relief for a few hours or days. These compounds, by destroying cholinesterase, mimic the action of acetylcholine and it is presumed that in myasthenia gravis, acetylcholine is deficient or abnormally inactivated at neuromuscular junctions.

As in the case of central synapses, there is a delay of less than 1 millisecond between arrival of nerve impulse and beginning of end plate potential. The specialization of the myoneural junction is indicated by the fact that certain drugs, such as curare, may block transmission here without affecting conduction in the axon, or without preventing contraction of the muscle fiber in response to direct stimulation.

The action potential of the muscle fiber is similar to the action potential of a nerve fiber, and can be recorded by similar methods. When several fibers are active, the result is a complex type of potential change, complex because fibers may be oriented differently with respect to recording electrodes, at different distances, and active at different times. Nevertheless, the recording of muscle action potentials, *electromyography*, is a very valuable tool in studying muscle physiology.

Smooth and Cardiac Muscle and Glands. Certain chemicals are liberated at the terminals of postganglionic autonomic fibers, and act as transmitters. Acetylcholine is the transmitter or chemical mediator at postganglionic parasympathetic terminals. These fibers are, therefore, called *cholinergic* fibers. *Noradrenaline (norepinephrine)* is the mediator released at most postganglionic sympathetic terminals. These fibers are, therefore, termed *adrenergic*. Not all sympathetic fibers are adrenergic (p. 234). Adrenaline (epinephrine), formed by the medulla of the adrenal gland and by certain other cells, has actions similar to those of noradrenaline.

Many drugs have been used in investigations of the nervous system. *Nicotine,* for instance, has been valuable in the analysis of autonomic functions. This drug acts on synaptic junctions in sympathetic ganglia. When locally applied, its initial effect is one of stimulation, but it soon blocks or inhibits transmission across synapses without preventing conduction in nerve fibers. It has, therefore, been effectively used to determine just where certain fibers synapse. *Strychnine* is another drug with striking effects. In poisonous doses it causes violent muscular contractions or convulsions, probably by blocking inhibitory mechanisms, and thus indirectly increasing the sensitivity of cells (p. 111). Therefore the slightest volley of afferent impulses from the periphery may be followed

by almost continuous discharges from motor neurons. There is, therefore, a basis for the old "laying on of hands" in the treatment of strychnine poisoning. This attempt to quiet the patient unwittingly reduces
the number of afferent impulses. In smaller doses, strychnine is a valuable analytical tool because it affords a relatively simple means of causing
groups of cells to discharge. The electrical activity of these cells and any
of their projections may then be recorded.

DEPENDENCE ON NERVE SUPPLY

Skeletal muscle is peculiar in that it cannot function without a motor
nerve supply. Denervated fibers lose tone and eventually atrophy (p.
170). But other effectors are not so dependent. Cardiac muscle fibers
contract rhythmically in the embryo before they receive their nerve
supply. In the adult they do not lose their contractility when denervated.
The autonomic nervous system appears rather to coordinate or time
the contractions of various parts of the heart. Smooth muscle and glands
are even more striking in their independence of nerve supply, being able
to function in an almost normal manner when nerve connections are
completely severed. This is particularly true of glands, since their
secretory activity may be initiated by other means, as, for example, by
hormones.

When afferent fibers are severed, the peripheral receptors ultimately degenerate, but the effect on associated non-nervous tissue is
variable. Skeletal muscle, for instance, undergoes relatively little morphological change as long as its motor supply is intact. Denervated skin,
on the other hand, is susceptible to infections and may become the site of
persistent ulcers.

Strength-Duration Curves. If electrodes are applied to a normal
muscle and electric shocks are given, the contractions which follow are
the result of stimulation of the motor nerve of the muscle. Nerve impulses initiate the muscular contractions. If the times taken for varying
strengths of current to stimulate are determined, a strength duration
curve is obtained which is characteristic for nerve (Fig. 91). The chronaxie, which is one point of the curve, is less than 1 millisecond. But if
electrodes are applied to a muscle deprived of its nerve supply, the
contractions following electric shocks are the result of direct stimulation
of muscle fibers. The time during which current must flow is considerably longer. Hence, the curve has a different shape and the chronaxie is
much greater (Fig. 92). Therefore, in a muscle which is partially denervated, some muscle fibers will respond to direct stimulation and

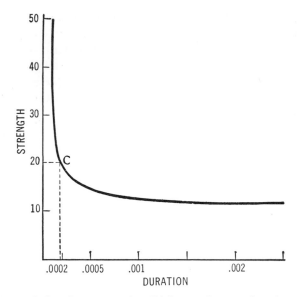

Figure 91. Strength-duration curve of a tibialis anterior muscle. The nerve supply is intact, so the curve is actually that of nerve. The chronaxie, *C,* is less than 0.2 of a milli-second. This, and Figure 92, modified from Adrian, E. D., Brain, *39*:1-33, 1916.

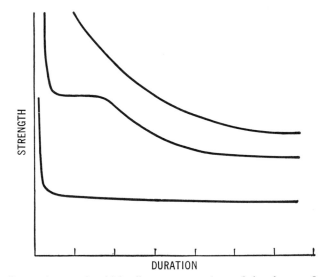

Figure 92. Composite graph which allows a comparison of the shapes of the various strength-duration curves. *Upper curve:* Denervated muscle, the curve being that for muscle. Although it cannot be shown in a composite graph, the chronaxie may be more than 50 times as great as that of normal muscle; *middle,* partially denervated, there being a mixture of two curves, one for normal muscle and nerve and another for denervated muscle; and *lower,* normal muscle and nerve, the curve being similar to that of Fig. 91.

others to nerve impulses. As Figure 92 shows, the curve is complex in shape, indicating that it is composed of the two simpler ones with different time relationships. These curves represent data that are more useful indices of denervation and recovery than single points, such as chronaxie.

SUMMARY

Receptors are specialized terminations of afferent fibers. Exteroceptive receptors are concerned with the reception of touch, pain, and temperature from the skin, as well as pain and pressure from deeper tissues; proprioceptive receptors are concerned with the reception of changes in tension of muscles and tendons and with changes in the position of limbs; interoceptive receptors are sensitive to various internal or visceral changes. Stimuli at or above threshold strength result in nerve impulses the frequency of which varies with the strength and duration of the stimuli.

Neuroeffector junctions are specialized terminations of efferent fibers in skeletal muscle fibers, smooth muscle fibers, cardiac muscle, and glands, these structures being the effectors. In skeletal muscles a single neuron supplies a number of muscle fibers (a motor unit), each branch terminating as a motor end plate. In smooth and cardiac muscle fibers and gland cells, the junctions are free endings. Certain chemical compounds, acetylcholine and noradrenaline, are probably released as mediators at neuroeffector junctions.

Skeletal muscle is the only effector fully dependent upon the nervous system for normal activity. Skeletal muscle exhibits a strength-duration curve of different time relationships from that of nerve, and this curve becomes apparent when the muscle is denervated.

Names in Neurology

WILHELM KRAUSE (1833-1910)

Krause was a German anatomist who studied most of the peripheral receptors, including the end bulbs now named after him.

GEORGE MEISSNER (1823-1893)

Meissner was a German histologist known primarily for the skin receptors he described.

FILIPO PACINI (1812-1883)

An Italian anatomist, Pacini is known for his studies of peripheral receptors.

ANGELO RUFFINI (1864-1929)

An Italian anatomist, Ruffini was one of the most skilled investigators of peripheral receptors. He used a gold chloride stain, and his studies of such endings in deep tissues as neuromuscular spindles formed the morphologic basis for subsequent physiologic studies.

REFERENCES

See the references to physiology and neuroanatomy textbooks cited on p. 6, and the special references cited on p. 94.

Andrew, B. L. (Ed.): Control and Innervation of Skeletal Muscle. Baltimore, Williams & Wilkins Company, 1966.
Bishop, G. H.: Neural mechanisms of cutaneous sense. Physiol. Rev., 26:77-102, 1946. (An advanced review of this subject.)
Clinical Examinations in Neurology. 2nd ed. Members of the Sections of Neurology, Physiology, Mayo Clinic, Rochester. Philadelphia, W. B. Saunders Company, 1963. (The chapter on electromyography is well organized and clearly written.)
Hoyle, G.: Comparative Physiology of the Nervous Control of Muscular Contraction. London, Cambridge University Press, 1957.
Sinclair, D. C.: Cutaneous sensations and the doctrine of specific energy. Brain, 78:584-614, 1956.

Chapter 11

THE CONTROL OF
MUSCULAR ACTIVITY

The pattern of muscular activity is controlled by the central nervous system, but this does not mean that one first thinks of movements to be performed in a particular activity and then initiates the nervous impulses causing them. On the contrary, most movements fit into complex, almost automatic patterns. Walking exemplifies such a pattern. Once walking is learned (it has to be learned laboriously), it is carried out according to fairly definite patterns of nervous activity. Nearly all movements, including portions or the whole of automatisms, can be voluntarily controlled. This control resides mainly if not entirely in the cerebral cortex. It should be realized, however, that the term "voluntary control" is misleading. It generally refers only to a pattern of activity.

For example, suppose that we reach out and pick something from a table. The use of the fingers is the component of which we are mainly conscious. But in order to get the fingers to the object, the forearm is extended, that is, straightened out, and in order to do this smoothly the muscles which flex or bend the arm at the elbow are relaxed. Yet this relaxation is not consciously carried out; we are not actually aware of this component of movement. Furthermore, in this reaching out and picking something up, other muscles stabilize the shoulder. At the same time the body leans forward, the center of gravity shifts, and compensatory, stabilizing muscle actions in the trunk and lower extremities insure maintenance of posture.

155

The muscles that take part in any movement may be classified as prime movers, synergists, antagonists, and fixation muscles (Fig. 93, *A*). The prime movers directly bring about the action desired, as flexing the fingers in Figure 93, *B*. When a prime mover crosses two or more joints, synergists prevent undesired action at the intermediate joints. Fixation

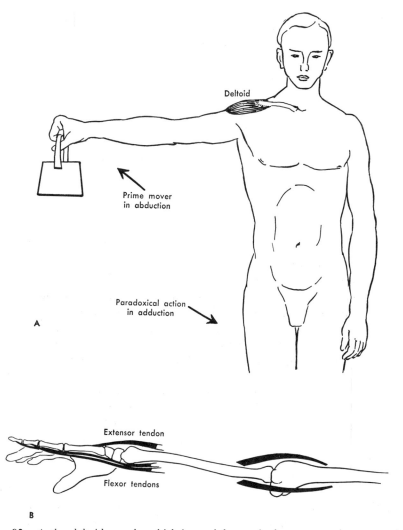

Figure 93. *A*, the deltoid muscle, which is an abductor, is shown as a prime mover in lifting a pail of water (other muscles stabilize elbow and hand). It also does negative work in controlling the lowering of the pail (adduction)—a paradoxical action. The adductors are inactive unless resistance is offered to the movement. *B*, if the flexor muscles, which are inserted into the fingers, contract so as to flex the fingers, the wrist would also flex were it not that the extensor muscle contracts and acts as a synergist, preventing undesired action at intermediate joints. The elbow joint can be fixed or stabilized in the desired position by simultaneous contraction of flexors and extensors.

muscles stabilize certain joints and also have postural functions, for example, maintaining the equilibrium of the trunk. Muscles may also have a paradoxical action in the sense that they can control movements in a direction opposite to that in which they usually operate (Fig. 93). In this capacity, they do negative work. Antagonists are those that act directly opposite to the prime mover. Antagonists may either relax completely during movement (when the movement is carried out against resistance), or they may gradually relax while lengthening so as to control or modify the action of the prime mover.

Thus an apparently simple act involves many muscles in a complex maneuver. We do not pay special attention to any of the components except the prime movement. Walking, using a typewriter, playing a piano, fielding a baseball, and talking are examples of skilled acts that we usually take for granted to the extent that we lose sight of their enormous complexity and forget the months or years of learning and practice.

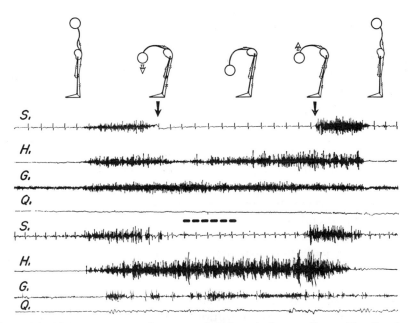

Figure 94. Electromyograms of two normal subjects during standing and bending down. In standing, no activity is recorded from sacrospinalis *(S)*, hamstrings *(H)*, or quadriceps femoris *(Q)*. The short vertical deflections in *S* are the electrocardiogram. As the subject leans forward, activity appears in *S* (negative work; the muscles control the leaning forward as they lengthen), in hamstrings (same reason) and gastrocnemius *(G)*. Activity stops in sacrospinalis at full flexion (ligaments now the support of the back), to reappear as the subject extends and returns to standing. These records show the lack of muscular activity in an easy standing position, and the complicated activity during movement. The upper four records are from one subject, the lower four from another subject. (Based on Figure 2, from Portnoy, H., and Morin, F., Am. J. Physiol., *186*:122-126, 1956. By permission of authors and publisher.)

Both in movement and in posture, muscles may act against the influence of gravity, and the muscles most concerned are often called antigravity muscles. It is held that reflexes involving neuromuscular spindles
are prominent in antigravity muscles during standing. Most experiments, however, have been made on four-footed animals, and it is
difficult and often inadvisable to conclude that findings from such
experimental studies are directly applicable to man. In an easy standing
position, little if any muscular contraction or tone can be detected in
the so-called antigravity muscles of man. The human skeleton and
human joints are arranged so that a man can stand upright with a minimal expenditure of energy (unless he is overweight, or has bad posture
or other defects) (Fig. 94).

LEVELS OF CONTROL

The normal contraction of a muscle is initiated only by impulses
reaching it over axons of specific motor cells in the brain stem or spinal
cord. This motor pathway from the central nervous system to muscle is
termed the *final common path;* it and the nerves to viscera carry the nerve
impulses that activate all outward expression of behavior. Therefore,
all motor tracts in the central nervous system, no matter what their
origin, are directed toward motor cells in the brain stem and spinal cord.

In naming pathways, tracts or fibers of the central nervous system,
direction is indicated by the order of naming. Reticulospinal, for example, means a pathway descending from the reticular formation to
the spinal cord. Other descriptive terms may be included. Thus, a tract
in the lateral part of the spinal cord originating in the cerebral cortex
is the lateral corticospinal tract. A spinocerebellar tract begins in the
spinal cord and ends in the cerebellum.

It is convenient, particularly in an introductory work of this nature,
to study motor paths and their part in the control of muscular activity as
if the nervous system were made up of a series of levels. These levels are
the spinal cord, the reticular formation of the brain stem, the cerebellum, the basal ganglia, and the cerebral cortex.

The lowest level of organization is the gray matter of the spinal
cord. Many cells in this gray matter, exclusive of motor cells, are capable
of certain types of organized activity. The degree of organization or
coordination depends upon the animal. For example, a frog with its
head removed does not exhibit spontaneous activity, but does show
coordinated responses to many types of stimulation. The functions of
the spinal cord are discussed in more detail in Chapter 15.

The next level is the reticular formation of the brain stem. This mixture of gray and white matter contains countless numbers of cells and fibers concerned with many different functions. The axons of many of these cells descend to the spinal cord and are therefore called *reticulospinal fibers*. Many cells in the reticular formation are important in the control of muscular activity. A useful concept, supported by experimental data, postulates that some of these cells inhibit motor neurons of brain stem and spinal cord and increase the threshold of reflex arcs (p. 263). They are therefore responsible for any muscular relaxation which may be necessary during movement. Others excite or activate motor cells and lower reflex thresholds, and can thereby initiate or maintain muscular contractions. Destruction of certain motor pathways of the brain may result in situations in which the excitatory mechanisms appear to be predominantly active, while the inhibitory mechanisms are relatively ineffective. As a result reflex muscular contractions become accentuated, particularly in antigravity muscles. These reactions are discussed in greater detail in Chapter 16.

The basal ganglia and certain portions of the cerebellum, which appear to be necessary for coordinated movement, send fibers to the brain stem reticular formation. These structures represent a still higher level of control (p. 300).

The highest level is the cerebral cortex, which is most highly developed in man. The regions of the cortex from which motor paths arise are called motor areas, most of which are located in the frontal lobes. The cortex contains vast numbers of nerve cells, the bodies of which tend to be arranged in six layers. In motor areas, the fifth layer is thick and contains many *pyramidal cells* (Fig. 152, p. 302). The axons of these pyramidal cells leave the cortex and enter the white matter of the hemisphere, where they descend in the internal capsule. Impulses may reach motor cells either by relaying in various subcortical levels, or by traveling in direct pathways to the brain stem and spinal cord.

This has been a rapid survey of various levels of the nervous system, the lowest level being the most specific in function and the highest the least specific. That is, a motor cell, the lowest level, supplies certain muscle fibers and no others. Its activity cannot directly cause any other muscle to contract. The cerebral cortex represents the greatest degree of lability. It controls activity through an almost infinite variety of combinations.

The present chapter will deal mainly with the longitudinal motor pathways. In this and in other chapters the terms "integration," "coordination," and "correlation" are often used. These are well-known terms, and many investigators attempt to use them in connection with different functions. No really satisfactory distinction has ever been arrived at, however, and in this textbook they will ordinarily be used synonymously.

MUSCULAR ACTIVITY IN THE TRUNK AND LIMBS

A few general rules can be cited which hold for normal activity. First, pathways concerned with movements of the lower limb begin in the cerebral cortex near the midline and on the medial surface, while those dealing with movements of the head and neck begin in the cortex near the lateral fissure. Second, the control of limb musculature is largely contralateral. Third, movements of midline muscles, such as those concerned with breathing, are bilaterally controlled, that is, can be initiated by either hemisphere.

Nerve fibers to muscles in the trunk and limbs are axons of motor cells in the spinal cord. Motor pathways in the central nervous system reach these cells in a variety of ways.

Pyramidal System. Present evidence indicates that the direct path from the cerebral cortex to the spinal cord is phylogenetically new, and is most prominent in primates. It bypasses the older pathways and is concerned especially with the limbs and particularly with the hands. In the movement complex cited previously, the reaching forward and picking something from a table, the movements involving the forearm and hand are particularly dependent upon this system. The fibers of this direct system are axons of cells in several regions of the cerebral cortex, especially the precentral gyrus, which lies immediately in front of the central sulcus. The fibers descend in the internal capsule and cerebral peduncle and, when they reach the medulla oblongata, they collect into prominent bundles of fibers, the pyramids, located on the anterior aspect of the medulla oblongata, one pyramid on each side of the midline fissure (p. 257). The pyramids are named because of their shape, and not because their constituent fibers arise from pyramidal cells in the cerebral cortex. Just before the medulla oblongata joins the spinal cord, many of the fibers in each pyramid cross to the opposite side, interlacing as they cross. After crossing, these fibers descend in the lateral funiculi of the spinal cord as *lateral corticospinal tracts* (Fig. 95). Because these fibers descend in the medullary pyramids, the term *pyramidal tract* is synonymous with corticospinal tract. Of the fibers which do not cross, some descend in the anterior funiculi of the spinal cord as *anterior corticospinal tracts*, which, in some instances, may be traced to lumbar levels. Other uncrossed fibers descend in lateral funiculi and hence are also lateral corticospinal fibers. It has been estimated that 75 per cent of corticospinal fibers cross.

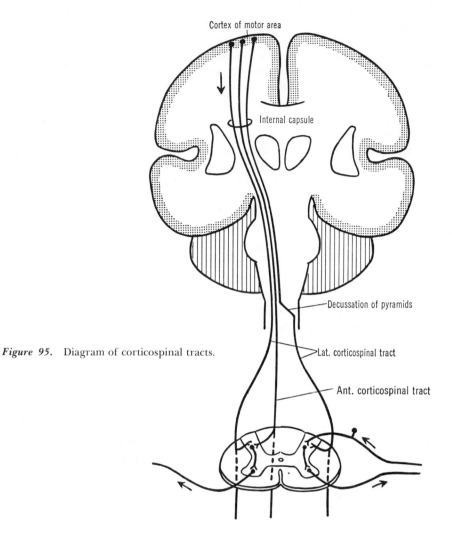

Figure 95. Diagram of corticospinal tracts.

The manner in which corticospinal fibers end depends upon the species. In primates, many end directly upon motor neurons; others upon interneurons. In lower forms, most synapse with interneurons in dorsal gray matter. In any event, the ultimate effects are upon motor cells supplying skeletal muscles, especially those with many motor units per unit number of muscle fibers. This makes for greater delicacy and precision of movement.

There is good evidence that the pyramidal system is primarily excitatory, and that the excitation can be manifested in a variety of ways. Impulses descending over pyramidal fibers may activate interneurons and motor cells. Impulses over pyramidal fibers may also facilitate cells, that is, lower their thresholds, without actually causing them to discharge. This is particularly true if impulses descend asynchronously and at a low frequency. Each sets up a local excitatory state, but, unless this occurs at approximately the same time another impulse sets up a similar change at the same region, summation does not result.

Some of these events can be indirectly demonstrated in man as follows: In many persons it is difficult to obtain a knee jerk. If, just before the patellar tendon is tapped, the subject clenches his fists, the knee jerk may then be marked. This enhancement or reinforcement results from the fact that impulses from the cerebral cortex reach not only the motor cells of the actively contracting muscles, but also other motor cells of the spinal cord and brain stem, and probably in particular the cells of origin of *gamma* efferents to the intrafusal fibers of neuromuscular spindles. The central facilitation coupled with more sensitive spindles enables the motor cells to fire off.

A widely held concept views the pyramidal system as primarily inhibitory. This is based mainly on interpretation of certain clinical findings in neurological disorders. According to such a concept, reinforcement would be explained as resulting from effectiveness of afferent stimuli in the presence of inattention to (and therefore lack of inhibition of) the leg extensors while movement is carried out elsewhere. Although this particular concept of pyramidal functions is inadequate, the possibility that lack of inhibition is a factor in reinforcement cannot be discounted.

Extrapyramidal System. Other components of movement patterns, such as the relaxation or inhibition of opposing muscles and the stabilizing and postural acts of the previously cited movement complex, are beautifully and automatically coordinated by a variety of mechanisms. The paths concerned originate mainly from the precentral motor cortex (by this is meant the motor cortex anterior to the central sulcus; it includes more than the precentral gyrus). The fibers descend in the internal capsule and, through a variety of paths (chiefly by way of the basal ganglia), reach the excitatory and inhibitory mechanisms in the brain stem. The excitatory components then descend from the brain stem to the spinal cord as reticulospinal and vestibulospinal tracts, the relative sizes and importance of which vary from one species to another. Both descend mainly in the anterior funiculus of the cord. The inhibitory component also descends as a reticulospinal tract, mainly in the lateral funiculus of the cord. These descending tracts end in the gray matter of the cord, either by synapsing with motor neurons directly or with internuncial neurons (Fig. 96).

The reticulospinal and vestibulospinal tracts do not enter the medullary pyramids. The system to which they belong is, therefore, frequently termed the *extrapyramidal system.* In the spinal cord, however, the inhibitory reticulospinal tracts which descend in the lateral funiculi are intermingled with the fibers of the lateral corticospinal tracts.

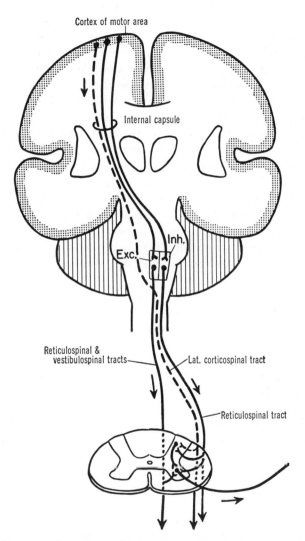

Figure 96. Diagram of extrapyramidal pathways. The brain stem excitatory and inhibitory mechanisms are indicated schematically, and the lateral corticospinal tract is included to show its relationship to the reticulospinal tract.

MUSCULAR ACTIVITY IN THE HEAD AND NECK

The activity referred to here is that carried out by the muscles supplied by cranial nerves. The pathways concerned are not separated anatomically into pyramidal and extrapyramidal, because most of the descending paths end before the medullary pyramids are reached. Other distinctions are usually made, however. Frequently all the fibers from the cerebral cortex to the brain stem are called corticobulbar. Less commonly, more specific terms are used, such as corticopontine (fibers from cortex to pons) or corticomesencephalic (cortex to midbrain). It seems likely that those fibers which do go directly from the cerebral cortex to the brain stem correspond functionally to the pyramidal system. In addition, there are many motor paths that reach the brain stem after a number of relays and then connect with reticular formation. Functionally these are extrapyramidal tracts.

From the standpoint of the various muscles concerned, a convenient organizational plan distinguishes the paths concerned with eye muscles, the tongue, and the branchiomeric muscles. The last are striated muscles that develop embryologically from branchial arch mesoderm. Many of them are closely associated with the alimentary and respiratory systems.

The motor paths for cranial nerves originate in the cerebral cortex. They descend by way of internal capsule and brain stem and, either directly or indirectly, reach the *nuclei of origin* of many of the cranial nerves. Here again is a matter of terminology. The term nucleus means either a compact collection of many neurons within the central nervous system, or a nucleus of a single cell. The term ganglion, on the other hand, usually refers to a collection of neurons outside the central nervous system.

Eye Muscles and Tongue. Eye movements are nearly always conjugate; that is to say, the eyes move together. The simplest example of conjugate movement is horizontal (lateral) gaze. In looking to the right, the right lateral rectus muscle, supplied by the abducent nerve, and the left medial rectus muscle, supplied by the oculomotor nerve, act to turn the eyes to the right (Fig. 97). At the same time the opposing muscles relax. The motor path originates in the precentral motor cortex. The fibers descend in the internal capsule, and there is a possibility that they relay in basal ganglia. Sometime during their descent they cross the midline and then reach a group of nerve cells in the lower pons, the center for lateral gaze (Fig. 98). Some consider this center to be one of the vestibular nuclei. Connections are then established with the abducent nucleus, and thereby the lateral rectus muscle, and other fibers

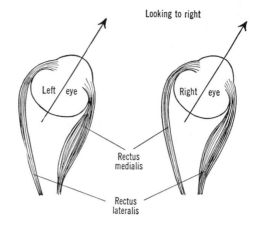

Figure 97. Conjugate activity in looking to the right. The right lateral rectus muscle and the left medial rectus contract, while the right medial rectus and left lateral rectus relax. This illustrates how a number of muscles coordinate in an apparently simple movement.

cross and ascend in the medial longitudinal fasciculus to the oculomotor nucleus, which supplies the medial rectus muscle.

Several other pathways are concerned in eye movements. There is, for example, a type of horizontal gaze in which the eyes are kept fixed on an object as the head turns. The motor path concerned has never been determined anatomically in man, but it probably originates in the

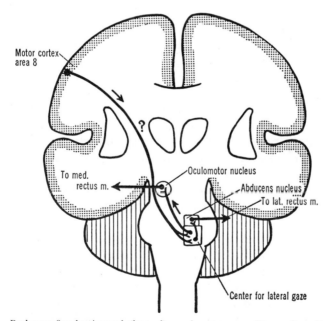

Figure 98. Pathway for horizontal (lateral) conjugate gaze. Descending fibers project to the center for lateral gaze in the pons, which in turn relays to eye muscle nuclei. The question mark indicates the possibility that the descending fibers relay in basal ganglia.

cortex of the occipital lobe. Conjugate gaze in vertical directions seems to be under the control of both frontal and occipital lobes, particularly the latter. The paths concerned descend to the midbrain, where they make connections with the nuclei of oculomotor and trochlear nerves. Eye movements are rarely confined to strictly horizontal or strictly vertical axes. Consequently, both frontal and occipital lobes and their pathways are coordinated in eye movements.

There are probably pathways by which conjugate gaze in a particular direction can be controlled by the ipsilateral hemisphere. Whether these are normally in operation is uncertain. They undoubtedly account for the fact that after destruction of cerebral cortex or pathways on one side, conjugate gaze to the opposite side is lost for but a few days or weeks. Recovery is often complete.

Each hypoglossal nerve supplies one half of the tongue and each receives fibers from both cerebral hemispheres. The fibers enter the internal capsule, and descend through the brain stem (probably through the reticular formation) to reach the hypoglossal nucleus in the medulla oblongata.

Loss of one of the descending paths has little if any effect upon control of tongue movements, except for a few days or weeks. Section of the hypoglossal nerve itself is followed by paralysis of one half the tongue.

Branchiomeric Muscles. The nerves concerned receive fibers from both precentral motor areas. The fibers reach the motor nuclei by descending in the internal capsule and reticular formation of the brain stem. The muscles of mastication are supplied by axons arising from a motor nucleus on each side of the pons. The fibers from this nucleus reach the muscles by way of the trigeminal nerve. The muscles of expression, the facial muscles, are supplied by motor nuclei in the lower part of the pons. The axons reach the muscles by way of the facial nerve. Parts of these nuclei are exceptions to the rule about bilateral control of midline muscles. The cells in the upper portions of the nuclei supply the muscles around the eyes (closing the eyes and wrinkling the forehead). These cells receive fibers from both motor areas. But the cells in the lower part of the facial nucleus, which supply muscles of the lips, nose, and cheek, receive fibers only from the contralateral motor cortex (Fig. 99). The muscles of swallowing (pharynx, palate, and upper esophagus) and vocalizing (larynx) are supplied by nuclei in the medulla oblongata whose axons are distributed by way of the glossopharyngeal, vagus, and accessory nerves. In addition, portions of two muscles, the sternocleidomastoid and trapezius, are partly of branchiomeric origin and are supplied by the portion of the accessory nerve that arises from the upper part of the cervical spinal cord.

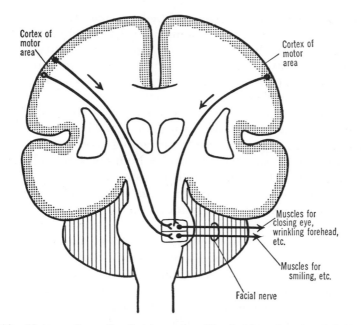

Figure 99. Motor pathway for facial muscles. The facial nucleus is subdivided. The upper part, which supplies one group of facial muscles, receives fibers from both cerebral hemispheres, whereas the lower part of the nucleus receives fibers only from the contralateral hemisphere.

CLINICAL IMPORTANCE OF MOTOR AREAS AND PATHWAYS

UPPER MOTOR NEURON LESIONS

The functions of the motor cortex have been studied in a variety of ways. Motor areas have been removed surgically, both in experimental animals and in necessary operations in man, and the functional losses observed directly. This method has been supplemented by cutting descending fibers in the internal capsule, cerebral peduncle, pyramid, or spinal cord in experimental animals and studying the resulting degeneration and loss of function. Motor areas and paths have been stimulated and effects observed and recorded. Similar conditions or events in man are frequently the result of disease or injury, and valuable information has been derived from clinical and postmortem studies in such cases. Clinically speaking, any interruption of connections between the cortex or subcortical levels and the motor cells in the spinal cord is said to be an *upper motor neuron lesion.* Such a lesion may interrupt corticospinal fibers or extrapyramidal fibers, or both.

Upper Motor Neuron Lesions of Corticospinal Tracts. Not much is known about the effects of lesions limited to corticospinal fibers in man, because these fibers throughout most of their course are closely associated with fibers of other functional systems, and injury to one is almost automatically injury to the others. It has been deduced from the available clinical evidence, and from experimental work, that lesions of certain portions of the precentral gyrus, or of the medullary pyramids, destroy corticospinal fibers with a minimal involvement of other types. Lesions elsewhere, as in the remaining motor cortex or in the internal capsule or spinal cord, involve both corticospinal and extrapyramidal fibers. Destruction of corticospinal fibers in a medullary pyramid is followed by weakness or *paresis* on the opposite side of the body, together with abnormal reflexes, such as the Babinski (p. 132). The weakness is especially pronounced in muscles of the limbs, and there is great difficulty with movements of the hands. The affected muscles may become limp and almost flaccid because of the loss of reflex arcs. This is not a paralysis, however, because, as has been emphasized before, the corticospinal fibers are not the only mediators of voluntary activity. Movements can still be initiated through extrapyramidal projections, particularly movements of the trunk and girdle regions. The voluntary control which remains can effect a remarkable degree of compensation, and, after a few months, functional defects may be difficult to detect.

Upper Motor Neuron Lesions of Extrapyramidal and Corticospinal Tracts. In the internal capsule, cerebral peduncle, and lateral part of the spinal cord, extrapyramidal and corticospinal fibers are so closely intermingled anatomically that destruction of one system almost automatically affects the other. The most common upper motor neuron lesion is, therefore, a combined one. When this happens, the effects of extrapyramidal destruction predominate. Figure 100 illustrates some of the resulting degeneration.

There is weakness or paralysis to a varying degree, depending entirely upon the number of descending fibers destroyed. The closer the destruction to the spinal cord, the more chance there is of severing all the descending axons. Only those muscles near the midline remain relatively unaffected, provided the lesion is on but one side.

So far as cranial nerves are concerned, functional losses are difficult to predict because of the variable amount of bilateral cortical control. Unilateral lesions above the level of the pons partially affect the facial nerves. It was pointed out earlier in this chapter that only the upper part of each facial nucleus is bilaterally controlled. In these lesions, therefore, there is paralysis of the opposite lower facial muscles, but not of the upper ones around the eyes and forehead.

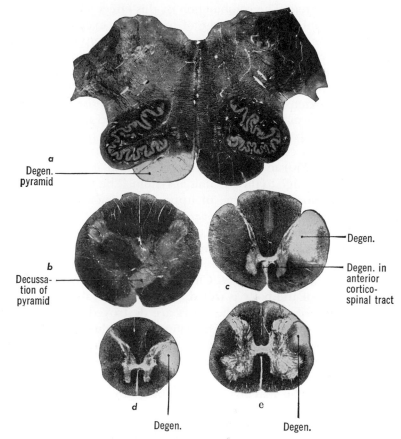

Figure 100. Photomicrographs of sections of spinal cord and medulla oblongata from a case of thrombosis of the arterial supply of the left internal capsule. Weigert stain. The degenerating fibers lie in the unstained areas, and at the indicated levels are corticospinal fibers. In *a* the left pyramid is involved. In *b* the degenerating fibers are crossing to the right side. Some remain on the same side, as shown in *c*, cervical cord. In *d*, thoracic cord, and *e*, lumbar cord, the lateral corticospinal tract decreases in size as it descends in the lateral funiculus. (Courtesy of Department of Anatomy, University of Southern California, Los Angeles.)

Paralysis is not the only symptom in upper motor neuron disorders. The extrapyramidal fibers mediate both excitatory and inhibitory functions, and the loss of inhibitory mechanisms leads to some pronounced effects. One of the fundamental characteristics of upper motor neuron lesions is that reflex arcs remain anatomically intact. Control or modification of these arcs, however, is hindered. The normal operation of gravity against the weight of the body may initiate stretch reflexes. Since there is no longer an inhibitory mechanism, the reflex contractions are exaggerated. The combination of this effect with contractions resulting from continuous discharge of brain stem excitatory mechanisms leads to a *spastic* or *hypertonic* state. Descending impulses to gamma efferents may activate spindle muscle fibers and thus enhance stretch reflexes.

The examiner detects spasticity by bending a joint. The stretch thus put on the extensor muscles leads reflexly to a resistance to flexion of the joint. Abnormal reflexes such as the Babinski also appear, and these again are probably a result of loss of inhibitory mechanisms. The Babinski reflex represents part of a general withdrawal or flexion of the lower limb (p. 250) and, whatever its explanation, is characteristically associated with damage to the pyramidal system. The spasticity and loss of voluntary motion in this type of upper motor neuron lesion have led to the synonymous term *spastic paralysis.*

These lesions are common in the internal capsule, where all the descending fibers are closely gathered together and are thus particularly vulnerable to neurological disorders. Lesions here result in signs mainly in the opposite half of the body. Clinically speaking, weakness in one longitudinal half of the body is called *hemiparesis;* paralysis in one half of the body is a *hemiplegia.* If the fibers are destroyed after they have crossed and are descending in the lateral funiculus of the cervical cord, there is spastic paralysis on the same side of the body, involving both limbs. A lesion of the lateral funiculus of the thoracic cord is followed by paralysis in the lower limb on the same side, a condition called *monoplegia.* The extent of the symptomatology is a clue to the location of the disorder.

In connection with the widely held concept of the pyramidal system as inhibitory, it is also widely held in clinical circles that upper motor neuron disorders are entirely the result of lesions to the pyramidal system. Consequently, the terms *pyramidal signs* or *pyramidal lesions* are synonymous with spastic paralysis or upper motor neuron disorders. The terminology is so deeply rooted that little attempt has ever been made to eradicate it.

LOWER MOTOR NEURON LESIONS

The pathway from the cortical motor areas is completed by motor neurons whose axons reach skeletal muscle fibers. Destruction of these neurons or their axons is followed by a characteristic clinical picture, whether the destruction is in the spinal cord, the ventral roots, or in spinal or peripheral nerves. In any case, impulses cannot reach the muscle fibers supplied by the destroyed nerve fibers, and voluntary control is completely lost. For the same reason, reflexes involving such

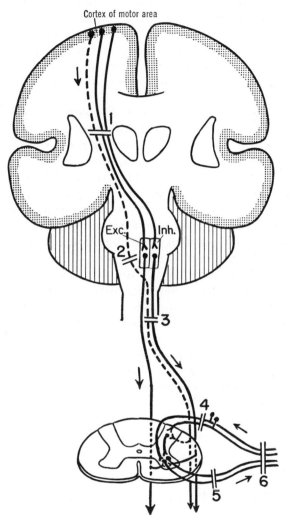

Figure 101. Diagram illustrating lesions of motor and reflex paths. *1,* A lesion here (internal capsule) causes an upper motor neuron defect, the severity of which depends on the extent of the lesion. *2,* A lesion here (near decussation of pyramids) affects only corticospinal fibers. *3,* A lesion here (lateral funiculus of cord) causes an upper motor neuron defect more severe than that at *1* because more descending fibers are cut (this feature is not actually illustrated). *4,* Section of dorsal root or roots causes diminution or loss of reflexes, sensation, muscle tone and coordination, but no paralysis. *5,* Section of a ventral root or roots causes a lower motor neuron defect. *6,* Section of a spinal or peripheral nerve results in combined motor and sensory losses.

muscles are impossible. Muscle fibers deprived of their nerve supply eventually shrink or atrophy, and during the course of this change the degenerating fibers show fibrillary twitchings. The characteristics of strength-duration curves are also changed (p. 151). If there is no regeneration, the muscles eventually disappear and are replaced by connective tissue and fat. Because the nerve impulses necessary for muscle tone are lost, muscles become limp or *flaccid*. This lower motor neuron type paralysis is, therfore, frequently referred to as a *flaccid paralysis*.

Flaccid paralyses are not the only disorders in which reflexes are lost. For instance, if one or several dorsal roots are cut, no sensation can be perceived in the areas supplied by these roots. The afferent impulses cannot reach the spinal cord, and reflexes depending upon them are lost. Paralysis is not present, however, because ventral roots are still intact, and motor impulses for voluntary activity can still reach the muscles. A diagnosis of dorsal root involvement can be made because the areas in which sensation is diminished or lost conform to the embryologic distribution of segments in which each spinal nerve supplies its own dermatome.

Lesions involving spinal nerves result in both motor and sensory losses in segmental areas. Lesions of major peripheral nerves, such as the sciatic, cause flaccid paralyses of the muscles supplied by that nerve, accompanied by loss of cutaneous sensations. Differentiation can be made from spinal nerve lesions because the motor and sensory losses are in areas characteristic of peripheral nerve distributions rather than the embryological segmental distributions (p. 33).

Figure 101 is a composite diagram illustrating the paths involved in the various motor disabilities.

SUMMARY

The control of muscular activity can be considered as if the nervous system were a series of levels. These are the spinal cord, the brain stem reticular formation, the cerebellum, the basal ganglia, and the cerebral cortex. All muscular activity is mediated by impulses leaving the brain stem and spinal cord.

Within the brain stem are excitatory and inhibitory mechanisms which project to the spinal cord and which in turn are influenced by higher centers, including the cerebral cortex. The paths from the cerebral cortex originate mainly from the frontal lobe. These levels and their connections constitute the extrapyramidal system.

The pyramidal system consists of a direct path from cerebral cortex to spinal cord and is primarily excitatory in function.

Muscles in the limbs are mainly controlled by the contralateral cerebral hemisphere, while muscles near the midline of the body are under bilateral cerebral control.

Interruption of connections between the cortex and motor neurons causes upper motor neuron lesions. Such lesions mostly involve both extrapyramidal and corticospinal fibers, and are characterized by a varying degree of paralysis, spasticity of antigravity muscles, exaggerated deep or tendon reflexes, and abnormal reflexes.

Cutting the pathway from motor neurons to muscles causes a lower motor neuron lesion. This is followed by paralysis of voluntary motion with limpness or flaccidity of the involved muscles, muscular atrophy, loss of reflexes, and fibrillary twitching. When the lesion is in spinal or peripheral nerves, the flaccid paralysis is accompanied by sensory losses.

REFERENCES

See the references cited on p. 6 and on p. 319.

Walshe, F.: The problem of the origin of the pyramidal tract. *In* Garland, H. (ed.): Scientific Aspects of Neurology. Edinburgh, E. & S. Livingstone, 1961. (A first-rate review.)

The following books deal with muscle functions in man. The accounts by Duchenne and Beevor are classics. Duchenne used electrical stimulation of muscles, and Beevor, palpation of active muscles, to determine functions. Wright also used the method of palpating contracting muscles. Both Basmajian and Joseph used electromyography in their studies, which are excellent examples of modern experimental and anatomical studies.

Basmajian, J. V.: Muscles Alive. 2nd ed. Baltimore, Williams & Wilkins Company, 1967.
Beevor, C.: The Croonian Lectures on Muscular Movements, 1903, and Remarks on Paralysis of the Movements of the Trunk in Hemiplegia, 1909. Ed. and repr. London, Macmillan and Co., Limited.
Duchenne, G. B.: Physiology of Motion. Tr. and ed. by E. B. Kaplan. Philadelphia, W. B. Saunders Company, 1959.
Joseph, J.: Man's Posture. Springfield, Ill., Charles C Thomas, 1960.
Wright, W. G.: Muscle Function. New York, Paul B. Hoeber, Inc., 1928.

CHAPTER 12

THE GENERAL SENSES
AND THEIR AFFERENT
PATHWAYS

In the discussion of reflexes it was pointed out that a stimulus, such as a burn, may be painful. Although the pain of the burn is frequently more important to the subject than is the reflex motor response, the sensation of pain is not a part of the reflex; it depends upon the activities of many parts of the central nervous system. One must therefore distinguish between the physiological and the psychological aspects of sensation. The physiological aspects show considerable specialization, that is, the peripheral receptors are more sensitive to a particular kind of stimulus. They should not, however, be called "pain" receptors or "touch" receptors. This implies a specificity that does not exist, namely, that stimulation of such a receptor invariably results in that sensation and only that sensation.

According to the traditional (and lay) conception, the different senses are vision, hearing, smell, taste, and touch. The inadequacy of this classification is indicated by the discussion of receptors and their relation to sensation (p. 135). The special senses (p. 190) include balance (equilibrium), vision, hearing, smell, and taste. The general sensations are considered to consist of certain primary modalities, for example, touch, pain, and temperature from the skin, and pain, pressure, and the kinesthetic sense from deeper tissues. Pain may also arise from certain viscera, but other visceral sensations are not readily classifiable.

174

Each of the terms given above is merely a linguistic term for a most complicated experience. The purpose of the present chapter is mainly to discuss some of the spinal cord and brain stem pathways which permit impulses from receptors to reach higher levels. In general, the impulses enter the spinal cord or brain stem and then ascend in groups of fibers called tracts. Perception is not possible until the impulses reach the brain. The entire pathway, from spinal cord to brain, is interrupted by synaptic junctions which modulate and control transmission and which are themselves influenced by descending pathways.

It now seems clear that nonmyelinated and myelinated fibers are both concerned with carrying impulses for all types of general sensations. Indeed, the extremely small size of the nonmyelinated fibers (or C fibers) makes it possible for a peripheral nerve to contain a vast number of such fibers, and thereby to convey a vast amount of information from the area supplied by the nerve.

SENSORY PATHS FROM THE SKIN

Touch.   Nerve impulses resulting from touching the skin or hairs are carried by myelinated and nonmyelinated fibers which enter the spinal cord by way of dorsal roots. These fibers give off many branches upon entering the spinal cord. Some of these establish reflex connections, while others synapse in the gray matter at the level of entrance, or at higher levels, with cells whose axons ascend to the cerebral hemispheres. These particular axons leave the gray matter, cross the midline, and ascend in the opposite anterior funiculi. Their destination is the thalamus; hence they form the *anterior spinothalamic tracts.* One of these tracts is illustrated in Figure 102.

Another pathway is by way of dorsal root fibers which enter and ascend in the posterior funiculus on the side of entrance to the medulla oblongata, where they end in the nucleus gracilis or nucleus cuneatus. This is the first part of what may be termed the posterior funiculus–medial lemniscus system. There is a morphological feature of the spinal cord which is the result of lamination in the ascending tracts. The fibers that enter the cord from lower levels and then ascend in the posterior funiculi are displaced medially by those entering at higher levels. Beginning in the upper thoracic cord and continuing into the cervical cord, each posterior funiculus is separated into a *fasciculus gracilis* and a *fasciculus cuneatus* (Fig. 133, p. 245). The fasciculus gracilis contains fibers derived from the lower limb and the lower trunk. It derives its name from its long, slender shape; it is the more medial of the two. The fasciculus cuneatus is shorter, and wedge-shaped. It con-

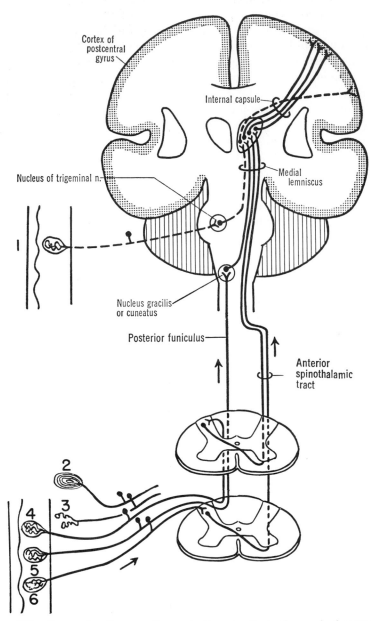

Figure 102. Composite diagram of several afferent paths to the cerebral cortex. *1, 4, 5,*
and *6* indicate Meissner's corpuscles. Note that tactile paths have several routes in the
spinal cord and that *2* (pacinian corpuscle) and *3* (joint receptor) have paths which, in the
spinal cord, are similar to the path taken by *5*, but, for purposes of simplification, are not
drawn.

tains fibers from the upper trunk and upper limb. Both fasciculi continue upwards and end in the *nucleus cuneatus* and the *nucleus gracilis*. These nuclei form the gracile and cuneate elevations on the surface of the medulla oblongata.

Axons that arise from the cuneate and gracile nuclei cross the midline and ascend in a prominent tract, the *medial lemniscus*. Each medial lemniscus is joined by the anterior spinothalamic tract of the corresponding side shortly after the latter tract enters the medulla oblongata. In the spinal cord, tactile pathways are therefore both crossed and uncrossed, but in the medulla oblongata they are largely crossed.

As the medial lemnisci ascend to the thalami, they are joined by fibers that carry tactile impulses from the head and face. These impulses enter the brain stem over branches of the trigeminal nerves, the unipolar cells being in the ganglia of these nerves. The central processes enter the pons and end in an area of gray matter on each side of the pons, the *main sensory nucleus*. Secondary axons then cross the midline and join the medial lemnisci.

Still another pathway, although perhaps not in man, is the spinocervicothalamic system. Fibers arising from cells in the dorsal gray matter ascend on the same side in the dorsal part of the lateral funiculus to the *lateral cervical nucleus* in the upper cervical cord. Axons from these cells cross to ascend with the medial lemniscus to the thalamus (Fig. 103).

Figures 102 and 103 illustrate the tactile pathways from their inception on one side of the body to their termination in the postcentral gyrus of the opposite parietal lobe. The projections from the thalamus to this gyrus are by way of the internal capsule. The postcentral gyrus is the *primary cortical receptive area* for general senses (except pain) from the opposite side of the body. Tactile impulses derived originally from the head and face terminate in the lower part of the gyrus, those from the lower limb in the upper portion, and those from the upper limb occupy an intermediate position.

The cells of the postcentral gyrus are arranged in layers, but the layers differ in thickness and composition from those in the motor areas. The fifth layer, that which in the motor areas contains large pyramidal cells, is present in the postcentral gyrus, but is thinner and overshadowed by a prominent fourth layer. This layer is pronounced because the nerve fibers which enter the sensory cortex extend vertically into it and branch profusely. The branches extend horizontally throughout this layer, forming extensive intracortical connections. This arrangement is characteristic of all the cortical areas which receive many nerve fibers (Fig. 156, p. 313).

The systems described above provide for the rapid transmission of information from the skin to the cerebral cortex, with precise somato-

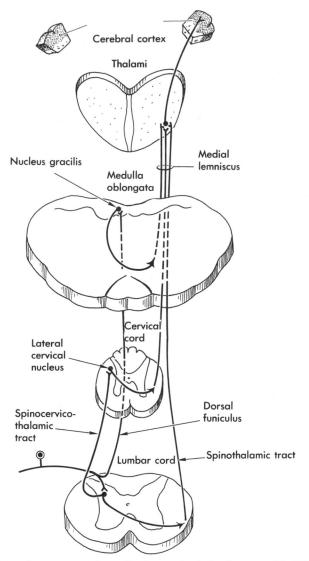

Figure 103. Schematic representation of spinocervicothalamic tract. (Modified from Gardner, E.: Ciba Foundation Symposium on Myotatic, Kinesthetic and Vestibular Mechanisms, London, J. and A. Churchill Ltd., 1967.)

topic localization. The rapidity of their action makes possible central control of the dorsal gray matter which acts as a gate for other pathways (see p. 246).

Pain. Impulses resulting from noxious stimuli travel centrally over myelinated and nonmyelinated fibers at rates varying from less than 1 to as much as 30 meters per second. Some impulses, therefore, reach the central nervous system before others. The time intervals may be so marked that a severe stimulus under certain conditions may be followed by a painful sensation, and then by a second or delayed pain. The first pain may be sharp, whereas the second is more diffuse. It tends to spread or radiate and is much more unpleasant. However, it is often difficult to demonstrate two types of pain under normal conditions. They are more easily demonstrated in certain disorders which affect nerve fibers, either destroying them or altering their conduction time. When two pains do occur, an important factor is differences in conduction rates between large and small pain fibers.

The axons carrying these impulses enter the spinal cord and branch profusely. Many of the branches establish reflex connections. Others synapse in the dorsal gray matter with cells the axons of which cross the midline and ascend in the lateral funiculi as the *lateral spino-thalamic tracts* (Fig. 104). On their way to the thalamus they are joined by fibers carrying impulses originating in the head and face. Painful stimuli in these areas initiate impulses that travel centrally over fibers of the trigeminal nerves. These fibers enter the brain stem and descend, some reaching the spinal cord before they end. They thus form the *spinal tracts of the trigeminal nerves* (Fig. 104 and Fig. 135, p. 257). The axons of the succeeding cells cross the midline, join the lateral spino-thalamic tracts, and ascend with them to the thalami. Impulses are then relayed to the postcentral gyri of the parietal lobes. The central pain pathway for skin is probably entirely crossed, both in the cord and brain stem. If this tract is cut, pain due to the usual stimuli cannot be felt in the skin on the opposite side of the body below the level of the cut. This is shown by Figure 105. Such a cut is a therapeutic measure in certain cases of severe intractable pain, such as might be present in the later stages of cancer, or after severe injuries. Since tactile paths in the cord are both crossed and uncrossed, the sense of touch is but slightly affected by such a procedure. Figure 106 illustrates the degeneration resulting from such a tractotomy.

The afferent input to the spinal cord involves the dorsal gray matter which modulates the incoming afferent activity, the fast systems which, at least in part, activate central mechanisms that influence the modulation, and transmission cells that activate response and initiate perception. In an attempt to reconcile opposing theories of pain (specificity theory versus pattern theory), it has been proposed that pain results after prolonged monitoring of the afferent input by central cells. Certainly, the specificity theory neglects the psychological aspects, the fact that surgical operations such as mentioned above may fail to relieve pain, and that the quality and degree of pain are susceptible to a variety of influences. The pattern theory, on the other hand, while explaining much more, neglects the specificity of receptors and their responses, which has been clearly demonstrated.

Temperature.   Changes in temperature above or below the normal body variations excite temperature receptors, from which impulses travel centrally over myelinated and nonmyelinated fibers. The central pathways, including those for the face and head, are almost identical to those for pain. Any lesion of the lateral spinothalamic tract, therefore, affects temperature as well as pain perception.

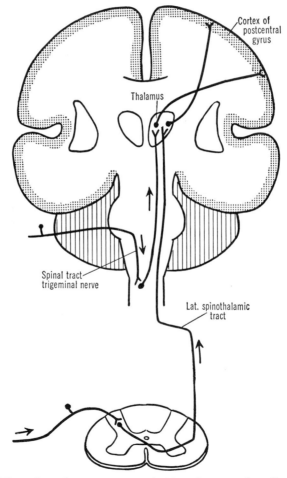

Figure 104.   The pain and temperature path. Note that secondary fibers from the trigeminal nerve join the lateral spinothalamic tract. The uncrossed path for pain is not shown.

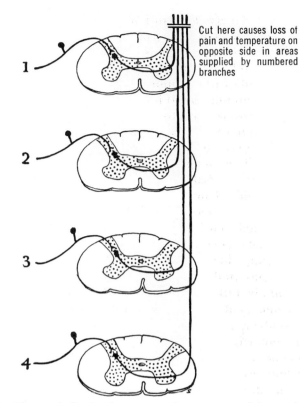

Cut here causes loss of pain and temperature on opposite side in areas supplied by numbered branches

Figure 105. Diagram indicating how sensory losses may result from a lesion of the pain and temperature path. The indicated lesion above segment *1* causes much more loss than one between segments *3* and *4*, even though both affect the lateral spinothalamic tract.

SENSORY PATHS FROM THE SUBCUTANEOUS AND DEEP TISSUES

Pressure. The pacinian corpuscles are the endings most sensitive to pressure, although other types of endings are also involved, including some derived from nonmyelinated fibers. The impulses that arise from pacinian corpuscles enter the spinal cord where reflex connections are established. Impulses ascending to the brain use the posterior funiculus–medial lemniscus and the spinocervicothalamic systems. The pathway from the face and head is probably similar to that for touch from these areas.

The sense of vibration, such as results when a vibrating tuning fork is placed on a bony prominence, is most likely a temporal modulation of the sensation resulting from stimulation of pacinian corpuscles.

Pain. The pathways for pain from the subcutaneous and deeper

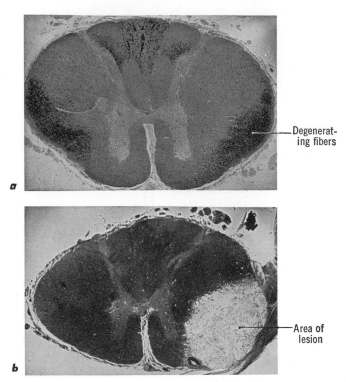

Figure 106. Photomicrographs of sections of spinal cord from a patient in whom both pain pathways had been cut to relieve intractable pain. *a,* Thoracic cord, above both incisions. Degenerating fibers in both lateral funiculi, Marchi method. Pain fibers are located here, and also spinocerebellar fibers which are unavoidably cut in this type of operation. Degeneration in the posterior funiculi is a result of the disorder which necessitated the operation. Compare this appearance of degeneration with that of Figure 100 (p. 169). *b,* Section through one of the incisions in the midthoracic cord.

tissues are identical to those described for skin, save that the fibers are more likely to be nonmyelinated. There is also evidence that an uncrossed pathway exists.

Kinesthetic Sense (Also Known as Position Sense, Muscle-Joint-Tendon Sense, or Conscious Proprioception).   This is the quality which enables a subject to know just where his body and limbs are in space. It depends upon impulses from the inner ear (p. 215) and from certain proprioceptive receptors. The functions of the latter may be tested by having the subject close his eyes; the examiner then passively moves a finger or toe of the subject to a new position. The subject is then asked to state what the new position is, or to duplicate it with the opposite corresponding member. The passively induced movement stimulates receptors in joints, periosteum, ligaments, and fascia. Impulses from muscle spindles and tendon endings play little, if any, role in the sensory quality; they are mostly concerned with reflex and subcortical mechanisms. The kinesthetic receptors are chiefly Ruffini endings and small pacinian corpuscles; endings derived from nonmyelinated fibers may also be involved. The impulses travel centrally over fibers that enter the spinal cord, establish reflex connections, and then ascend in both the posterior funiculus–medial lemniscus and spinocervico-thalamic systems (Fig. 102). Similar receptors are present in the head and face areas, but the central pathways are unique. The primary neurons, the unipolar cells, are not in the ganglia of the trigeminal nerves, but in the brain stem itself. The central processes of these cells presumably have connections which allow a relay to the opposite medial lemnisci. Impulses concerned with position sense anywhere in the body eventually reach the postcentral gyri of the opposite parietal lobes.

SENSORY PATHS FROM VISCERA

Visceral Pain.   Visceral pain has a quality quite different from that of cutaneous pain, as anyone who has had an intestinal cramp will testify. The pain is usually diffuse, it tends to radiate, and it is difficult to localize. In addition, it is often severe, even sickening, and may persist for minutes, hours or even days. In spite of those differences, visceral pain, no matter what the cause, apparently starts, as does cutaneous pain, with the stimulation of free nerve endings. The resulting impulses travel centrally over fibers which end in the dorsal gray matter of the spinal cord. Some axons of the secondary cells cross and ascend in the opposite lateral spinothalamic tract; others ascend in the tract on the same side. The path to the thalamus and to the cerebral cortex is, therefore, a bilateral one. If an operation is necessary for the relief of visceral pain, both tracts must be cut. Even then, the operation may be unsuccessful.

Little is known about the central pathways for other visceral sensations.

REFERRED PAIN AND PROJECTED SENSATIONS

Visceral disorders frequently cause pain that is felt in certain areas in the skin. The skin pain occurs in regions supplied by nerves originating from the segment of the cord in which the impulses from the involved viscera enter. For example, if the diaphragm, which is supplied by the fourth cervical segment of the spinal cord (phrenic nerve), is inflamed, pain may be felt in the skin areas supplied by the fourth cervical segment, namely, the tip of the shoulder. Referred pain is frequent enough to be valuable as a diagnostic sign. Heart disease may be accompanied by pain referred down the left arm. In the early stages of appendicitis, pain may be felt just below the sternum. The pain of a kidney stone passing down the ureter may be referred to the back and groin. Physicians are able to localize internal disorders more accurately when referred pain is present.

Current explanations of referred pain are inadequate, although the recent theories about pain in general may lead to a greater understanding of referred and projected pain. Undoubtedly the cerebral cortex is unable to distinguish accurately between impulses from viscera and impulses arriving from skin. Some of the causes of this inability are discussed on p. 325. Other factors appear to be structural and functional characteristics of the gray matter of the spinal cord. Figure 107 illustrates the closed circuit arrangements found in gray matter. Impulses started in such circuits may produce after-discharge, the phenomenon of continued discharge of motor neurons after afferent impulses have ceased (p. 129). Furthermore, the afferent tracts of the cord evolve from such interneuronal pools rather than from the simple relays which form the conventional representation. It is probable that many of the impulses from viscera enter these circuits along with impulses from skin. If this be true, then the cerebral cortex would be unable to distinguish accurately between the two. This is possible because nerve impulses arriving at the cortex are the same no matter where initiated. A stimulus applied to a peripheral nerve causes impulses which are indistinguishable from those originating at receptors

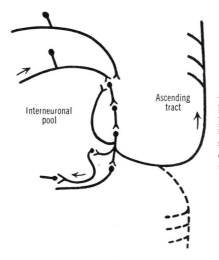

Interneuronal
pool

Ascending
tract

Figure 107.   Diagram of an interneuronal pool, a closed circuit of the type mentioned on p. 130. Connections are such that an ascending tract may convey impulses derived from several afferent fibers, each of which impinges on the closed circuit. Arrows indicate direction of conduction.

on the ends of the fibers of that nerve. The cortex actually interprets them as coming from the receptors. Striking the ulnar nerve at the elbow, that is, "hitting the funny bone," is such a phenomenon. The pain appears to radiate down the forearm and hand. This is known as projection of a sensation.

A classical example is found in *tabes dorsalis*, which is one of the manifestations of syphilitic infection of the nervous system. The inflammatory process involves dorsal roots. The irritation of the nerve fibers initiates impulses that reach the cerebrum, but, since the impulses are the same as those caused by stimulation of the receptors at the ends of the same fibers, they are interpreted as coming from receptors. The patient, therefore, complains of severe pains in his limbs and viscera, the exact location depending upon the dorsal roots involved.

Even more striking are *phantom limb sensations.* Patients who have had a limb amputated subsequently feel as if that limb were still present. The phantom limb may even become painful. Apparently some type of irritation of the ends of the nerve fibers in the stump initiates nerve impulses. When these reach the cerebrum, they are interpreted as coming from receptors in the absent limb, that is, the areas normally supplied by the fibers. In other words, during the lifetime of the person, previous to the amputation, there has been built up a body scheme in which the brain has become used to the fact that impulses arriving from certain nerves were coming from certain portions of the body. Impulses initiated anywhere along the path are identical with those starting at the peripheral receptors. Sensations due to stimuli at portions of afferent paths other than receptors may be termed referred, projected, or spontaneous. It is apparent that when a person complains of pain somewhere in his body, the cause may be anywhere along the pain pathway.

Occasionally, the predominating sensation in a phantom limb is pain. It is interesting that in medical history and in folklore, there are references to the practice of digging up amputated parts which had been buried, in order to straighten out the fingers or toes in the belief that this would relieve painful spasms of the absent limb. These spasms were attributed to the devil.

CLINICAL IMPORTANCE OF THE AFFERENT PATHWAYS

Because of the anatomical differences in the afferent pathways, symptoms resulting from lesions of these paths will differ according to the location of the lesion (Fig. 108).

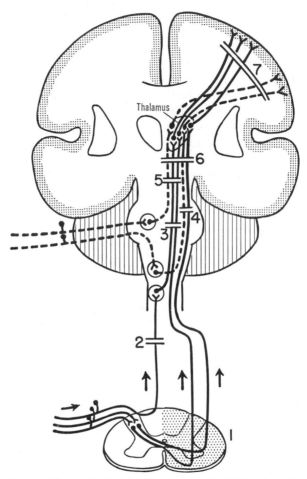

Figure 108. Diagram illustrating lesions of sensory paths. *1*, The shaded area represents a hemisection of the cord (Brown-Séquard syndrome; described in text). *2*, Section of fibers ascending in the posterior funiculus, causing loss of position sense, pressure and vibratory sense, but not touch, because the latter has additional routes in the spinal cord. *3*, Section of the medial lemniscus here causes loss of general senses (except pain and temperature) in opposite side of the body. *4*, Section of the lateral spinothalamic tract causes loss of pain and temperature in opposite side of the body and face. *5*, Section of the medial lemniscus similar to *3*, except that the loss includes the opposite face as well. *6*, Lesion of all sensory fibers with loss of all general senses in opposite side of the body and face. *7*, This represents a lesion in the internal capsule or cortex. The signs are quite variable, but the characteristic feature is that some perception of pain and temperature often remains.

Suppose that the posterior, lateral, and anterior funiculi (one half of the cord) are destroyed on the left side of the thoracic cord. Pain and temperature perception may be lost over the right lower limb because of the destruction of the left lateral spinothalamic tract. Pressure and position sense are lost in the left lower limb — destruction of the left posterior funiculus. Touch is but slightly affected, because the fibers ascending in the left posterior funiculus are destroyed, but those which crossed below the lesion and ascended in the right anterior spinothalamic tract are intact; impulses can still reach the cerebral cortex. Such a lesion, of course, causes a spastic paralysis of the left lower limb because of destruction of corticospinal and extrapyramidal fibers. If this lesion were in the upper cervical cord, there would be similar signs in the upper limbs as well. The symptoms resulting from hemisection of the spinal cord constitute the *Brown-Séquard syndrome* (p. 188).

Suppose, however, that the lesion is in the brain stem above the level of entrance of fibers from the head and face, and that it destroys one of the medial lemnisci. Since touch is by now entirely crossed, it, as well as pressure and position sense, is lost in the opposite limbs and opposite side of the trunk and head. If the lesion is large enough to include the lateral spinothalamic tract, then pain and temperature perception are lost over the same areas. If the lesion is extended to include the descending motor fibers, spastic paralysis of the opposite limbs occurs. Of course, any brain stem lesion often involves one of the cranial nerves, in which case there are signs and symptoms relating to its destruction.

It should be emphasized that our knowledge of sensory pathways in man is far from complete, as indicated by the fact that it is rare for any sensation to be lost completely following a lesion that destroys pathways on one side of the brain stem or spinal cord.

PRIMARY RECEPTIVE AREAS

When impulses from peripheral receptors arrive at the cerebral hemispheres, they terminate in *primary receptive areas* (p. 312). Here the impulses are perceived as sensations. Only perception and recognition are functions of these areas, which are not responsible for the localization of stimuli, that is, the determination that stimuli are affecting a particular portion of the body, such as the hand. The recall or memory of a sensation does not occur in the primary areas, nor is the accurate differentiation of intensity one of their functions. These are all functions of higher or *association areas,* to which impulses are relayed by the primary areas (p. 320).

The primary areas for the general sensations include both the thalamus and the postcentral gyrus. The functions of the postcentral gyrus are not known with any certainty. If the gyrus on one side is destroyed, the patient may subsequently be able to detect pain and temperature on the opposite side of the body, although the capacity to localize and to discriminate intensities of stimulation is impaired or lost. It may be postulated, then, that the thalamus is the primary receptive area for pain and temperature, and the postcentral gyrus a primary area for other general senses. These are only partial explanations, however, and other phenomena are difficult to clarify. Our knowledge is so inadequate that the only generalization possible is that both the thalamus and the postcentral gyrus are concerned in the initial recognition of pain, temperature, touch, pressure, and position sense.

SUMMARY

The various general sensations from skin, subcutaneous and deep tissues, and viscera are the result of interpretations of impulses by primary receptive areas in the thalamus and postcentral gyrus. The pathways for these impulses differ in their course through the spinal cord and brain stem. Tactile impulses reach the cord and ascend via both crossed and uncrossed paths, but once in the brain stem they are entirely crossed, ascending in the medial lemniscus to the thalamus. Position sense and pressure follow the same path as does uncrossed touch. Pain and temperature ascend in the lateral spinothalamic tract, the pathway being crossed for skin and deeper tissues and both crossed and uncrossed for viscera. This tract ascends to the thalamus, and, like the medial lemniscus, the impulses it carries are relayed to the postcentral gyrus.

Referred and projected sensations are related to the fact that impulses originating in any part of an afferent path are indistinguishable from those originating in receptors.

Names in Neurology

CHARLES-EDOUARD BROWN-SÉQUARD (1817-1894)

This physician, though associated mainly with France, led a roving existence, teaching at Harvard as well as in various French colleges.

He produced experimental lesions of the nervous system, studied their effects, and also carried out considerable work on the sympathetic system.

REFERENCES

See the references cited on pages 6, 154, and 319.

For recent reviews, see the following Ciba Foundation Symposia:
Touch, Heat and Pain. Boston, Little, Brown and Company, 1966.
Myotatic, Kinesthetic and Vestibular Mechanisms. London, J. & A. Churchill, Ltd., 1967.

Calne, D. B., and Pallis, C. A.: Vibratory sense: a critical review. Brain, 89:723-746, 1966.
Douglas, W. W., and Ritchie, J. M.: Mammalian nonmyelinated nerve fibers. Physiol. Rev., 42:297-334, 1962. (An excellent review of the properties and functions of nonmyelinated fibers.)
Melzack, R., and Wall, P. D.: Pain mechanisms: a new theory. Science, 150:971-979, 1966. (A superb review and presentation of a new theory.)
White, J. C., and Sweet, W. H.: Pain, Its Mechanisms and Neurosurgical Control. Springfield, Ill., Charles C Thomas, 1955. (An outstanding volume, of advanced nature, by distinguished neurosurgeons.)
Wyburn, G. M., Pickford, R. W., and Hirst, R. J.: Human Senses and Perception. Toronto, University of Toronto Press, 1964. (An excellent general presentation, with emphasis on central and psychological factors.)

CHAPTER 13

THE SPECIAL SENSES
AND THEIR AFFERENT
PATHWAYS

The separation of senses into general and special types is partially based on the causative stimuli. General senses are those aroused by stimuli acting on and within the body. These energy changes are mostly mechanical in nature. We usually think of special senses as those which are aroused by stimuli originating at a variable distance from the body, as, for example, light and sound waves. The term "special sense" when used in this manner is, however, inadequate, because, even if the source of a stimulus is some distance away, the effective energy must still impinge upon receptors; that is to say, sound waves must reach the ear. Taste cannot be considered the result of stimuli originating at a distance. Balance or equilibrium, as a function of the labyrinth, is associated with movements of the head. The classification is nevertheless valuable if by special senses we refer broadly to sensory qualities dependent upon receptors in the cranial region, whose afferent paths are over cranial nerves and which may allow perception of distant objects.

In man these senses are rather uniformly developed to a high degree. This does not mean that taste is as subjectively important as vision. It means that taste is associated with a system of pathways and cortical areas which allow for functional elaboration if necessary. Man, therefore, differs from other animals in which one or more of these

190

senses may be highly developed. Hearing in a bat is certainly more acute than in man. A dog has a remarkable olfactory sense. Birds may have extraordinarily keen vision. But in these animals many of the other senses are functionally inferior to those of man.

VISION

The peripheral stimuli necessary for this sensory quality are radiations in the visible spectrum varying in wave length from 400 to 700 millimicrons. The receptors are in the sensory layer of the retina. The retina is the innermost layer of the eye, that complex and efficient optical instrument which is designed to gather and focus light upon the retina.

If one compares the eye to a camera, the retina would represent the light-sensitive plate or film. There is a focusing system composed of the *cornea* and the *crystalline lens*. These are shown in Figure 109. The cornea is composed of connective tissue and is covered on both

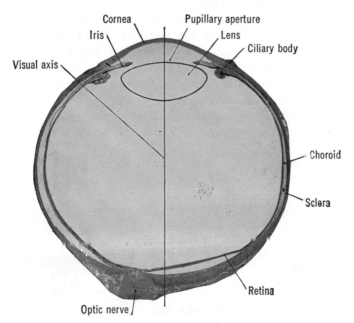

Figure 109. Photograph of a horizontal section of a human eye. The lens, which was removed to facilitate making the section, has been drawn in its correct position, but the suspensory strands around it have been omitted. Note that the retina has partially separated from the other coats of the eyeball. The dark line in the posterior part of the iris is due to the presence of pigment.

surfaces by epithelial cells. It is transparent and is devoid of any blood vessels that might interfere with this property. The cornea is curved, with the convexity forward or outward, and, when viewed from the front, is the clear portion of the globe, surrounded on all sides by the "white" of the eye, the *sclera.*

Much of the refraction of entering light occurs during its passage through the corneal surfaces. Light undergoes further refraction as it passes through the lens. The total refraction is such that when light from any object reaches the retina, it forms a real and inverted image on the retina. Just behind the cornea is the *iris.* This has an opening in its center, the *pupil.* There are smooth muscle fibers in the iris, some of which are arranged circularly so that the pupillary aperture narrows when they contract. Others are arranged radially, spreading out like a fan, and their contraction widens the pupillary opening (Fig. 110). Thus, like the variable aperture of a camera, there is a mechanism for regulating the amount of light admitted to the eye.

The color of the eyes is caused by pigment, most of which is concentrated in cells on the posterior surface of the iris. Pigment is also present in the outer or nonsensory portion of the retina, and in the middle coat of the eye, the *choroid.* The pigment probably serves to prevent blurring or multiplication of images by internal reflection; in the camera this is prevented by painting the interior a dead black.

Sharp pictures at different distances can be taken with a camera by changing lenses or by varying the distance between lens and film. In the eye this is done by changing the curvature of the lens. The structures which make this possible are as follows: Surrounding the outer margin of the lens and attached to it by fine suspensory strands are bundles of smooth muscle fibers which form the *ciliary muscle.* When this muscle contracts, the area to which the strands attach is pulled

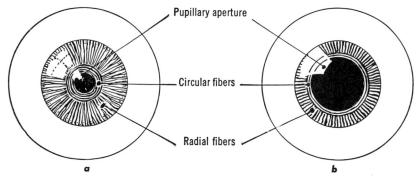

Pupillary aperture

Circular fibers

Radial fibers

a   *b*

Figure 110.   Circular and radial fibers in the iris. *a,* Pupillary constriction with contraction of the circular fibers. *b,* Pupillary dilatation with contraction of radial fibers and relaxation of circular ones.

forward. The strands are thus shortened, and the tension which they maintained on the lens is thereby lessened, allowing the elastic lens capsule to bulge forward.

Some fibers in the ciliary muscle are arranged circularly. When they contract, the entire ciliary area moves inward, thereby providing another means of shortening suspensory strands. The resulting increased thickness of the lens refracts the light to a greater degree, thus allowing near objects to be brought into sharper focus. This process is known as *accommodation*. It is accompanied by a narrowing of the pupillary aperture, that is to say, by pupillary constriction, and by a medial movement or convergence of each eye.

Between the iris and the cornea is the anterior chamber (Fig. 109); between the iris and the lens is the posterior chamber. Both are filled with a thin watery fluid, the *aqueous fluid* or *humor*, which is a filtrate of blood plasma. It circulates through the chambers and after absorp-

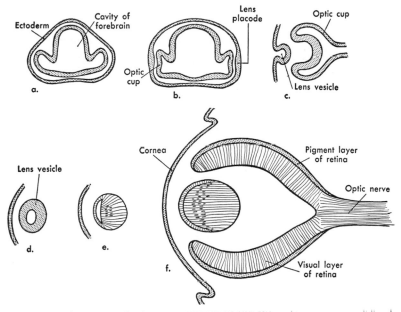

Figure 111. Various stages in the development of the eye. *a*, Cross section of forebrain showing outpocketings in the region of the future diencephalon. *b*, Outpocketings are definite optic cups, and the thickened ectoderm on each side is the beginning of the lens (lens placode). *c*, Just the region of the eye is shown. The lens placode has invaginated further. The optic cup shows how the retina begins as two layers. *d* and *e*, The lens vesicle detaches and its cavity begins to disappear. *f*, The lens is well formed. The cavity in the retina has disappeared. The posterior or outer layer of the optic cup becomes the pigment layer of the retina, and the anterior or inner layer contains the rods and cones, bipolar cells, and ganglion cells. When, for any reason, the retina separates in the adult, it generally separates between pigment layer and sensory layer, and not between pigment layer and choroid. The above is a very schematic representation, the actual development being considerably more complicated.

tion into tissue spaces in the coats of the eye is eventually returned to the venous circulation. Behind the lens is the *vitreous body,* a gelatinous, clear substance that is permanent; that is, it is not undergoing a constant formation, circulation, and absorption.

This complicated structure of the eye may be made somewhat clearer by reference to its formation and development in the embryo and fetus. This is illustrated in Figure 111. It can be seen that the retina is an extension of brain substance and that, because of its manner of formation, it is a double layer. The posterior or outer layer becomes the pigmented epithelium, and the anterior or inner layer the receptive portion of the retina.

THE RETINA

The retina is a part of the brain, having layers of specialized nerve cells, and being connected to the rest of the brain by a fiber tract called the optic nerve. The retina is the only portion of the nervous system which can be seen directly in the intact living subject. With an *ophthalmoscope* all portions of the retina may be seen. This instrument is designed so that light from it, when flashed into the eye of the subject, is reflected from the retina back to the eye of the observer.

Light entering the eye along the visual axis (Fig. 109) falls upon a portion of the retina known as the *macula lutea,* so called because it is a yellow spot. In the middle of the macula is a depression, the *fovea.* Just medial to the macula lutea is a whitish area from which small arteries and veins spread throughout the retina. This is the *optic disk,* the point of exit of the optic nerve. The vessels are the retinal arteries and veins, which reach the disk by running in the substance of the optic nerve. The optic disk and the vessels accurately reflect many pathological changes. Increased intracranial pressure, for instance, may so compress the retinal veins that circulation in the retina is seriously impaired. Fluid is forced out of capillaries because the venous pressure rises; this escaping fluid permeates the retina, and especially the optic disk. This becomes swollen and in such conditions is usually called a *choked disk.* The amount of choking is a good index of the amount of increase in the intracranial pressure. Vascular changes, such as atherosclerosis, usually affect the retinal vessels in the early stages of the disorder. Since these pathological processes can be seen directly, the disorder may often be detected before there is evidence of its presence elsewhere in the body. Ophthalmoscopic examination, therefore, is an important diagnostic tool for the general practitioner as well as for the ophthalmologist and the neurologist.

As shown in Figure 112, the retina is composed of cells arranged in layers. It is not necessary to name all the layers, it being sufficient to

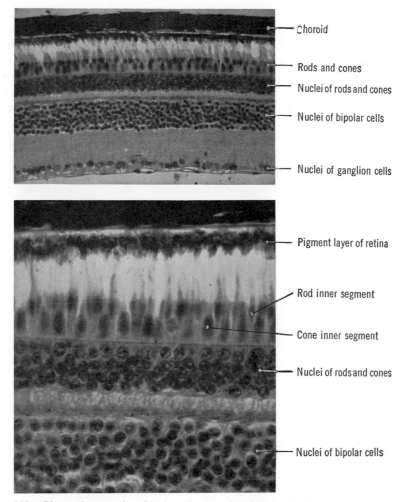

Figure 112. Photomicrographs of retina of copperhead snake (similar in many respects to human retina). *a,* Includes all the layers. *b,* At a higher magnification, showing particularly the rods and cones. The staining method does not demonstrate neuronal processes. (These sections, made by Dr. Gordon Walls, were obtained through the courtesy of Dr. Parker Heath.)

state that outermost in the retina proper is the layer of *rods* and *cones;* next the layer of *bipolar cells,* and innermost the layer of *ganglion cells.* In general, these cells are arranged nearly perpendicularly. At the region of the optic disk, however, the cells are arranged so obliquely that they are absent just in front of the disk. Light striking this region does not impinge on receptor cells, and no visual function is possible. This is the *blind spot* of the eye.

Rods and Cones and Their Connections.   The receptive cells, that is, those sensitive to radiations in the visible spectrum, are the rods and cones. In order to reach these specialized cells, light must traverse the other layers of the retina, except in the fovea, where the cells are arranged obliquely so that cones are directly exposed. The schematic representation of Figure 113 illustrates that the rods and cones are named because of the shape of their outer segments. The outer segments of the rods contain a pigment, *rhodopsin* or *visual purple*. The precise nature of photosensitive pigments in mammalian cones has not yet been determined. It should be emphasized that there is great species variation in the morphology of rods and cones, and that electon microscope studies are leading to certain doubts about current concepts of structure.

In the retina as a whole, there are about four times as many rods as cones. In the macula, however, cones predominate, and the fovea is occupied exclusively by them. As one progresses toward the periphery of the retina, the rods become predominant.

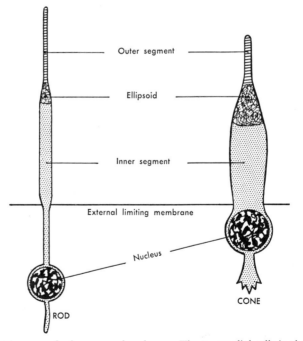

Figure 113.   Diagram of a human rod and cone. The neuroglial cells in the retina have long processes that, in the inner and outer parts of the retina, fuse to form internal and external limiting membranes. The external limiting membrane is shown here, perforated by the rod and the cone. Cone nuclei are placed nearer the membrane. (Based on Walls, The Vertebrate Eye, cited on p. 225.)

The general arrangement of retinal cells is such that rods and cones connect with bipolar cells, which in turn synapse with ganglion cells. The axons of the ganglion cells course toward the back of the eye; at the optic disk they collect to form the optic nerve. There are 115 to 130 million rods and cones, but, at the most, only one million optic nerve fibers. This necessitates a general convergence within the retina (Fig. 114). In other words, one or a few ganglion cells receive impulses from a number of bipolar cells, and these in turn from many rods and cones. This means that most ganglion cells are related to hundreds and perhaps thousands of photoreceptors, and that the receptive field of a ganglion cell may be relatively large. There is evidence that a restricted path exists in the fovea, perhaps as a one-to-one connection as shown in Figure 114. This figure is a schematic representation of a few of the possible kinds of retinal connections. Neurons that connect or associate parts of the retina in a horizontal manner are omitted.

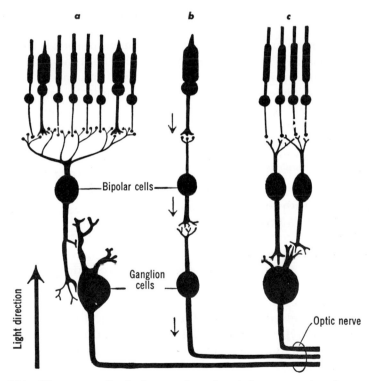

Figure 114. Three types of retinal connections. Association neurons have been omitted. *a,* Mixed rod and cone system, both types synapsing with one bipolar cell and this in turn with a ganglion cell. *b,* Single cone system, found only in the fovea. *c,* Multiple rod system, several rods converging upon bipolars and these upon a ganglion cell. The optic nerve is formed by axons of the ganglion cells. (Modified after Polyak.)

All the retinal connections are synapses. The cells are neurons, though in the rods and cones considerably modified ones. The retina is comparable to the cerebral cortex in its complexity. Between the cells, and forming a supporting framework for them, are neuroglial cells such as are found in the rest of the central nervous system. The optic nerve, being a fiber tract and not a true peripheral nerve, also contains neuroglial tissue. Its fibers lack neurilemma and are, therefore, incapable of regeneration when once destroyed.

Retinal Functions. Light striking a photoreceptor initiates a series of processes that result in nerve impulses leaving the eye by way of an optic nerve fiber. These receptors contain visual pigments which decompose upon absorbing light, the process presumably resulting in an electrical change which activates the succeeding neuron.

The eyes of most mammals have both rods and cones. This situation, plus the association of rod-rich retinas with nocturnal animals and cone-rich retinas with diurnal animals, has led to the duplicity theory of vision. This holds that rods are associated with visual sensitivity (night vision), and cones with visual acuity and often color vision also (day vision).

As mentioned previously, the visual pigment in rods is rhodopsin. This is the common pigment in marine fishes and land vertebrates, the various rhodopsins having a characteristic absorption maximum at about 500 millimicrons (mμ). Human rhodopsin has an absorption maximum at 497 mμ. Many fresh water fishes have porphyropsins rather than rhodopsins, the porphyropsins having absorption maxima at about 522 mμ. Both types of pigments are related to the vitamin A complex, vitamin A_1 (retinal) being a chromophore for rhodopsin, and vitamin A_2 (retinal) being a chromophore for porphyropsin.

Light that reaches rods is absorbed by rhodopsin. A photochemical change results, with some of the rhodopsin being bleached in the process. The process is reversible, rhodopsin being resynthesized. In some way, the photochemical reaction is followed by excitation of bipolar cells and then ganglion cells. This excitation is signaled by electrical changes of such magnitude that they can be recorded by electrodes placed on the surface of the eye. The recorded electrical changes constitute the electroretinogram (ERG), with characteristic deflections (Fig. 115). The velocity at which the photochemical reaction proceeds is proportional to the intensity of light and the concentration of rhodopsin. Only a small part of the total amount of rhodopsin is bleached when exposed to light.

Rhodopsin is found in the outer segments of rods, and light must therefore traverse the layers of the retina to reach it. The mechanism of excitation is extraordinarily sensitive. Recent evidence indicates that one to three quanta of light reaching rods are sufficient for excitation

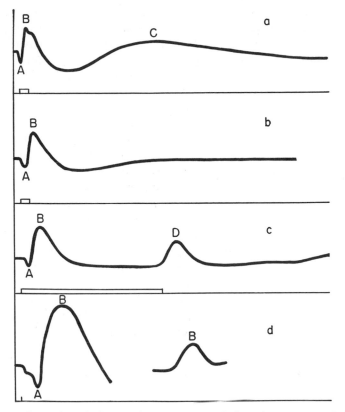

Figure 115. Examples of electroretinograms, recorded so that an upward deflection indicates positivity at an electrode in front of the retina, in contrast to an electrode behind or at the side of the retina. *a* is an ERG of a guinea pig (with a pure rod retina, or nearly so), in response to a flash of light, the onset and duration of which is signaled on the base line. There is an initial, negative *A* wave, a larger positive *B* wave, and a long lasting, positive *C* wave. *b* is an ERG of a ground squirrel (with a pure cone retina) in response to a short flash of light, showing *A* and *B* waves. With a long flash of light *(c)*, there is a *D* wave or off-effect when the light is turned off. *d* shows human ERG's. That on the left is in response to a flash of high intensity light, showing *A* and *B* waves. That on the right shows just a *B* wave when the stimulus is of low intensity. The nature of the ERG is still obscure. It is a general reaction, and the various waves or components cannot be assigned specifically to either rods or cones. All ERG's are in dark-adapted state, and the human ERG's are based on Armington, Johnson and Riggs, J. Physiol., *118*:289-298, 1952.

and it may be, therefore, that one quantum can activate a single rod.

A photosensitive pigment, *iodopsin,* has been isolated from cones of birds. The evidence strongly suggests that three visual pigments are related to human cones.

Dark and Light Adaptation. If the eyes have been in complete darkness for forty minutes or more, it will be found that the sensitivity of the eye has greatly increased. The energy of light necessary to stimulate is much less, by about a thousand-fold, than that required in daylight. If the dark-adapted eye is exposed to light of varying wave lengths, of equal energy, it is found that sensitivity is greatest in the green portion of the spectrum, where the greatest absorption by rhodopsin occurs. The light seen is not green, however, but some intensity of gray. The dark-adapted eye cannot distinguish colors. When the dark-adapted eye is stimulated with other wave lengths, it is found that sensitivity decreases according to the manner illustrated in Figure 116 *(scotopic curve)*. Part of the decrease in sensitivity toward the violet or shorter wave length portion of the spectrum is more apparent than real, because some of the shorter wave lengths are absorbed by the refracting media, such as the lens. Patients who have had lenses removed because of cataracts *(aphakia)* may, by ultraviolet radiation, be able to see objects that are invisible or less visible to others. The dark-adapted eye is quite insensitive at the longer wave lengths, or red end of the spectrum. Hence one can dark-adapt by wearing red goggles with the proper transmission characteristics. The red light that gets through stimulates cones, thus enabling one to see. Rods are not stimulated, hence can adapt just as if they were in darkness.

If an eye is exposed to strong light or to daylight, it becomes light-adapted, and the greatest sensitivity is found in the region of 557 mμ

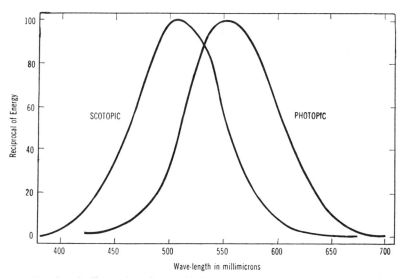

Figure 116. Graph illustrating the Purkinje shift. The scotopic curve is the visibility curve of the dark-adapted eye (achromatic vision), with maximum sensitivity at 510 millimicrons. The photopic curve is the visibility curve of the light-adapted eye (chromatic vision), with maximum sensitivity at 557 millimicrons. The two curves, for convenience, are plotted in the same units of sensitivity, although the scotopic eye is many times more sensitive. (Modified from Hecht and Williams: J. Gen. Physiol., 5:1-33, 1923.)

(*photopic curve*, Fig. 116). This shift to the red-green portion of the spectrum is the *Purkinje shift,* and represents functional differences between rods and cones. The threshold is at least a thousand times greater than in the dark-adapted retina.

It has been shown that in animals with pure rod and pure cone retinae, there is no Purkinje shift, nor is there one in man when the stimulating light is so arranged that it falls only on the fovea, where only cones are present. On the basis of the evidence cited, and of other evidence, there is reason to believe that rods are primarily concerned with visual sensitivity, being active in the dark-adapted eye, and that cones are primarily concerned with visual acuity, being active in the light-adapted eye. This, however, is not a clear-cut functional separation. Rods are active in day vision. Nocturnal animals, for example, can see in the daytime. Color vision is supposed to be primarily a cone function, but rods may be concerned to some extent.

Visual Sensitivity. This is the ability to see in dim light and is primarily a function of the rods. There are several reasons for this. As mentioned above, rhodopsin is extremely sensitive to light. Hence, in the dark-adapted eye, little energy is necessary for rod stimulation. Furthermore, as shown in Figure 114, the rods in multiple rod systems converge upon one bipolar cell, or at least upon one ganglion cell. Therefore, if light of low intensity falls upon each of many rods, the resulting excitation may summate at the succeeding bipolar cells and thereby reach the threshold of that neuron. Visual sensitivity is aided by reflex widening of the pupil in dim light. This illuminates rods previously unaffected and thereby increases the chances for summation.

Several mechanisms seem to be responsible for the increase in sensitivity during dark adaptation. Only a small part of the total amount of rhodopsin is bleached, even in strong light, and the amount resynthesized in the dark accounts only in part for the increase in sensitivity. It is held that in dim light, or in darkness, there are conditions that are favorable for a horizontal spread of excitation. Probably, in the absence of cone activity, certain inhibitory mechanisms are lost, so that an increasing number of neurons have a lower threshold. Thus, one can speak of both photochemical and neurological components in dark adaptation.

Since vitamin A is involved in the metabolism of rhodopsin, vitamin A deficiency may result in night blindness. This vitamin, however, has the general property of being necessary for the maintenance of epithelium, and its role in night blindness may therefore be related to the latter property. Cone functions may also be affected in so-called night blindness.

Rods are more numerous in the periphery of the retina. Therefore, in dim light, such as at twilight, objects are best seen from an oblique angle rather than viewed directly ahead, since in the latter case light falls on the macular region where cones predominate.

Visual Acuity.   With the light-adapted eye, color sensation becomes possible, as well as an increased sharpness of object contour and detail. One is therefore able to distinguish small objects as entities and to observe them in sharp outline.

Everyone is familiar with the fact that if one moves away from two closely approximated objects, they eventually fuse and appear as one. If the objects are lines, visual acuity may be tested by measuring the least separation by which two lines may be discerned. The smallest visual angle, the angle subserved by the distance separating the two lines, is 1 minute or less. There are many factors, more than can be discussed here, involved in visual acuity. One is probably the *grain* of the retina or the denseness of receptors within it. That is, if receptors were relatively far apart, light from one or the other of the lines or from the area between might fall on nonsensitive portions of the retina, and this would certainly diminish resolving power. Another factor is undoubtedly the one-to-one type of cone projection of the foveal region. This allows separate paths for impulses due to light from different, small sources, such as two lines. The fact that visual acuity is more pronounced in the fovea corroborates the functions of the cones in this matter.

The theoretical conditions for the smallest visual angle may be shown as follows: Suppose two thin black lines on a white background are separated by such a small or narrow distance that the light from the intervening white would illuminate but a single row of cones. It follows that the row of cones on each side would not be illuminated (corresponding to the black lines), but those still farther laterally would be. The brain is thus furnished a means of distinguishing the two separable lines, since there are no nerve impulses from the retinal region corresponding to the lines, in contrast to the impulses arriving from the intervening and neighboring retina. These conditions, however, are not actually found. The focusing and fixation of the eyes are not accurate enough to meet these theoretical demands. Slight movements of the eyeballs result in illumination of the row of cones corresponding to the intervening white background, and in illumination of the row on each side (corresponding to the black lines) as well. Hence impulses from all these cells eventually reach the brain.

There is this difference, however. It was pointed out on p. 142 that receptors respond to increasing intensities of stimulation by higher frequencies of discharges. Accordingly, the row of cones corresponding to the white background is more intensely stimulated, and discharges at higher frequencies than the less intensely illuminated row on each side. As discussed on p. 328, differences in frequency are interpreted by the cerebral cortex as differences in intensity. Visual acuity thus becomes a matter of intensity discrimination, in which the cerebral cortex is most important.

Visual acuity may also be tested by determining the smallest object which can be seen when viewed against a homogeneous field. The apparent size of a star, for instance, is minute. The angle subtended by it may be much smaller than the minimum visual angle necessary to deal with separable objects. The angle subtended by the minimum visible object has been shown to be a few seconds or less, even one-half second. The extremely fine dark line which may be seen in such tests probably lessens the illumination of a row of cones, the surrounding ones being uniformly illuminated by the homogeneous background.

Critical Fusion Frequency for Flicker.   A flash of light on the eye generally elicits a burst of impulses over the optic nerve. With successive flashes of light, successive bursts of impulses reach the brain, and successive electrical changes can be recorded from the eye. But as the frequency of flashes increases, the ability to distinguish separate flashes decreases. If a sectored disk is rotated in front of a light source, it is found that as the rate of rotation increases, there is a frequency at which the flashes fuse, and give a sensation of continuous brightness. The critical frequency at which such fusion takes place is dependent upon the intensity of the light (a higher frequency for higher intensities), and upon a number of other factors, including attention, the condition of the retina, and the condition of the brain. A familiar example of fusion is that of motion pictures. The number of frames per second is high enough so that individual frames are not seen.

Color Vision.   The problem of color vision cannot be given more than a limited discussion here.

The sensation of color is influenced by a number of factors, including:

Hue or *tone*, which is a function of the wave length. Thus red and green, each of different wave lengths, are different hues.

Brightness, which depends upon the intensity of the light. Thus, a single hue, such as green, can have many degrees of brightness. Brightness may be compared to mixtures of black and white to produce gray, in the sense that as one adds black, brightness is lessened. This is because black absorbs all wave lengths and lessens the amount of reflected light. Brilliance is the subjective sensation due to brightness.

Saturation or *purity*, which depends upon the mixture with white light. The more white light and, therefore, the more of other colors, the less saturated or pure is a given hue. Colors exhibiting saturation are commonly referred to as pale or pastel.

It has long been known that there are certain primary colors, such that any color of the spectrum can be matched by mixing two primary colors in correct proportions. The primary colors (when dealing with light) are red, green, and blue (or violet). The matching is not quite precise, however, unless a third color is used. For example, if one wished to match a spectral yellow with a mixture of red and green, a precise match is obtained only if some blue is added to the yellow. Methods of color matching are useful in studying defects in color vision, since color blindness can be classified on the basis of defects in primary colors.

There have been, and are, a number of theories of color vision. The one most widely accepted is the three-color theory (Young-Helmholtz Theory, p. 224). This theory postulates that there are three types of receptors (presumably cones), each sensitive to one of the primary colors. However, three different types of cones cannot be distinguished histologically, nor have the mammalian cone pigments been isolated, although, as mentioned previously, the evidence strongly suggests that three pigments are associated with human cones.

Color perception may be affected by a number of factors. For example, if a small object of a specific color is placed in the field of vision so that light from it falls on a specific part of the retina, the color perceived may vary according to the part of the retina stimulated. This difference is due in part to the incidence of the light. Light entering the eye through the center of the pupil is more or less parallel to receptors, but light entering at the edge of the pupil strikes receptors at an angle (because the eyeball is curved). The color perceived is different in the two instances.

Other theories have received considerable support, among them a four-color theory with red and green and yellow and blue pairs of receptors, and a polychromatic theory (with seven receptors). But it must be emphasized that although many facts regarding color vision have accumulated, theories are still tenuous, including the one most widely accepted, the three-color theory.

Color Blindness. Color blindness is a common defect, being found in some degree in about 4 per cent of all men. It may be acquired, but is otherwise a strongly sex-linked characteristic. Color blindness may be classified according to primary color defect.

Trichomats (three-color vision) include those with normal vision, those with anomalous (weak) red vision (protanomaly), and those with anomalous green vision (deuteranomaly).*

---

*The words indicating the type of color defect are of Greek origin. *Protos* means first, hence protanomaly (weakness of) and protanopia (loss of or without) are defects in the first of the three primary colors. *Deuteros* means second, hence deuteranomaly and deuteranopia are defects in the second of the primary colors. *Tritos* means third, and tritanopia is a defect in the third primary color.

Dichromats (two-color vision) include those who cannot perceive red (protanopia); those who have green blindness (deuteranopia), but who can match spectral colors with red and blue, and to whom the luminosity of colors appears normal; and, finally, and quite rarely, those who are blue (violet) blind (tritanopia). The fovea of man appears to be tritanopic, the blue end of the spectrum being absorbed by media and by the yellow pigment of the macula. Diurnal mammals with pure cone retinae have yellow lenses, thus limiting the amount of blue reaching the retina.

Monochromats (total color blindness) are quite rare. There appear to be two kinds, with and without photophobia (pain on exposure to strong light). The ones with photophobia seem to react as if they had no cones in their retinae.

It should be emphasized that the above is a classification based on subjective defects in perception, and not on any proven defect in or absence of a specific kind of color receptor.

Binocular Vision.   When one looks at an object, an image is formed in each eye, and impulses go from each eye to both cerebral hemispheres. But only one object is seen. To obtain this result, the points of the image must fall on corresponding parts of the retinae. Thus the temporal half of the left eye and the nasal half of the right eye are corresponding halves. If there is a disturbance of binocular vision, such as may follow paralyses of extrinsic eye muscles, then double vision or *diplopia* may result. This is because image points do not fall upon corresponding parts of the retinae, and two images are seen. Diplopia can be demonstrated by lightly pressing upon the lateral side of one of the eyes while gazing steadily at an object some distance away. The pressure shifts the eye so that images are formed on noncorresponding portions of the retina, and diplopia results. If diplopia is due to a persistent disorder, one lasting for weeks or months or longer, false images usually become suppressed.

CENTRAL CONNECTIONS OF THE RETINA

The optic nerves converge at the base of the brain to form the optic chiasma. A partial decussation occurs here in a manner indicated in Figure 117. Behind the chiasma, the axons continue into the optic tracts, which curve around the outside of the cerebral peduncles and disappear from the surface.

Some of the axons terminate in or near the region of the superior colliculi. Because of these connections, reflex pupillary reactions or body movements in response to light can occur. Most of the optic fibers, however, end in the lateral geniculate body of the thalamus and are relayed by way of the internal capsule to the occipital lobes. Here they

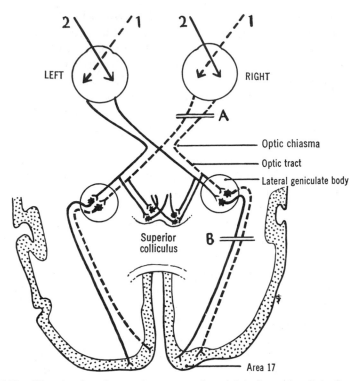

Figure 117. The visual pathways. Arrows numbered *1* indicate that light from objects in the right visual fields (when looking straight ahead) reaches the left halves of the retinae. The reverse is true for the opposite visual fields. The collaterals from the visual path (to the superior colliculi for reflexes) are really separate fibers and not branches of true visual fibers. Cutting the optic nerve at *A* causes complete blindness in that eye. A lesion at *B*, however, causes blindness in the left half of each field of vision (arrows numbered 2).

end around the calcarine fissure in a cortical area numbered 17, the primary receptive area (Fig. 158, p. 315). As in the postcentral gyrus, the entering fibers dispose themselves throughout the fourth cell layer (Fig. 156, p. 313). They are so concentrated here that they form a white band, the band or stripe of Gennari, visible to the naked eye. Because of this, the visual cortex is also called the *striate cortex.* It is now known that optic nerves exhibit continuous discharges which change in frequency with stimulation. Hence, coding depends upon the specific fiber involved and upon changes occurring in the lateral geniculate body and visual cortex. Furthermore, it is clear that retinal receptors respond in a variety of ways, not merely to the presence or absence of light, but to movement or pattern. These various responses can be detected all along the visual path.

As indicated in Figure 117, the fibers from the medial or nasal half of each retina cross, whereas those from the lateral or temporal half do not. This means that objects on the right are visualized by left Area 17, and vice versa. This perception is therefore contralateral, as it is in other sensations.

Contralateral vision perception can be demonstrated by a simple experiment. Close the eyes and turn the right eye toward the nose, then press lightly on the temporal side (right side) of the right eyeball. A bright ring or a blue ring with a bright halo is seen in the nasal or left field of the right eye. This shows that stimulation of the right half of the retina produces an effect which appears to come from the opposite or left part of the visual field.

That retinal images are also reversed may be demonstrated in a number of ways. The retina is sensitive to any x-rays that may happen to penetrate the eye. Metal letters placed in front of closed eyes and exposed to x-rays are recognized as shadows against a bright background. (The x-rays that reach the retina apparently cause it to fluoresce.) Since x-rays are not refracted or bent during their passage through the eyes, the shadows are not inverted upon the retina. The brain performs its customary reversal during interpretation, and the letters appear upside down. If the letters are to appear upright, they must be inverted in front of the eyes. There is not, however, a conscious analysis of retinal inversion. Perception is of objects in visual fields and not of impulses from the retinae. From infancy on, object position determination by vision is substantiated by impressions produced by the objects on other senses, such as touch. Thereafter, impulses from specific retinal areas become visual perceptions for objects in certain portions of the visual fields.

The interpretation of these cues from retinal stimulation probably depends to a great extent upon learning. If subjects wear lenses which invert the retinal fields, the images on the retina become upright and the perceived field is inverted. In spite of the resulting confusion, the subjects can, by wearing the lenses for considerable periods of time, adjust themselves fairly well to the situation and perform coordinated movements.

LESIONS OF THE VISUAL SYSTEM

The anatomy of the visual system is such that damage in various portions of the optic pathways causes visual defects with differences which enable one to locate such lesions rather accurately. Destruction of one optic nerve, for instance, will cause complete blindness in that eye. Destruction of the pathway on one side behind the chiasma (Fig. 117) will cause, not total blindness, but blindness in half of the visual field of each eye, a *hemianopia.* If such a lesion is on the left side, the patient will be unable to see objects on his right side when he is looking straight ahead.

HEARING

Hearing follows the stimulation of certain specialized epithelial cells by sound waves. These cells are part of a receptor system situated in the *labyrinth,* or inner ear (Fig. 118). The labyrinth is a group of small, fluid-filled chambers and canals, one of which, the *cochlea,* is especially concerned with auditory mechanisms. There is an intricate, delicate mechanism by which sound waves enter the external ear and are then funneled into the middle ear, from which three tiny bones transmit the vibrations to the fluid-filled cochlea.

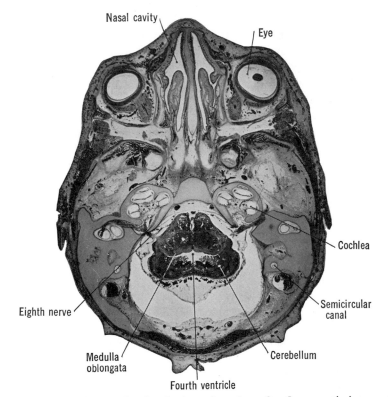

Figure 118. Photomicrograph of a horizontal section of a four-month human fetal head. Note the left eighth nerve dividing into cochlear and vestibular portions, the latter going to the macula utriculi.

THE EXTERNAL AND MIDDLE EARS

As shown in Figure 119, the external ear includes the auricle, which is attached to the side of the head, and the external acoustic meatus or ear canal. Whether the auricle is of any great importance in man is doubtful. The external ear canal transmits the air vibrations to the middle ear. Separating this canal from the middle ear cavity is a thin *tympanic membrane*. To it is attached one of the three ossicles which form a chain across the middle ear cavity. When vibrations of air strike the tympanic membrane, they cause it to move at the same frequency as the impinging waves. These vibrations are transmitted through the ear ossicles in such a manner that the innermost ossicle, the *stapes*, moves inward when the tympanic membrane moves inward. It can be seen from Figures 119 and 120 that the foot of the stapes impinges upon one of the fluid-filled canals of the cochlea, and its vibrations are, therefore, transmitted to the fluid. It can also be seen from these figures that at the other end of the fluid system is an aperture, the *round window*, which is closed off by a thin membrane. Since fluid is incompressible, an increase in pressure at the end where the stapes is located is compensated for by a bulging outward of this membrane in the round window.

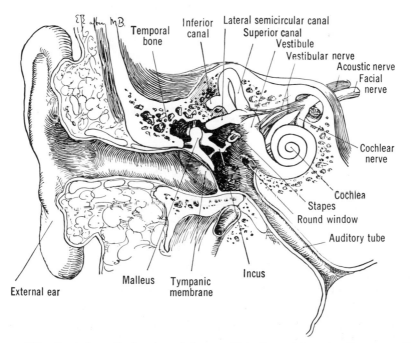

Figure 119. Semischematic drawing of the ear. Note the ossicles extending across the middle ear cavity. The greater part of the course of the facial nerve through the ear has been omitted. (Modified from Max Brödel.)

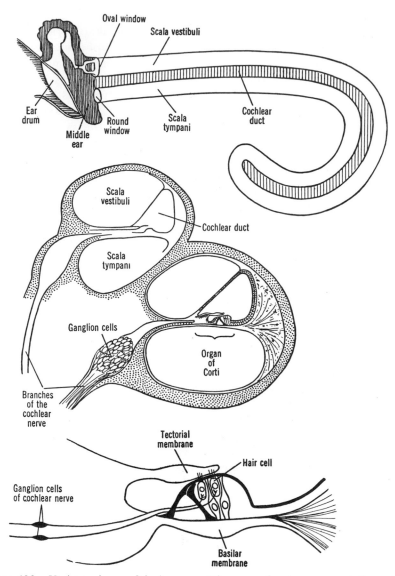

Figure 120. Various schema of the inner ear. The upper drawing represents the cochlea as if it were uncoiled. Note how the stapes fits into the oval window. The scala vestibuli communicates with the scala tympani which terminates at the round window. Compare with Figure 119. The middle drawing represents the cochlea cut at a right angle to or across the first plane, indicating the shape and relationships of the cochlear duct. The peripheral processes of the bipolar ganglion cells extend to the spiral organ of Corti. The lower drawing is of the spiral organ of Corti. Most of the cells have been omitted, since all are either hair cells or supporting cells.

Marked changes in external air pressure might seriously affect the tympanic membrane were it not for the fact that the middle ear cavity communicates with the pharynx by means of the auditory tube (Fig. 119). Pressure on both sides of the membrane may be equalized through this passageway. All are familiar with the "popping" of the ears when ascending or descending considerable distances. This is due to periodic openings of the auditory tube at the point where it reaches the pharynx.

THE INNER EAR AND COCHLEA

The cochlea is a fluid-filled cavity in the temporal bone, being arranged in coils resembling those of a snail shell. Within the cavity is a small fluid-filled duct, the *cochlear duct,* in which are found the specialized epithelial cells of the *spiral organ* (of Corti) (Fig. 120). Some of the cells have fine, hairlike processes at their free ends. Other cells surround and support the hair cells. Fibers of the cochlear division of the eighth nerve end around the bases of the hair cells. The bipolar cell bodies giving origin to these fibers form the spiral ganglion, which is located in the bony portion of the cochlea. Their central processes are directed toward the brain stem.

As shown in Figure 120, the hair cells rest upon a membrane, the *basilar membrane.* This is composed of *auditory strings* that vary in length in different portions of the cochlea. Above the hair cells is a mass of gelatinous material, the *tectorial membrane,* into which the hairs project. Nearly all these structures can be related to the functions of the cochlea.

Cochlear Functions. Broadly speaking, nerve impulses are produced as follows: The vibrations of air strike the tympanic membrane and are transmitted by the ear ossicles to the cochlea, where pressure waves are set up in the fluid, causing the hair cells to move up or down, toward or away from the less movable tectorial membrane. This produces a deformation of the hair cells. In some manner this stimulates the nerve fibers ending around them. It is possible that the cells are like piezoelectric crystals which, upon being deformed, develop a voltage. If this were true of the hair cells, the voltage could act as a stimulus for the nerve fibers. Whatever the explanation, deformation of hair cells is accompanied by a rapidly developing potential change which can be recorded. This is the *microphonic potential.* The system is extraordinarily sensitive, more than could be expected of a passive system. It behaves much as if the cells were amplifiers.

There is also a resting potential in the cochlea, the spiral organ being negative to the fluid in scale tympani and scala vestibuli. It is not known whether this potential, or the microphonic potential, or both, are directly involved in depolarizing cochlear nerve fibers.

Certain properties and qualities of sound must be mentioned before proceeding with the discussion of cochlear functions.

PITCH.   This refers to the level in the muscial scale in which a sound may be placed. It is mainly dependent upon the frequency of the sound waves, that is to say, the number of waves per second.

INTENSITY.   In ordinary usage this is synonymous with loudness, but this is not strictly accurate. Intensity is a physical value which refers to the energy or power of the sound waves and is proportional to the amplitude of these waves. Loudness is a subjective sensation. That the two are not the same is shown by the fact that while tones of high pitch are inaudible to man, no matter what their intensity, they may be audible to other animals, such as the dog.

There is in common usage a unit for expressing differences in intensity of two sounds which is based on a logarithmic scale. If one sound has a power ten times greater than another, it is said to be 1 bel greater (log of 10 = 1). But the bel (named after Alexander Graham Bell, the inventor of the telephone) is too large a unit, and one-tenth of this or 1 decibel (db) is used. Within the auditory range 1 decibel is a change just detectible subjectively. Bels and decibels used without a reference level are meaningless. To say that a sound wave is 1 decibel more than another means nothing, since both may still be inaudible. Accordingly, a standard reference may be used. This is 0.0002 dyne/cm.^{2}, and the threshold of hearing at 1000 cycles is of this order of power. From this point the audible range extends 120 decibels, that is, 12 bels or 10^{12} times. The upper limit represents the loudest sound tolerable to the human ear.

TIMBRE OR QUALITY.   This is determined by the wave form, and is the property by which two sounds of the same pitch and intensity can be distinguished. It probably depends upon the overtones or harmonics of a particular sound.

Just how all these properties are detected is uncertain. The range of vibrations or frequencies audible to the human ear is from approximately 20 to 20,000 per second, with considerable individual variation. Furthermore, there is a striking difference in sensitivity at different frequencies. When the relation between sensitivity and frequency is plotted, the resulting curve (audiogram) is that shown in Figure 121. This shows that the human ear is most sensitive to vibrations in the neighborhood of 2048 cycles per second. At this frequency the cochlea is comparable in sensitivity to the retina. By this is meant that under optimum conditions one can detect sounds of such low intensities that the amplitude of vibration at threshold is no more than the longer wave lengths in the visible spectrum.

It was mentioned previously that the basilar membrane on which the hair cells rest is composed of auditory strings of varying lengths.

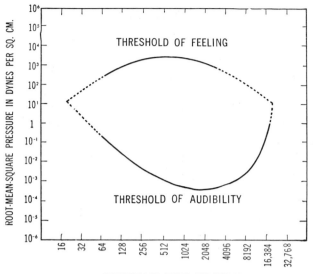

Figure 121. An audiogram of the human ear. The curves are plotted from data obtained from a large number of subjects. The audibility threshold curve represents the pressure variations necessary to produce sound of minimum audibility between 20 and 20,000 cycles per second The feeling threshold curve represents pressure variations beyond which pain is felt. The broken lines indicate regions where data are inexact or lacking. Note that hearing is most sensitive in the region of 2048 cycles per second. (Slightly modified after Fletcher: Speech and Hearing. New York, D. Van Nostrand Co., Inc., 1953.)

The concept most widely held is the *place theory.* According to this theory, a pure tone will throw a stretch of the basilar membrane into vibration, with a maximum amplitude of vibration at some point. One version of this, the Helmholtz resonance theory, is that the auditory strings are of such lengths that for any audible frequency, there is a string or group of strings that will be thrown into vibration, that is, will resonate. Another theory holds that a pure tone produces a standing wave in the basilar membrane, the position of the wave changing according to the frequency of the tone. There is, however, considerable evidence that sound waves produce traveling waves along the membrane. These waves have a flat maximum that shifts in location along the membrane as frequency changes. The theories are not radically different. Whatever the type of vibration, there is a maximum at some point, and nerve fibers from this point will discharge at a higher rate than other nerve fibers from the area of the wave vibration. The basilar membrane in the apical part of the cochlea is wider than elsewhere, and this region responds mainly to low tones.

Central Auditory Connections. When the central fibers of the cochlear division of the eighth nerve reach the brain stem, they end

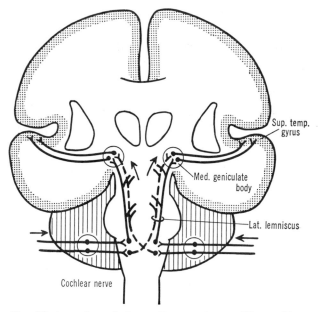

Figure 122. Simplified version of the auditory pathways. The cochlear nerves carry impulses from the receptors, the primary neurons being bipolar cells. The brain stem path (lateral lemniscus) is probably a multineuron path, but the relays have been omitted. The branches indicated are those which form reflex connections.

in masses of gray matter, the *cochlear nuclei.* These project to cranial nerve nuclei that provide for reflexes in response to sound, and also give axons that ascend in a myelinated tract on each side, the *lateral lemniscus* (Fig. 122). There are several synaptic interruptions along this pathway, but eventually the fibers reach the medial geniculate body of the thalamus and are then relayed to the temporal lobe, specifically to the portion of the superior temporal gyrus that forms Area 41 (see Figs. 122 and 157, p. 315). This is the primary receptive area for hearing.

LESIONS OF THE AUDITORY SYSTEM

If a cochlear duct or nerve on one side is destroyed, complete deafness on that side results. But a unilateral lesion within the central nervous system which affects one of the auditory paths does not cause complete deafness, since each lateral lemniscus carries fibers derived from both cochleae, as shown in Figure 122. A unilateral lesion, therefore, does not interrupt all impulses derived from the cochlea of the same side.

Diseases of the middle ear may cause middle ear or transmission deafness. Sounds are heard incompletely, if at all, because pathological changes of the ossicles or tympanic membrane interfere with their transmission. If the vibrations are strong enough to set bone in motion, or are started in bone, then they may reach the cochlea, and perception is ultimately possible. This can be demonstrated by placing the base of a vibrating tuning fork on the skull. The vibrations are audible, but disappear when the fork is held in the air beside the ear. Patients with middle ear deafness have difficulty in ordinary conversation, but may hear well over the telephone because the sounds are conducted through the bones of the skull. Hearing aids are, therefore, useful in such cases, but not when deafness is due to destruction of a cochlea or cochlear nerve (nerve deafness).

BALANCE OR EQUILIBRIUM

What is ordinarily called the sense of balance or of equilibrium is functionally integrated with the kinesthetic sense. An important component of the sense of balance arises from the stimulation of certain receptors in the labyrinth. One of the labyrinthine canals, the cochlea, was discussed in the preceding section of this chapter. The rest of the labyrinth consists of a small chamber, the *vestibule,* which communicates with three small *semicircular ducts,* each of which is in the form of a half-circle (Fig. 123) and is contained within a semicircular canal in the bone. There are two small membranous sacs in the vestibule, the *utricle* and *saccule.* In each of these is a specialized epithelial layer or *macula,* around the cells of which fibers of the vestibular portion of the eighth nerve terminate. At one end of each semicircular canal there

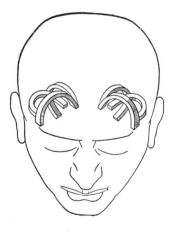

Figure 123. A drawing indicating the semicircular ducts in relation to each other and to the rest of the head. Compare with Figure 119, in which they are shown with the rest of the ear. Note that the two lateral ducts are in the same plane, and therefore form a functional unit. Likewise the anterior or superior duct of one side forms a functional unit with the posterior or inferior duct of the opposite side. The ducts are much smaller than indicated here.

is also a specialized epithelial layer, a *crista,* around whose cells other fibers of the vestibular nerve terminate. All the nerve fibers are peripheral processes of bipolar cells in the nearby vestibular ganglion. The central processes enter the brain stem near the junction of the pons and medulla oblongata.

THE SEMICIRCULAR DUCTS

The semicircular ducts are small membranous tubes filled with a slightly viscous fluid. The structure of each crista is similar to that of the spiral organ of Corti. That is, there are hair cells held together or supported by sustentacular cells, and the processes of the hair cells are embedded in an overlying structure consisting of fibrils embedded in a gelatinous ground substance. Vestibular nerve fibers terminate at the bases of the hair cells. Pressure changes in the fluid of the ducts constitute effective stimuli. The mechanisms are probably similar to those of the hair cells of the cochlea.

Each of the three ducts on either side of the head occupies a different plane in space (Fig. 123), so that when the head is moved or rotated in any direction, the cells in one or more cristae are stimulated because of pressure changes which come about in the following manner. When the head is turned, say to the right (clockwise), the fluid in the horizontal ducts tends to remain stationary because of its inertia. The actual result is that a hydrostatic pressure develops. In clockwise rotation the pressure is exerted against the anterior end of the right horizontal duct, the end which contains the crista.

Similar phenomena are seen when a glass of water is rotated. At first the water remains stationary. Then, as inertia is overcome, the water rotates with the glass. Translated into familiar, everyday experience, similar phenomena are experienced when a car accelerates rapidly. Anyone in the seat tends to remain where he was, so to speak, and the result is the development of pressure against the car seat. But within a short time, particularly if the car reaches a uniform rate of speed, the sensation of pressure stops because inertia has been overcome and the car and person are in effect traveling at the same rate. If, now, the car slows or stops suddenly, anyone in the car tends to keep on going in the same direction, just as one tends to keep going in the same direction when the car goes around a curve. Likewise, when the rotation of the glass of water is suddenly stopped, the water keeps on rotating for a time.

In the case of the ducts, continued clockwise rotation can be carried out if the whole body is rotated. This is most easily done by sitting in a special chair which can be turned (children commonly do this by sitting in a swing which is wound up and then allowed to unwind). When rotation reaches a uniform rate, there is no pressure in the ducts.

When rotation stops, the fluid tends to keep on going in the direction of rotation; as a result pressure develops against the crista in the anterior end of the left horizontal duct.

It is often necessary in experimental and clinical work to test a duct separately. This can be done by irrigating the external ear canals with hot or cold water. The temperature changes are sufficient to reach the internal ear and set up convection currents in the fluid in the semi-circular duct. These currents create pressures, with an end result just as if the subject were being rotated. With hot water the currents tend to rise, and with cold water to fall. Consequently it is necessary to have the subjects so tilt his head that the duct under study is vertical in order to create pressure changes at whatever end of the canal the experimenter wishes.

THE UTRICLE AND SACCULE

The maculae of the utricle and saccule resemble the cristae in structure. Each consists of sustentacular cells and hair cells. The hairs project into an overlying mass consisting of fibrils embedded in a gelatinous ground substance and containing small masses of calcium carbonate called *otoliths*. Vestibular nerve fibers end around the bases of the hair cells, and the mechanism of stimulation is probably basically similar to that in the cochlea.

The functions of the saccules in man are not known with any certainty. The maculae of the utricles are sensitive to any position the head occupies in space, whether it is moving or not. It is maximally sensitive (or stimulated) in the upside-down position, as standing on one's head. Apparently, pulling or tension on hairs is most effective, since in this position the gelatinous mass is below the cells. The otoliths probably increase the effectiveness of gravity.

CENTRAL VESTIBULAR CONNECTIONS

Impulses over nerve fibers from the maculae and cristae travel centrally to the brain stem and cerebellum. In the brain stem they end in masses of gray matter, the vestibular nuclei, which are specialized portions of the reticular formation. These relay impulses to the spinal cord by way of the vestibulospinal tracts and the medial longitudinal fasciculi (Fig. 124). They also relay impulses to various nuclei of cranial nerves, particularly those supplying extrinsic eye muscles, by way of the medial longitudinal fasciculi and also diffuse projections through reticular formation. Connections are also made with visceral centers of the brain stem. Impulses are known to reach the cerebral cortex, but the central pathways are not known with any certainty. There is some evidence that they are topographically the same as the auditory paths and

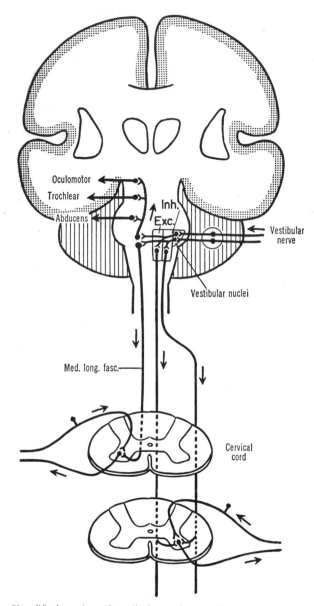

Figure 124. Simplified version of vestibular pathways. The primary neurons are bipolar cells. Direct connections with the cerebellum have been omitted. The vestibular nuclei are represented as projecting to excitatory and inhibitory mechanisms of the brain stem and to various motor nuclei by way of the medial longitudinal fasciculus (both fasciculi are used). The vestibulospinal tract (from the lateral vestibular nucleus) was omitted because it follows much the same course as does the tract from the excitatory center. The ascending path to the cerebral cortex has also been omitted. It is probably similar to that for auditory fibers.

that the primary receptive area is probably the superior temporal gyrus, either in or near Area 41.

FUNCTIONS OF THE VESTIBULAR SYSTEM

This system is important in the control of muscular activity, for reasons mentioned in Chapter 11 and discussed in more detail in Chapter 16. In spite of the importance of this system in balance or equilibrium and position sense, reflex functions often overshadow sensory functions. The cristae in semicircular ducts are stimulated mainly by changes in rate of movement, during acceleration or deceleration and especially in rotational movement. The ducts thus function in kinetic or phasic activity. The maculae utriculi are stimulated mainly when the head is being held in one position, during movement uniform in rate and during linear acceleration or deceleration. Macular functions are, therefore, mainly static in nature. These distinctions are extremely general. There is actually considerable overlap in functions. The central connections and nuclei of the vestibular system are an important part of the extrapyramidal motor system.

LESIONS OF THE VESTIBULAR SYSTEM

Rapid or prolonged rotations or other type of movement may produce severe side effects, such as vertigo, nausea and vomiting. These symptoms are the familiar ones of seasickness. Some persons are so sensitive that these symptoms may follow relatively mild rotations.

Although a number of disorders affect the vestibular system, the symptoms may be difficult to interpret. For example, an inflammatory process in the vestibular system of one side may produce symptoms such as dizziness or nausea because it irritates or stimulates on that side. But a lesion which destroys the opposite side, by leaving an unopposed or unbalanced normal side, may produce apparently identical symptoms. Consequently, it is necessary to have confirmatory signs referable to other nerves. For example, a destructive lesion of the right vestibular nerve will almost surely destroy the right cochlear nerve. The patient will have, therefore, complete nerve deafness on that side, a symptom which in itself so localizes the lesion that there may be little point in analyzing the vestibular symptoms in detail.

TASTE

The peripheral receptors for this special sense are located in the mucous membrane of the tongue, palate, pharynx, and larynx. Taste, as ordinarily perceived, is a complex sensation, which can be equated with flavor and often includes smell, texture, temperature, and even pain, as well as "true taste." The interference with taste during a cold is the result of a temporary loss of smell. The receptors for taste are found in *taste buds*. These are small cellular areas located in the mucous membrane. They contain specialized cells which are surrounded by nerve endings (Fig. 125). These cells originate from ordinary epithelium. The buds themselves are constantly renewed and reinnervated. Food substances dissolved in saliva are able in some way to stimulate these cells, and this in turn initiates impulses in the nerve fibers. Single receptors may be sensitive to one or more of a number of substances characterized as sweet, salt, bitter, and sour, and perhaps others as well. The characterizations are made on the basis of sensations. They can scarcely be separated from behavioral responses, such as the acceptance or rejection of foodstuffs or other substances such as quinine or sugar.

Nerve impulses are transmitted centrally over the facial nerves from the anterior two-thirds of the tongue, by way of the glossopharyngeal nerves from the posterior third of the tongue and part of the pharynx, and over the vagus nerves from the pharynx and larynx. The primary neurons are unipolar cells located in ganglia along the course of these nerves. The central processes of these cells enter the medulla oblongata. Some secondary fibers establish reflex connections, and others ascend in the opposite medial lemnisci to the thalami and thence to the postcentral gyri, the primary receptive areas. Here, the interpretation of discharges arriving over any one sensory channel would depend upon concurrent activity in the other channels.

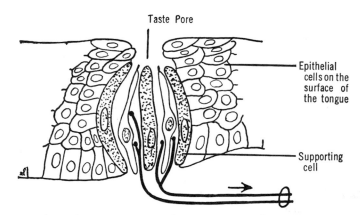

Taste Pore

Epithelial cells on the surface of the tongue

Supporting cell

Figure 125. Schematic representation of taste-sensitive cells in mucous membrane of the tongue. These and the supporting cells comprise a taste bud. Nerve fibers ending around the receptive cells are peripheral processes of unipolar neurons.

SMELL

The olfactory receptors are located in the upper part of the nasal mucous membrane on each side of the nasal cavity. This membrane, which is pigmented in many vertebrates, consists of bipolar nerve cells surrounded and supported by non-nervous cells (Fig. 126). The surface of the membrane is covered with a watery fluid. Small particles of gases go into solution in this fluid and are then able, by a means as yet unknown, to stimulate the bipolar cells. This is an exceedingly sensitive

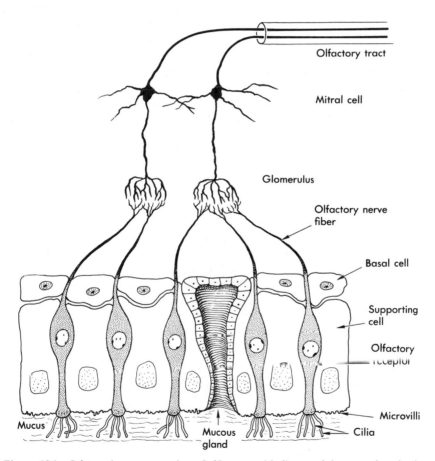

Figure 126. Schematic representation of olfactory epithelium and the central projections of the olfactory receptors. The orientation is like that of Figure 127, with the epithelium downward and the olfactory nerve fibers ascending. (Modified from Moulton, D. G., and Beidler, L. M., Physiol. Rev., *47*:1-52, 1967, and from Schneider, R. A., New Eng. J. Med., *277*:299-303, 1967.)

mechanism by which incredibly small amounts of gaseous substances can be detected. The fact that wood has an odor, for instance, means that oils in the wood are given off in the air and reach the olfactory membrane. The olfactory sense is much more sensitive than that of taste and distinguishes a greater variety of modalities.

The bipolar cells are chemoreceptors with short processes, the olfactory rods. The rods extend to the free surface of the mucous membrane where they end as a brush of filaments. The central processes of the bipolar cells form the filaments of the olfactory nerves. These ascend through tiny openings in the base of the skull (Fig. 127) and end in masses of gray matter, the olfactory bulbs. Axons from cells in the bulbs travel posteriorly as the olfactory tracts to the rhinencephalic area (p. 335). The subsequent pathways are so complex and widespread and yet so uncertain as regards function that they will not be discussed here. Even the location of the primary receptive area is not definitely known. Olfaction is nevertheless an important and sensitive quality. The reflexes which it may initiate are often rapid and forceful, as, for example, violent nausea from a putrid odor. Yet because of many factors in civilized life, such as smoking, contamination of city air, and the like, interferences with and even losses of smell are so common that unless such a loss is restricted to one side of the nose, it cannot be regarded as a definitely important clinical sign.

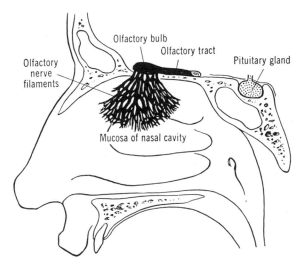

Figure 127. Drawing of olfactory structures in the nasal cavity (a sagittal section, exposing the interior of the nose). Numbers of axons interlace as they ascend through the floor of the skull. The olfactory tract is cut anterior to its termination (see Figure 8, p. 16).

SUMMARY

The special senses include vision, hearing, balance, taste, and smell. Vision is the cortical interpretation of impulses which are the result of excitation of specialized receptors, the rods and cones in the retinal layers of the eyes. These cells are connected to bipolar cells, and these in turn to ganglion cells. The axons of these ganglion cells form the optic nerves. The optic nerves intermingle at the chiasma in such a way that impulses resulting from light entering the eye from one side of the body finally reach the opposite primary area (Area 17), located on either side of the calcarine fissure of the occipital lobe. The retina itself probably has a double function related to its structure, the rods serving for visual sensitivity, the cones for visual acuity and color vision. In normal binocular vision all image points fall upon corresponding retinal points.

Hearing is the cortical interpretation of impulses resulting from sound waves striking specialized cells in the cochlea of the inner ear. These cells are sensitive to vibrations ranging from approximately 20 to 20,000 cycles per second, and presumably the auditory strings of the cochlea are sensitive to different pitches according to their lengths. The nerve impulses are transmitted centrally over the cochlear nerves and eventually reach both primary areas, numbered 41, in the superior temporal gyri of the temporal lobes.

Impulses resulting from stimulation of the maculae utriculi and the cristae of the semicircular ducts eventually reach the temporal lobes, as well as reflex pathways in the brain stem. The superior temporal gyri are probably the primary receptive areas.

Solutions of food substances stimulate receptors in taste buds of the tongue, palate, pharynx, and larynx. The nerve impulses are transmitted centrally over the facial, glossopharyngeal and vagus nerves to the brain stem. From here they eventually reach the primary receptive areas, the postcentral gyri, by way of the medial lemnisci, thalami, and internal capsules.

Smell depends upon the stimulation of bipolar cells in the olfactory mucous membrane by substances dissolved in the overlying watery fluid. The central processes of these bipolar cells form the olfactory nerves, which end in the olfactory bulbs. From here the impulses follow a complex path to a primary receptive area whose location is still uncertain.

Names in Neurology

HERMAN VON HELMHOLTZ (1821-1894)

Helmholtz was a German physician, physiologist and physicist and one of the giants in scientific attainment. He was a man of widespread interests who, at various times, occupied chairs of physiology, anatomy, pathology, and physics. He applied the law of conservation of energy to all living material. He showed that muscles were the main source of animal heat. During the years 1850-1852, he measured the velocity of the nerve impulse. In 1851 he invented the ophthalmoscope and, with the aid of other instruments of his own devising, measured ocular constants and explained the mechanism of accommodation. During the years 1856-1867, he wrote his "Handbook of Physiological Optics," which is a permanent scientific classic. Incredibly, in spite of all this work, he found time to publish on acoustic mechanisms, including the functions of the tympanic membrane and the ear ossicles. From him we have our most widely accepted theory of cochlear functions. From 1887 on he made outstanding contributions in the fields of dynamics, hydrodynamics, thermodynamics, and electrodynamics. It is difficult to see how one man could have done so much work fundamental to present day knowledge.

THOMAS YOUNG (1773-1829)

Young, a Quaker physician in England, was one of the great men of science. He was called the father of physiological optics. He studied accommodation, gave the first description of astigmatism, and stated that color vision was possible because of retinal structures sensitive to red, green, and violet. He studied blood flow and stated the laws governing it. He announced the wave theory of light. He introduced concepts of energy and work done and defined the modulus of elasticity, "Young's modulus." He was interested and accomplished in many other activities, including Egyptology. Altogether, he ranks with Helmholtz as a scientific great.

REFERENCES

See the references cited on p. 6.

Polyak, S. L.: The Retina. Chicago, University of Chicago Press, 1941. (This is an outstanding volume on the structure and neurological connections of the human retina. It contains a section on operative and microscopic techniques, and considerable space is devoted to the history of visual investigation.)

Stevens, S. S., and Davis, H.: Hearing. New York, John Wiley & Sons, Inc., 1938. (This is a well-written discussion of the psychophysiology of hearing.)

von Békésy, G.: Experiments on Hearing (transl. and edited by E. G. Wever). New York, McGraw-Hill Book Company, Inc., 1960. (A detailed study of the physiology and psychology of hearing.)

Walls, G. L.: The Vertebrate Eye. Bloomfield Hills, Mich., Cranbrook Institute of Science, 1942. (This is another outstanding work dealing with the comparative anatomy and functions of the eye. In both this and Polyak's volume the illustrations are superb.)

The following are reviews, monographs, and symposia on specific subjects.

Ciba Foundation Symposium. Colour Vision. Boston, Little, Brown and Company, 1965. (An excellent symposium on all aspects of the problem.)
Davis, H.: Biophysics and physiology of the inner ear. Physiol. Rev., 37:1-49, 1957. (Especially valuable for the bibliography.)
Moulton, D. G., and Beidler, L. M.: Structure and function in the peripheral olfactory system. Physiol. Rev., 47:1-52, 1967.
Pfaffman, C.: Taste, its sensory and motivating properties. Amer. Sci., 52:187-206, 1964.

CHAPTER 14

CONTROL OF VISCERAL ACTIVITY

The functions of viscera are as necessary as those activities about which a person is more or less aware. But these functions are either carried out without conscious recognition or are perceived in an ill-defined manner. An excellent illustration of a complex pattern of visceral activity is afforded by the process of regulation of body temperature.

Cold-blooded vertebrates, such as fishes, amphibians, and reptiles, have body temperatures which vary with the ambient temperature, but warm-blooded animals, such as birds and mammals, keep their body temperatures constant within certain limits and are to a large extent independent of their thermal environment. Heat production and heat loss are relatively balanced. The heat produced during metabolic activities is lost through radiation from the blood vessels which lie near the surface of the body. If these vessels dilate, that is to say, increase in diameter, a greater volume of blood flows through them per unit time, and more heat is then lost by radiation. A certain amount of heat is also lost with the evaporation of sweat, through the air and water vapor expired from the lungs, and with the excreta. The nervous system can regulate the caliber of the cutaneous arterioles, capillaries and venules, thus controlling the volume of blood flowing through them and, thereby, the amount of heat loss.

This nervous control may be initiated in a number of ways. For example, skin exposed to the cold air becomes blanched or pale, owing

226

to a reflex narrowing or constriction of the cutaneous vessels. The cold air stimulates receptors sensitive to a temperature lower than that of the skin surface; the central path is through the spinal cord and the efferent path through the sympathetic system (Fig. 128). The reflex reduction in heat radiation enables the internal temperature to be maintained even though the skin may be cold, both subjectively and objectively.

The term "viscera" is a general one. It is often used to refer to structures supposedly not under voluntary control, such as smooth muscle, in contrast to structures such as skeletal muscle. The distinction is, however, more apparent than real. Many skeletal muscles, such as the diaphragm, are not subject to complete voluntary control. Organs containing smooth muscle are often as much under voluntary direction or control as many so-called voluntary muscles. Furthermore, certain organs, such as the pharynx and esophagus, contain striated muscle but are classified as viscera.

The term "vsicera" now refers to cardiac muscle and to those organs which contain smooth muscle or glands, all of which receive their motor supply from the nervous system according to a specific type of distribution. This motor supply forms what is usually called the *autonomic* or *visceral nervous system*. This classification, however, has led to confusion, since it no more tells the whole story than the term "motor fiber" or "final common path" tells the whole story about control of skeletal activity. Afferent fibers, for example, are just as important as efferent fibers, as in the situation cited previously in which blood vessels reflexly changed in diameter subsequent to stimulation of temperature receptors.

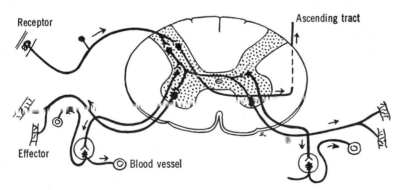

Figure 128. Diagram illustrating how impulses from a receptor in the skin (in this case a temperature receptor) reach motor neurons supplying skeletal muscles and also neurons in the intermediate gray. By way of the latter connections the impulses reach smooth muscle in blood vessels of the trunk and limbs. The impulses may also reach the cerebral hemisphere.

AUTONOMIC NERVOUS SYSTEM

The autonomic nervous system can be considered as a series of levels which differ in function in that the higher the level, the more widespread and general its functions; the lower the level, the more restricted and specific the functions. The highest level is the cerebral cortex, the next is the hypothalamus, then the brain stem and spinal cord, and finally the ganglionic level.

LEVELS OF ORGANIZATION

Cerebral Cortex. Little is known about the specific regions of cerebral cortex concerned in visceral mechanisms, except that portions of the frontal lobes, especially the basal and medial parts (see limbic system, p. 335), are involved in the control or regulation of visceral functions and send fibers to the hypothalamus and brain stem.

Hypothalamus. The hypothalamus is a portion of the diencephalon which is a coordinating center for the motor control of visceral activity. Its location and relation to other nervous structures may be determined by reference to Chapter 2 and Figures 13 and 14 (pp. 21 and 22). Study of microscopic sections reveals rather dense collections of nerve cells and fibers. Most of the fibers are nonmyelinated, so that with Weigert stains the hypothalamus appears as an area of gray matter. Various investigators have succeeded in defining the cells of the hypothalamus into nuclear groups, but as yet the functions of these nuclei have not been elucidated except in the most general way.

The hypothalamus is further characterized by a rich blood supply and by a specific relationship with the pituitary gland or hypophysis. This endocrine gland has a double embryological origin, partly from the pharyngeal region and partly from the diencephalon. The various divisions of the hypophysis are illustrated in Figure 129. In addition to nervous connections, there are vascular relationships between the hypothalamus and the pituitary. The blood supply of the pars distalis is derived mainly from vessels which have already broken up into a capillary network elsewhere. Specifically, blood vessels enter the median eminence and form what is termed the *primary capillary net.* These capillaries then collect into a number of vessels, the portal vessels, which enter the substance of the pars distalis and break up into a network of sinusoids, the *second capillary net.* These then drain into nearby veins. The pituitary has therefore a true portal circulation (Fig. 129). The significance of this system is that most of the blood destined for the pars distalis first passes through the median eminence. The neurohypophysis is independently vascularized.

The hypothalamus receives fibers from many afferent paths. For

example, many fibers in the olfactory tracts are destined for the hypothalamus. Afferent fibers relaying in the thalamus also send branches
to it. In addition, there are fibers from the cerebral cortex, particularly
the frontal lobes. All the afferent connections are complex, and little
is known of their ultimate connections and effects except that they
synapse with most, if not all, of the hypothalamic nuclei. Efferent
fibers from the hypothalamus are widely distributed. Many descend in
the neural stalk to the posterior part of the pituitary gland and, in addition, appear to supply the vessels of the median eminence. They are
concerned with the transport and release of neurohormones (p. 120).
It is doubtful that any significant number of nerve fibers reach the cells
of the anterior part. The majority of fibers from the hypothalamus
project posteriorly and caudally to the brain stem, some as far as the

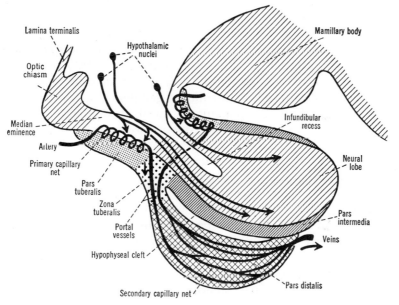

Figure 129. Drawing of a generalized mammalian pituitary gland to illustrate certain
basic features. The *adenohypophysis* develops in the embryo from the epithelium of the
pharynx; it includes the *pars tuberalis*, which lies in contact with the *median eminence*, the
pars intermedia, in contact with the neural lobe, and the *pars distalis*, the remainder of the
adenohypophysis. The *zona tuberalis* is a specialized portion of the pars distalis which
contains the portal vessels. The *neurohypophysis* is derived embryologically from the diencephalon and includes the *median eminence,* which receives its blood supply from the hypo-
physioportal circulation or which has a common vascularization with the adenohypophysis,
and the *neural lobe,* which has an independent blood supply. Some vessels may reach the
adenohypophysis directly, but they have not been indicated in this drawing. The projections from hypothalamic nuclei represent nerve fibers which descend to the neural
lobe, giving branches to the portal vessels as they descend. (These definitions are according
to J. D. Green: Am. J. Anat., *88*:225-312, 1951.)

medulla oblongata, and connect with the motor and visceral areas throughout the brain stem.

Brain Stem. The brain stem contains regions or centers that are found in the reticular formation and are not well defined anatomically. They are composed of cells scattered diffusely throughout areas the limits of which can be determined only by physiological methods.

These visceral centers, which are concerned with functions such as the reflex regulation of respiration, heart rate, and circulation, receive fibers from the cerebral cortex and hypothalamus and collaterals from ascending sensory systems and reflex paths. In turn they project to the nuclei of certain cranial nerves and also to neurons of the spinal cord, particularly those in the thoracic region, the first three segments of the lumbar cord, and the second and third sacral levels. The descending axons are scattered throughout the lateral and anterior funiculi.

Brain Stem and Spinal Cord. Within the brain stem itself, and also in the spinal cord, there are still lower levels of organization, which are concerned with more specific functions in more specific parts of the body, for example, the control of smooth muscle in the eye. These levels consist of groups of cells associated with cranial and spinal nerves. The axons of these cells are known as *preganglionic fibers* because they leave the central nervous system by way of a cranial nerve or ventral root and synapse with cells in peripheral ganglia. The cells in the brain stem are associated with the oculomotor, facial, glossopharyngeal, vagus, and accessory nerves. Those in the spinal cord form a long column in the intermediolateral part of the gray matter of the thoracic cord, upper lumbar cord, and middle sacral cord.

All of these groups of cells receive descending fibers from the brain stem, and collaterals from sensory and reflex paths.

Ganglia. This level is formed by the various autonomic ganglia, such as those in the sympathetic trunks. The ganglia are composed of cells which receive preganglionic fibers from the brain stem and spinal cord. The axons of the ganglion cells are called *postganglionic fibers.* They project to viscera in specific parts of the body and form effector junctions with cardiac muscle, smooth muscle, or gland cells.

LEVELS OF OUTFLOW

The foregoing account illustrates how impulses from higher centers such as the hypothalamus may reach a viscus by traversing various structural levels. The levels from which axons leave the brain stem and spinal cord as preganglionic fibers form the basis for a subdivision of the autonomic nervous system into *sympathetic* and *parasympathetic* systems. This subdivision, however, is inadequate because it does not take into account higher levels of organization or afferent fibers from viscera.

Sympathetic System (also called *Orthosympathetic* or *Thoracolumbar*). The cells which form a column in the intermediolateral part of the gray matter of the thoracic and upper lumbar segments of the spinal cord send their axons over ventral roots to the ganglia of the sympathetic trunks or else through these ganglia to other cells in more peripherally located ganglia, such as the celiac (Figs. 130, 131). Each preganglionic fiber is myelinated and synapses with a number of ganglion cells. The preganglionic fibers reach the ganglia by leaving the spinal nerve in rami communicantes (p. 40). The postganglionic fibers, that is, the axons of the ganglion cells, are nonmyelinated and are distributed in several different ways. Some return to spinal nerves (in rami communicantes) and thus reach blood vessels, sweat glands, and smooth muscle fibers in skin. Others go directly to blood vessels and organs in the head, neck, thorax, abdomen, and pelvis. All those from the celiac ganglia are distributed to the abdominal and pelvic viscera.

Parasympathetic System (also called *Craniosacral*). This system comprises those fibers which leave by way of the cranial nerves mentioned earlier and also by way of the second and third sacral ventral roots (Fig. 130). The preganglionic fibers are myelinated. Unlike the sympathetic system, the peripheral ganglia are not found in well-defined trunks, but instead the various cells form small ganglia or scattered groups in or near the organs to be innervated. The nonmyelinated postganglionic fibers are thus short (Fig. 131). Furthermore, each preganglionic fiber synapses with relatively few cells or just one cell, and the postganglionic fibers supply fewer structures than do postganglionic sympathetic fibers.

Those parasympathetic cells in the oculomotor nucleus send axons to a small ganglion in each orbit. The postganglionic fibers supply smooth muscle in the eye. The parasympathetic fibers in the facial nerve synapse in several peripherally located ganglia, and the postganglionic fibers supply the lacrimal gland, some of the salivary glands, and glands in the mucous membrane of the nasal cavity, oral cavity, and pharynx. The axons leaving by way of the glossopharyngeal nerve synapse in peripheral ganglia and the postganglionic fibers supply chiefly the parotid gland. Axons leaving by way of the vagus and accessory nerves are distributed to the heart, lungs, esophagus, stomach, pancreas, liver, small intestine, and part of the large intestine. The terminal ganglia are located in the walls of these organs.

With regard to the sacral portion, the axons arise from cells in the second and third sacral segments and leave by way of the ventral roots of these segments. They are distributed to those viscera not supplied by the vagus, that is, a part of the large intestine, and the pelvic viscera,

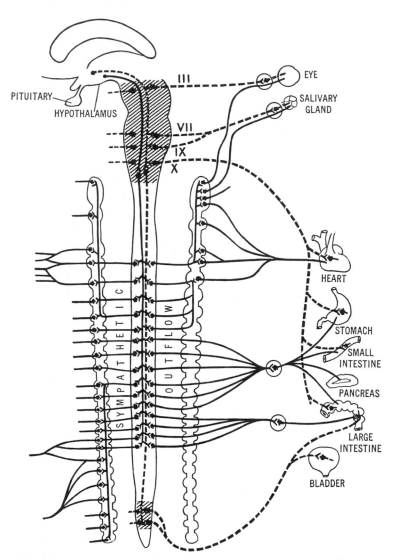

Figure 130. The general arrangement of the autonomic nervous system. The projections from the hypothalamus to the pituitary gland have been omitted, while those to lower centers are shown in solid lines (sympathetic) and broken lines (parasympathetic). The portions of the brain stem and sacral cord from which the parasympathetic preganglionic fibers leave are indicated by oblique lines, and the sympathetic outflow from the thoracic and upper lumbar cord is labeled. Autonomic fibers to organs of the head and trunk are shown on the right side, while those on the left side represent the sympathetic outflow to blood vessels, sweat glands, and smooth muscle fibers attached to hairs.

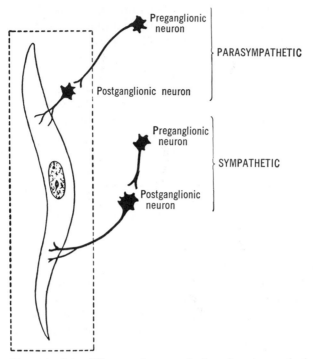

Figure 131. Diagram of the differences in sympathetic and parasympathetic distribution. The dotted line represents an organ containing effectors such as a smooth muscle cell. As indicated for this organ, nearly all parasympathetic postganglionic neurons lie within the organ they supply. The postganglionic axons travel at the most a few millimeters. Sympathetic synapses, however, occur in paravertebral ganglia, and the postganglionic axons travel considerable distances.

such as the bladder, rectum, and genital organs. The terminal ganglia are in the walls of these organs.

Aside from certain blood vessels in the thorax, abdomen, pelvic and external genitalia, there are no parasympathetic fibers to blood vessels or to sweat glands or to smooth muscle of skin

Transmitters. In certain respects the anatomical classification is unsatisfactory. It implies a rigid or sharp distinction between the subdivisions that functionally may not exist. Also, some organs are supplied by sympathetic fibers that functionally appear to be parasympathetic. There is now in common use a classification based on the type of transmitter and upon reactions to certain drugs. This classification was first mentioned in connection with neuroeffector junctions (p. 150).

Impulses traveling over preganglionic fibers arrive at synapses with ganglion cells and cause the release of acetylcholine (p. 111). Ganglion cells are activated and impulses travel over postganglionic fibers. Certain chemicals are liberated at the terminals of these fibers in synaptic vesicles. These chemicals act as transmitters, that is, they are released when nerve impulses arrive and in turn initiate activity in a viscus, or alter its existing activity. Acetylcholine is released at postganglionic parasympathetic terminals and at most of the postganglionic sympathetic fibers that supply the smooth muscle and sweat glands of the skin; all such fibers are called cholinergic. Norepinephrine (noradrenaline) is released at postganglionic sympathetic terminals (except at those just listed); such fibers are called adrenergic.

Epinephrine (adrenaline), which is formed by the cells in the medulla of the suprarenal glands, has actions similar to those of norepinephrine. Hence, the sympathetic system, by virtue of stimulating the release of epinephrine, can enhance its own actions. Epinephrine is the chief catecholamine released by the suprarenal medulla, and norepinephrine the chief one released by the peripheral autonomic system. Another catecholamine named dopamine, together with norepinephrine and the indole amine, serotonin (p. 120), are found in high concentrations in certain parts of the brain. It has been suggested that they are central nervous system transmitters, but this is far from clear. What is more certain is that they are related to the affective state (p. 121).

In pharmacological studies a number of drugs can be classified according to their actions on the autonomic nervous system. For example, a parasympathetic drug is one which, when administered, acts in a manner similar to the parasympathetic system. The drug *nicotine,* when applied in low concentration to ganglion cells, stimulates the cells, whereas in high concentrations it depresses and blocks synaptic transmission. Acetylcholine has similar properties, and these have been termed its *nicotinic effect.* The drug *muscarine* acts on viscera much as acetylcholine does; the action of acetylcholine at postganglionic terminals has been termed its *muscarine action.* This action is blocked by *atropine,* which, however, has no effect on synapses. As mentioned previously (p. 149), acetylcholine is rapidly hydrolyzed by *cholinesterase,* an enzyme normally present in tissues, and this in turn may be blocked by *eserine.* Several compounds act in a manner similar to the sympathetic system, and are classified as sympathetic drugs. Likewise, there are drugs, such as *ergotoxin* and *ergotamine,* which can block the action of norepinephrine.

That chemical mediators exist has been shown by a variety of experiments. If the sympathetic fibers to a frog heart are stimulated, and the blood leaving that heart is perfused through the heart of another frog, the second heart responds as does the first in that its rate of contraction increases. The only explanation is that the stimulation resulted in the formation of some substance which entered the blood and was thus able to reach the second heart. Likewise, if the vagus (parasympathetic) nerves are stimulated and a similar experiment is carried out, the second heart responds as does the first in that its rate of contraction decreases.

Neither of the mediators is specific in its effects on the different effectors. In the intestine, for example, acetylcholine ordinarily stimulates contraction of those smooth muscle coats which push forward the intestinal contents, but it usually inhibits the smooth muscle of the various intestinal sphincters, thereby allowing the material to pass through. Acetylcholine inhibits cardiac muscle, whereas noradrenaline has the opposite effect. The effects of either of these substances may, therefore, be inhibitory or excitatory, depending upon the specific structure involved. Table 2 lists the effects of these two mediators on different viscera.

Most organs are supplied by both systems. When this is so, the systems tend to have opposite effects on the effectors, as in the case of the heart. Nearly all the peripheral blood vessels, however, are supplied by the sympathetic system alone. Yet opposite effects are possible, as constriction or dilatation. Either some of the fibers supplying these vessels are cholinergic and others are adrenergic; or the adrenergic fibers are able to mediate excitation or inhibition of the smooth muscle in the vessels, depending upon the concentration of the mediator.

Table 2.   Functions of the Autonomic Nervous System

ORGAN	PARASYMPATHETIC	SYMPATHETIC
Eye	Constriction of pupil	Dilatation of pupil
Lacrimal, nasal, palatine, and salivary glands	Stimulates serous and mucous secretions	No important effect
Heart	Inhibits heart muscle — heart rate slows	Stimulates heart muscle — heart rate increases
Lungs	Stimulates serous and mucous secretions and smooth muscle of bronchioles	Inhibits smooth muscle of bronchioles
Alimentary canal	Stimulates digestion, peristalsis, evacuation	Inhibits peristalsis
Medullae of suprarenal glands	No effect	Stimulates secretion of epinephrine
Urinary bladder	Stimulates emptying of bladder	
Genital organs	Uncertain and variable; may stimulate smooth muscle and glands; vasodilatation	Uncertain and variable; may stimulate vasoconstriction
Peripheral blood vessels	No effect	Constriction and dilatation
Sweat glands and smooth muscle of skin	No effect	Stimulates sweating and erection of hairs

FUNCTIONS OF THE VARIOUS LEVELS

Cerebral Cortex. Little is known of the functions of the cerebral cortex with regard to visceral activities. Electrical stimulation of various parts of the frontal lobes, especially the basal and medial surfaces, may have profound effects upon visceral activity (see limbic system, p. 335). Extensive cortical destruction in the frontal lobes of human patients may be accompanied by severe visceral disorders, such as incontinence.

The cerebral cortex is probably involved in visceral responses to emotional situations, particularly when they are in the form of conditioned responses. There is no visceral activity that cannot be modified, or even completely disorganized, by emotional upsets. Blushing, for instance, is a sudden dilatation of facial blood vessels in response to an emotional situation or to the memory of one. Fright, anger, fear or apprehension may completely upset digestive processes and, at the same time, cause blood pressure to rise and heart rate to increase. Students are well acquainted with such phenomena before examinations; speakers may encounter them in the form of stage fright.

Hypothalamus. The hypothalamus is concerned in many physiological activities. Its exact role is by no means known with certainty, but it appears to effect a general regulation of water balance, body temperature, and the development of secondary sex characteristics, to mention but a few. The functions necessitating parasympathetic activity appear to be mediated by the anterior portion of the hypothalamus, and sympathetic activity by the posterior hypothalamus.

Many of the functions of the hypothalamus are carried out by way of connections to lower centers, such as the brain stem. In the regulation of body temperature, for example, changes in external temperature stimulate skin receptors, and central connections allow impulses to reach the hypothalamus. In addition, certain cells in the hypothalamus are themselves directly sensitive to changes in temperature of the blood flowing through the area in which they are situated. If the external temperature drops, the posterior hypothalamus initiates the sympathetic activities necessary to prevent heat loss and, under more extreme conditions, initiates the metabolic processes which increase the production of heat. Included with the latter would be contractions of skeletal muscle evidenced as shivering. If the external temperature rises, the anterior hypothalamus initiates the parasympathetic activities necessary to increase the loss of heat. Under normal conditions, these various mechanisms maintain body temperature within a degree or so of 98.6° F.

There are many circumstances in which this hypothalamic balance is altered. For example, a common sign of a bacterial infection is a fever. Bacterial toxins alter the sensitivity of the hypothalamic cells so that the balance point at which they operate is raised or set, as it were, at a higher level, like a thermostat. For the body temperature to conform to this new level, the processes of heat retention are started. Cutaneous vessels constrict, thus reducing the loss of heat by radiation. This is accompanied by a subjective sensation of cold. Shivering appears, thus increasing heat production. The chills which frequently signify the onset of a fever are shivering plus the sensation of cold. Body temperature rises because more heat is produced than can be lost. When the temperature reaches the new operating level of the hypothalamus, a compensatory process occurs. This is an increase in the loss of heat resulting from a dilatation of cutaneous vessels evidenced by the flushing of the skin. The loss is not great enough, however, to cause the temperature to drop to normal. That these phenomena are the result of an altered hypothalamic sensitivity is shown by the fact that surgical operations in or near the hypothalamus may be followed by marked changes in body temperature. The trauma incident to the operation probably interferes with the control of either heat loss or heat production. Postoperative rises or falls of temperature may be so extreme that the patient may die.

The hypothalamus is an important link between the central nervous system and the endocrine system. The study of this link or interaction is known as *neuroendocrinology*. The hypothalamus contains the supraoptic and paraventricular nuclei, which have a rich blood supply and consist of specialized cells that often contain neurosecretory material. This material is thought to be carried down the axons of the cells to the neurohypophysis. The material appears to be a mixture which, when released upon demand, constitutes the two hormones of the neurohypophysis. One of the hormones is the antidiuretic hormone (also known as vasopressin) which regulates the elimination of water by the kidney. The other is oxytocin, which stimulates contraction of the uterus. If the connections between the hypothalamus and the neurohypophysis are destroyed, a disorder known as *diabetes insipidus* may result. Owing to the deficiency in antidiuretic hormone, tremendous quantities of fluid (amounting to many liters) are eliminated by the kidneys each day; correspondingly large amounts of water must be drunk.

The adenohypophysis is influenced by the hypothalamus, not by direct nerve pathways, but by a humoral mechanism. It has been suggested, with good supporting evidence, that nerve fibers from the hypothalamus act upon the vessels of the capillary net in the median eminence in such a way as to cause the formation and release of a chemical mediator. This mediator is carried by the portal vessels to the adenohypophysis and activates its glandular cells. The various hormones of the adenohypophysis are carried by the blood to the other endocrine glands. Hence, the hypothalamus can influence all endocrine activities, such as intermediary metabolism, growth, electrolyte balance, and secondary sex characteristics, to mention but a few, and disorders of the hypothalamus can result in endocrine disorders. Finally, the hypothalamus itself is activated in these mechanisms by a variety of impulses reaching it from other parts of the nervous system.

Brain Stem.   The specific functions with which the brain stem is concerned are numerous. In the pons and medulla oblongata, for instance, are *respiratory, vasomotor,* and *cardiac centers.* Still others are concerned with intestinal movements, salivation, and many other visceral functions. These centers are functionally restricted in the sense that the respiratory centers do not control the vasomotor centers, although they may affect them. But the hypothalamus, projecting to both, may control or activate them simultaneously, as when respiration and blood pressure increase during emotional states. These centers also function on a reflex level, as in the control of blood pressure. They are, furthermore, frequently integrated with somatic activities. Respiration, for instance, involves skeletal muscles. Because of the multiplicity of their functions, some of these centers will be discussed in more detail in Chapter 16.

An idea of how brain stem levels function may be gained by studying decerebrate animals, that is, animals in which all the nervous system above the midbrain has been removed. Descending fibers from the cerebral cortex and hypothalamus are thereby interrupted. A decerebrate cat can breathe by itself. Its blood pressure is maintained reflexly at a fairly normal level. It cannot eat or maintain body temperature or adjust to any severe environmental changes. How some of these functions are carried out can be illustrated by a brief discussion of the processes involved in the control of blood pressure, processes which take place in a similar manner in a normal animal.

CONTROL OF BLOOD PRESSURE.   There must be a pressure gradient in order for blood to circulate. This can be measured in terms of the ability of the blood to raise a column of mercury above atmospheric pressure. A device used to measure blood pressure is a *sphygmomanometer.* A hollow cloth cuff is wrapped around the arm and pumped full of air until the flow of arterial blood is stopped. This cuff is connected to a tube filled with mercury, and air pressure in it is thereby exerted against the mercury column. The latter, therefore, rises as the air pressure increases. The height which the mercury column reaches when the blood is shut off averages about 120 mm. This, then, is the highest pressure in the bloodstream. Since it is related to the contraction of the heart, or *systole,* it is termed systolic pressure. Between contractions, that is, during *diastole*, the pressure drops to a base line or minimum pressure which averages about 80 mm. of mercury. In referring to blood pressure one should always include the two figures, systolic and diastolic; in the example cited the values would be written as 120/80. The 40 mm. difference is the pulse pressure and represents the efficiency of the heart in raising pressure above the base line and pumping the blood around the body.

Reflex mechanisms help to maintain blood pressure at these average levels. In the bifurcation of the common carotid arteries in the neck and also in the arch of the aorta are interoceptive receptors which are sensitive to changes in pressure. For instance, if the blood pressure increases, the nerve impulses initiated ascend by way of the vagus and glossopharyngeal nerves to the medulla oblongata, and reach the cardiac and vasomotor centers (Fig. 132). Efferent impulses over the vagus nerves inhibit the heart, thereby slowing its rate of contraction. Other impulses descend to the spinal cord where they inhibit the cells of the sympathetic system that control the diameter of peripheral blood vessels. As a result, the blood vessels dilate, their resistance to the flow of blood

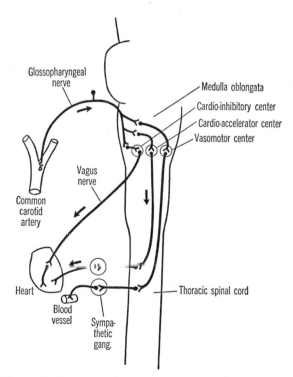

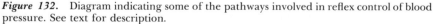

Figure 132.   Diagram indicating some of the pathways involved in reflex control of blood pressure. See text for description.

decreases, and the pressure drops, much as widening the nozzle of a garden hose decreases the force of the stream of water going through it. With the decrease in pressure, stimulation of the carotid and aortic receptors lessens. Fewer impulses thus reach the medulla oblongata, and the process reverses. The pressure then rises as the peripheral vessels constrict and the heart rate increases. Under resting conditions, then, there is a slight fall, rise, then fall, and so on, continually occurring; the net result is a blood pressure reflexly maintained at an average level. This illustrates how finely balanced and integrated the two systems are in equilibrating a given activity.

OTHER REFLEX PHENOMENA. Still other reflex activities may be cited. Reflex salivation may occur after taste of a food, even in decerebrate animals.

Pupillary reactions likewise can occur. If a light is flashed in an eye, the pupils of both eyes narrow and restrict the amount of light which can enter. This reaction is known as the *light reflex.* The impulses initiated by the light traverse those fibers of the optic nerve which go to the region between the superior colliculi and the thalami. After several synaptic connections, impulses leave by way of the oculomotor nerves and eventually reach the constrictor muscle of each iris. A widening of the pupils, on the other hand, may be the result either of sympathetic stimulation of the dilator muscle of the iris or of inhibition of the parasympathetic fibers supplying the constrictor muscles. The constrictor is much the stronger of the two opposing muscles, and the parasympathetic system is, therefore, the more important in pupillary reactions.

The various processes mentioned in the foregoing discussion illustrate how afferent impulses are necessary for the integrated control of visceral activities, and how meaningless it is to restrict a concept of such control to the motor side.

Brain Stem, Spinal Cord, and Ganglia. These levels, which constitute the origin of preganglionic fibers, are still more restricted in functions. In a spinal animal, that is, an animal in which the spinal cord has been severed, the blood pressure and temperature in the part of the body supplied by the isolated spinal cord fall markedly and respond but poorly to reflex stimuli. Other functions, such as the control of the urinary bladder, may occur reflexly, but without integration with other visceral activities. Furthermore, visceral activities may be initiated by stimuli which in normal animals would be ineffective. In spinal man, for example, scratching the skin may lead to sweating, vasodilatation, and even emptying of the bladder.

The ganglia are still more restricted in outflow and function and differ functionally in at least one major respect from preganglionic cells in the spinal cord in that no reflex connections are established within them.

GENERAL FUNCTIONS OF THE AUTONOMIC NERVOUS SYSTEM

The autonomic system is an important part of the mechanism whereby the body keeps its internal environment *("milieu intérieur")* constant, that is, maintains temperature, fluid balance, and ionic composition of the blood. The maintenance of the internal environment is termed *homeostasis.*

Parasympathetic System. The parasympathetic system is concerned with the initiation and maintenance of a number of specific functions, such as digestion, intermediate metabolism of foods, and excretion. These are usually initiated in response to specific stimuli; hence the necessity for rather specific anatomical arrangements. Widespread connections such as are found in the sympathetic system would interfere with parasympathetic functions. This does not mean that widespread parasympathetic discharge cannot take place. It can, but usually not as a normal process, since it would be rather undesirable if, for example, the stimuli which initiated glandular secretion in the stomach or duodenum at the same time automatically initiated evacuation of the bladder and rectum.

Sympathetic System. The sympathetic system tends to respond as a whole, particularly during emergencies or sudden environmental changes, and is therefore an important part of the mechanisms by which a person reacts to stress. There are many stressing situations which particularly implicate the sympathetic system. Among these are pain, rage, fright, exercise, cold, drugs, and asphyxia. Any of these may evoke a similar pattern of response. Certain phases of the response are acute and are mediated mainly by the nervous system. For example, there may occur a rise in blood pressure, increased cardiac output, increased blood sugar, increased oxygen consumption and sweating, to mention but a few. These changes come as a result of sympathetic discharge following cortical and hypothalamic activity after the stressing situation. These sympathetic effects are enhanced or maintained because the epinephrine released into the blood as a result of sympathetic stimulation of the medullae of the suprarenal glands has about the same effect on viscera as do the sympathetic nerve fibers.

In addition, in response to stress, there are more slowly developing changes involving both the nervous system and the endocrine system. For example, there is increased secretion of adrenocorticotrophic hormone (ACTH) of the pituitary, and this in turn is followed by increased activity of the adrenal cortex, evidenced in part by a fall in blood lymphocytes. Since adrenal cortical hormones are concerned with a wide variety of metabolic activities, there is therefore a mechanism by which stress can affect such activities.

SUMMARY

Visceral activities are controlled, directly or indirectly, by the autonomic nervous system. The levels of nervous control are the cerebral cortex, hypothalamus, brain stem, spinal cord, and ganglia. The higher the level, the more general, widespread, and nonspecific are connections and functions. The fibers which leave the central nervous system do so as preganglionic fibers, synapsing with peripherally located ganglion cells and reaching viscera as postganglionic fibers. Axons leaving by way of the oculomotor, facial, glossopharyngeal, vagus, and accessory nerves and by way of ventral roots of the second and third sacral nerves, form the craniosacral or parasympathetic division. The ganglia are in or near the organs innervated. The axons leaving by way of the ventral roots of the thoracic and first three lumbar roots form the thoracolumbar or sympathetic system. The peripheral synapses occur in the paravertebral and prevertebral ganglia.

The autonomic nervous system supplies smooth muscle, cardiac muscle, and gland cells. Most organs made up of these tissues are supplied by both divisions of the autonomic system. Acetylcholine is released at parasympathetic postganglionic terminals, and norepinephrine at most sympathetic postganglionic terminals. These postganglionic fibers are known respectively as cholinergic and adrenergic fibers. Fibers supplying sweat glands and smooth muscle of skin anatomically are sympathetic, but functionally are cholinergic. Acetylcholine and norepinephrine are not specific in their effects. Either may be excitatory or inhibitory, depending upon the viscus concerned.

Little is known of the functions of the cerebral cortex with regard to visceral activities. The hypothalamus is involved in a number of visceral and metabolic functions, and carries out its functions by means of projections to the brain stem and to the hypophysis. Thus, it acts both upon the endocrine system and upon other nervous levels. The brain stem is concerned with a number of visceral activities, each rather specific, such as the reflex control of respiration and blood pressure. The brain stem and spinal cord contain still lower and functionally more specific levels which project to peripheral autonomic ganglia. The latter constitute the lowest and most specific autonomic level.

The parasympathetic system as a whole is concerned with fairly specific functions, such as digestion and excretion, each of which is initiated by fairly definite stimuli. The sympathetic system is particularly concerned in responses to stress, and its pattern of activity may be initiated by a wide variety of situations and agents.

Names in Neurology

CLAUDE BERNARD (1813-1878)

Bernard was a French scientist and one of the greatest of experimental physiologists. He was the founder of experimental medicine. To him we owe much of our knowledge of the digestive and vasomotor systems. In 1843, he discovered that cane sugar appeared in the urine after being injected into the veins, but not if it had been first treated with gastric juice. This observation was the beginning of a long series of investigations of digestive processes. In 1849 he discovered that a puncture of the floor of the fourth ventricle produced a temporary diabetes. Shortly after this he investigated the factors controlling blood vessels and demonstrated the mechanisms of constriction and dilatation. Later he used curare in an investigation of muscle and showed that the paralysis it produced was the result of an effect on the myoneural junction, thus showing the independent excitability of muscle and nerve. Later he studied carbon monoxide poisoning. One of the most fundamental concepts in physiology results from his statement that all the vital processes maintain the constancy of the *milieu intérieur* or internal environment. Although Bernard was not primarily a neurophysiologist, if his work on the nervous system were all that he had done, his name would still go down in scientific history.

REFERENCES

See the references cited on pages 6, 94 and 121.

Cannon, W. B.: The Wisdom of the Body. New York, W. W. Norton and Company, 1939. (Dr. Cannon was one of the outstanding investigators of the autonomic system. In this classic volume he emphasizes homeostatic mechanisms.)

Goodman, L., and Gilman, A.: Pharmacological Basis of Therapeutics. 3rd ed. New York, Macmillan Company, 1965. (Drugs are discussed by showing how and where they act and by correlating their effects with physiological processes. It contains excellent sections on the pharmacology of the autonomic system.)

Harris, G. W.: Neural Control of the Pituitary Gland. London, Edward Arnold (Publisher) Ltd., 1955. (Clear, concise, well-written, instructive.)

von Euler, U. S.: Noradrenaline. Springfield, Ill., Charles C Thomas, 1956. (A discussion and summary of work showing that noradrenaline is the sympathetic mediator.)

Scharrer, E., and Scharrer, B.: Neuroendocrinology. New York, Columbia University Press, 1963. (A fine account by two of the pioneer investigators in this field.)

White, J. C., Smithwick, R. H., and Simeone, F. A.: Autonomic Nervous System. 3rd ed. New York, Macmillan Company, 1952. (This is a book of an advanced nature, especially valuable from a clinical standpoint. It discusses the anatomy and physiology of the system briefly but clearly.)

CHAPTER 15

THE SPINAL CORD, SPINAL NERVES, AND PERIPHERAL NERVES

The presentation of neurological structure and function has been, up to this point, from what might be termed a longitudinal point of view. That is, after the introduction to general form and arrangement, the long tracts of the nervous system were discussed according to their relations with motor and sensory functions. This is logically followed by a consideration of the local or horizontal levels or functions.

THE SPINAL CORD

The spinal cord is the least modified portion of the original neural tube. To a large extent, its segmental differentiation is retained. The spinal cord has essentially the same structure throughout. Its gray matter has a fundamental arrangement which is modified locally, as indicated in Figure 133. This is the result of differences in numbers and types of its contained neurons. Thus the gray matter of the cervical and lumbosacral regions is more abundant because these regions supply the limbs. That of the thoracic and upper lumbar segments of the spinal cord is relatively scanty because it supplies only the trunk. It is characterized, however, by a lateral projection of its intermediate portion

Fasciculus gracilis

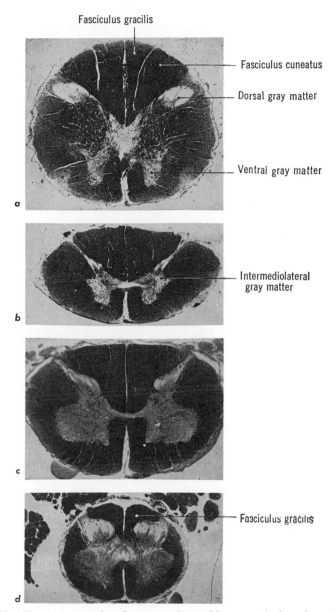

Fasciculus cuneatus

Dorsal gray matter

Ventral gray matter

Intermediolateral gray matter

Fasciculus gracilis

Figure 133. Photomicrographs of cross sections of human spinal cords. *a,* Upper cervical; *b,* thoracic; *c,* lumbar; *d,* sacral. Note how the gray matter varies in shape and volume. The structures around the sacral cord are spinal roots of the cauda equina. Tracts cannot be distinguished in this normal material. Compare with Figure 100 (p. 169) and Figure 106 (p. 182). For diagram of tracts, see Figure 134. Weigert stain.

which contains the autonomic neurons whose axons ultimately enter sympathetic ganglia.

The cells of the dorsal gray matter consist of interneurons and transmission neurons, and are arranged in layers, usually six. Each layer tends to receive incoming dorsal root fibers predominantly from one type or group of peripheral receptors. The cells also receive impulses from fibers descending from higher levels. These fibers control the threshold of the dorsal gray cells, and may switch their receptivity in terms of making them more sensitive to other peripheral receptors. The outermost layer of cells is particularly concerned with impulses arriving over nonmyelinated and small myelinated fibers. These cells modulate impulses initiated by noxious stimuli and are implicated in recent theories of pain.

The cells of the ventral gray matter are mostly motor cells to skeletal muscle, and, in certain regions, to autonomic ganglia. Interneurons are also present, including the inhibitory Renshaw cells (Fig. 75, p. 126).

The white matter differs but little in its fundamental arrangement throughout the spinal cord. It is contained within three funiculi on each side, as indicated in Figure 18 (p. 25). These funiculi, of course, vary in shape and size at different levels, because of variations in the shape of the gray matter and because of additions of ascending and terminations of descending fibers. These funiculi are simply morphological divisions which have no striking functional characteristics. The

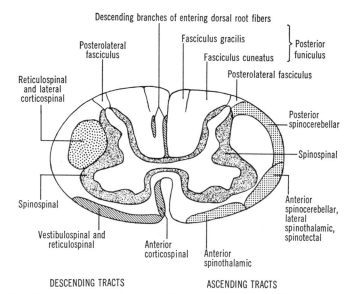

Figure 134.   The main tracts of the spinal cord. Afferent, ascending tracts on the right side; efferent, descending tracts on the left. It must be remembered, however, that both ascending and descending fibers are present on each side.

functional units of the white matter are tracts (Fig. 134). These, however, cannot be distinguished from each other in normal material. The
lateral corticospinal tracts, for instance, can be morphologically demonstrated only by their absence, as shown in Fig. 100 (p. 169). The fibers
of the lateral spinothalamic tract are intermingled with spinocerebellar
fibers (Fig. 106, p. 182). Thus the lateral and anterior funiculi contain
ascending and descending tracts which are anatomically congruent. In
man, motor tracts are not found in the dorsal funiculi.

A large part of the white matter is composed of spinospinal or
propriospinal fibers, that is, fibers arising and terminating within the
spinal cord, thereby linking various levels and providing for coordinated
activity (Fig. 77, p. 128). These spinospinal fibers are of short and long
types. The short ones interconnect levels within a given region, such
as from one cervical segment to another. The long ones pass from one
region to another, for example, cervical to lumbar.

FUNCTIONS OF THE SPINAL CORD

The functions of the spinal cord are difficult to analyze in an intact
animal, so that recourse is often had to electrical recording from the
cords of anesthetized animals. Such studies have demonstrated the
importance of the gray matter in modulating and modifying afferent
inflow, as mentioned previously. They have made possible the analysis
of reflex pathways and motor and sensory tracts. Important contributions have also been made by studies of spinal animals (animals with
their spinal cord either transected or severed from the brain stem).
An approximate idea of certain functions can be gained by all such
studies. For example, in a spinal animal, certain reflex patterns may be
elicited in a relatively unmodified form. How closely these patterns
resemble those of the normal animals depends upon the species under
study. If, for example, the spinal cord of a frog is severed, immediately
after the section spinal cord functions are depressed, but within a few
minutes it is possible to demonstrate reflex withdrawal to painful
stimuli, reflex squatting and swimming movements and a variety of
reactions similar to those seen in normal frogs. The spinal cord of the
frog is therefore capable of much autonomous activity. Little of this
activity, however, is spontaneous; that is, it does not take place without
adequate external stimuli.

In higher animals, such as the cat or dog, the period of depression
or *spinal shock* may last for several hours or days. Subsequently, certain
patterns of reflex behavior can be demonstrated. Although spinal cats
and dogs either cannot stand or can stand for but short periods of time,
if they are properly supported and adequate stimulation supplied,

alternating flexion and extension movements which resemble running patterns may be elicited. The reflexes forming these patterns are combinations of the fundamental types discussed previously (p. 123). There, it was pointed out that the two-neuron or stretch reflex is a highly restricted or *local reflex* of both phasic and static types. The phasic type, that is, the knee jerk, can be elicited in spinal cats and dogs, but the degree to which the static type is present is variable. Those animals which exhibit some degree of reflex extensor activity also show periods of reflex standing, whereas in others the knee jerk may be the only type of extensor response which can be demonstrated.

Another type of extensor activity is the *crossed extensor reflex*. This is most easily elicited by painful stimuli. The afferent impulses, after entering the spinal cord, are relayed by interneurons to various levels so as to provide for the reflex withdrawal (flexion) of the stimulated or ipsilateral limb and the simultaneous inhibition of the antagonistic extensors. At the same time, interneurons project to various levels of the opposite side of the spinal cord and provide for enhancement of the postural contractions of the contralateral limb. This total reaction is a mechanism for providing support when a limb is lifted from the ground. The crossed extensor reflex is a *segmental static reflex* and is not always easy to elicit in spinal cats.

From a study of spinal animals it is known that a simple reflex is an abstraction, an anatomical situation which cannot be demonstrated physiologically. Certain general principles regarding more complicated patterns can, however, be pointed out.

Reflexes exhibit *local sign* or *specificity*. For example, scratching movements may follow light scratching of the skin of the flank, but not of the foot. A painful stimulus to the skin of the flank is followed, not by scratching, but by withdrawal.

Reflexes exhibit *rhythm*, which appears to be an intrinsic property of the spinal cord. For example, one may scratch the skin of the flank of a spinal dog at a certain frequency, say several times a second. Yet the scratching movements which the animal carries out reflexly are not necessarily the same number of times per second. They may be much slower, and independent of stimulus frequency to the extent that the rate of scratching remains the same even when the stimulus frequency is varied. Likewise, for a particular animal it is likely that a basic rhythmic discharge from gray matter is responsible for the locomotor pattern of activity. Afferent stimuli, then, although extremely important in locomotion, modify the basic rhythm rather than determine it.

There are a variety of other principles, having mainly to do with allied and antagonistic reflexes. Some type of *coordination* is necessary because there are more afferent fibers entering the spinal cord than there are efferent fibers leaving it. As a general rule, if stimuli which normally result in different reflexes are applied simultaneously, and if one of the stimuli is painful, the response to pain is dominant.

Reflexes may be *allied*. For example, the scratch response is several simpler types of reflexes which are coordinated into a fairly complicated pattern.

Not infrequently, the cutaneous stimulation is subthreshold, that is, ineffective. In such cases a similar subthreshold stimulus applied nearby at the same time (simultaneous combination) or applied to the same region immediately after the first (successive combination) will summate with the first and produce a response. *Summation of subthreshold stimuli* is commonly seen in connection with many reflexes.

Some reflexes are *antagonistic,* as in the case of extensor and flexor components of locomotion, in the sense that they initiate movement in opposing directions. When they are coordinated into locomotor patterns involving forelimbs and hindlimbs, they form what are called *intersegmental reflexes.* Intersegmental relationships are further illustrated by the changes subsequent to spinal transection in a decerebrate animal (p. 266). If the transection is made in the thoracic region, stretch reflexes in the forelimbs become exaggerated, indicating that the caudal portion of the spinal cord had been carrying out an inhibitory function.

It is apparent that the spinal cord in cats and dogs does not function as well as that of the frog when separated from the rest of the nervous system. The higher the animal in the vertebrate scale, the more dependent on higher centers and the less autonomy there is of the spinal cord. This can be shown by reference to spinal man.

SPINAL MAN

When the spinal cord is completely severed above the fourth cervical segment, death rapidly follows because of the interference with respiration (p. 270).

Transection at lower levels is compatible with life. The initial effect is a complete cessation of spinal cord functions below the lesion. This *spinal shock* is much more pronounced in man than in lower vertebrates and is characterized by complete flaccid paralysis and absence of reflexes and sensation below the level of the lesion, and marked disturbance of bladder and rectal functions. The reasons for its appearance are not fully understood. One of the main factors is sudden section of descending tracts, because, if a transection develops slowly over days or weeks, shock may not appear. If, after transection, the isolated cord happens to be severed again, the cord distal to the second transection does not develop signs of shock. Evidently, then, fibers descending from higher levels are implicated. These would not be involved in the second transection.

There are certain fundamental reactions to any pathological changes in the nervous system, their specificity depending on whether there is a destruction of nervous tissue or an irritation. (1) If part of the nervous system has been destroyed, two fundamental reactions occur: *(a)* functions performed by the affected area are lost, and *(b)* abnormal phenomena appear because of the hyperactivity of areas normally held in check or inhibited by or opposing the affected part. In an upper motor neuron lesion, for instance, the paralysis is a loss of function; the spasticity and hyperactive reflexes are abnormal phenomena. (2) If a disorder irritates part of the nervous system by a stimulating action, the fundamental reaction is an exaggeration of the normal functions of the affected area. In infantile paralysis, for instance, there may be irritation of motor neurons, and muscle spasm results. Any or all of the fundamental reactions may occur in a neurological disorder. Furthermore, some lesions are initially irritative and later destructive; in such cases the type of fundamental reaction may change during the course of the disorder. Spinal man exhibits the two types of reaction that follow destruction.

Following cord transection, there are generally the following stages: spinal shock, minimal reflex activity, flexor spasms, and alternating flexor and extensor spasms. In most instances of uncomplicated long-surviving cases of complete cord transection, extensor activity below the level of transection becomes dominant.

Flaccid paralysis, with complete loss of all reflexes, persists during spinal shock. The paralyzed bladder contains stagnant urine, a potential source of infection, and care has to be taken to prevent infections from involving the urinary system.

As spinal shock subsides, the isolated part of the spinal cord becomes more or less automatic in function. Muscles are not severed from motor neurons except at the level of the transection itself, and reflex arcs are, therefore, intact. But all descending motor tracts are severed and reflex arcs are, therefore, modifiable by local influences (cutaneous stimulation, muscle stretch, or gamma efferents). All ascending tracts are cut, and sensation is completely lost below the level of the lesion.

The first signs of reflex activity appear in the distal parts of the limbs, one to six weeks after transection. These consist of mild reflex contractions of flexor muscles following cutaneous stimulation.

Flexor activity becomes more marked until flexor spasm or *mass flexion* is seen. In its best developed form this consists of withdrawal of the limbs, with flexion at hip, knee and ankle, and strong Babinski responses, these occurring in response to cutaneous stimulation. Tendon reflexes become very active, and at a variable time after transection can be elicited in extensor muscles, as, for example, a phasic type of knee jerk.

Commonly, extensor spasm (straightening of lower limbs) begins to appear and eventually becomes predominant *(mass extension)*. Extensor activity is best elicited by stretch of muscles. In a few instances, extension may be so pronounced that patients, on being placed in a standing position, may continue to stand reflexly, even though no voluntary control exists.

Autonomic functions are lost during the period of spinal shock. With recovery, evidences of sympathetic activity reappear. The cutaneous vessels constrict, and sweating may be reflexly induced. Thus a mass flexion is accompanied by sweating in the affected areas. The upper limit of the area of sweating indicates the approximate level of the cord lesion. This illustrates the localized distribution of the autonomic outflow.

With recovery from spinal shock, the bladder may function almost automatically and become a "cord bladder," tending to fill and empty spontaneously. The bladder normally functions as follows: Urine formed by the kidneys flows down the ureters into the urinary bladder. The walls of the bladder are composed of smooth muscle, which continues along the urethra. Under normal conditions the smooth muscle of the bladder wall is contracted to a certain degree. These contractions are mediated by the parasympathetic system. When the amount of urine in the bladder increases enough to raise the intravesical pressure, several things may happen. Afferent impulses due to the increase in pressure are interpreted as a vague sensation of bladder fullness. If voiding is initiated, the smooth muscle of the bladder contracts. At the same time, the urethral musculature contracts, the part of the urethra immediately below the bladder becomes shorter, and the opening between the bladder and the urethra widens. The external abdominal muscles likewise contract, thereby increasing intra-abdominal pressure and aiding in the evacuation of the bladder. Here, then, is a situation in which smooth muscle supplied by the parasympathetic system is partially under voluntary control and is coordinated in its activity with skeletal muscles.

If the bladder is not emptied, the afferent impulses inhibit the parasympathetic cells in the sacral cord. The smooth muscle relaxes and the pressure drops until afferent impulses cease and the muscle resumes its tonicity. As more urine enters, the same processes may be repeated. But there is a limit to the relaxation of the bladder. When a certain pressure is reached, the sensation of fullness becomes acutely and increasingly uncomfortable.

In spinal man the bladder is paralyzed during the period of spinal shock. It fills with urine which cannot be voided except by artificial means. But as spinal shock disappears, the reflex arc begins to function. Eventually, the parasympathetic cells in the sacral cord begin to function and may be excited by afferent impulses resulting from a rise in intravesical pressure. When the bladder begins to contract reflexly, an automatic or "cord bladder" is established.

Other types of visceral activities are affected by cord transections. In spinal man, during the period of shock, the nervous mechanism controlling evacuation of the rectum is almost completely depressed. With gradual recovery from the shock, local reflexes reappear whose stimulus seems to be distention of the rectum and whose response consists in rectal contraction and relaxation of the sphincters at the anal orifice.

Likewise, sexual functions are interfered with. Psychic stimuli are generally unable to influence sexual activity. But there appears to be an area in the lumbosacral cord capable of initiating integrated sexual activity, not only after direct stimulation of the external genitalia, but frequently after any type of cutaneous stimulation.

SPINAL NERVES

All the expressions of behavior are mediated through effectors, and no matter what they are, the final or ultimate path from the central nervous system is the motor neuron of the brain stem and spinal cord, the final common path.

The ventral roots contain efferent fibers. These fibers supply skeletal muscles which developed in the embryo segment corresponding to the cord segment of the ventral root.

The afferent fibers of the dorsal roots are derived from areas characterized by a segmental arrangement even more striking (p. 33). It is interesting that the overlap between any two dorsal roots is great. Thus, if the middle one of three adjacent dorsal roots is severed, the overlap from the other two makes it difficult to detect a loss of sensation. *Hypesthesia,* not anesthesia, is found.

The fact that afferent fibers are collected into dorsal roots is utilized clinically in spinal anesthesia. The introduction of an anesthetic, such as *procaine,* into the subarachnoid space in the sitting position is followed by anesthesia of the sacral areas, then lumbar, and so forth, depending on the amount of anesthetic injected and the height to which it is allowed to rise. Such anesthetics affect nonmyelinated and small myelinated fibers first. Consequently, the sense of pain disappears first, and that of pressure last. During an operation, therefore, pain may be absent, but pressure sense may still be present.

NERVE COMPONENTS

The fibers contained within a nerve may be classified according to the structures they supply. This has considerably simplified and clarified our concepts of cranial nerves (p. 260). In spinal nerves, four types or components of fibers are present. These are arranged in a manner relating to the position of the embryonic sulcus limitans. It will be recalled that within the neural tube those neuroblasts lying ventral to the sulcus limitans, that is, in the basal plate, become efferent in nature. The dorsally placed afferent fibers, on the other hand, enter the alar plate and synapse with the cells developing there. The same relationship is found in the adult.

Ventral roots contain large myelinated fibers supplying skeletal muscle, and small myelinated fibers to spindle muscle fibers. These are efferent fibers to somatic structures, hence are called *somatic efferent fibers,* and their cells of origin are in the most ventral part of the gray matter. Many ventral roots contain small myelinated fibers destined for visceral structures. These *general visceral efferent* fibers are preganglionic axons of the autonomic system. The reason for using the term "general" is explained later (p. 260). The cells of origin of these fibers are found just ventral to the sulcus limitans.

Dorsal roots contain *general somatic afferent* and *general visceral afferent* fibers, which supply somatic (skin, muscles, and so forth) and visceral structures, respectively.

Spinal nerves, since they are formed by dorsal and ventral roots, contain all four components. This is true of major peripheral nerves, but branches of these vary in composition. Thus a nerve to skin lacks somatic efferent fibers.

In the upper levels of the cervical spinal cord, large motor neurons are found in intermediate as well as in ventral gray matter. The axons of cells in the intermediate gray leave, not by way of spinal roots, but instead emerge laterally and form the spinal portion of the accessory nerve, which ascends through the foramen magnum and joins the medullary portion. These axons comprise a functional component which belongs with the brain stem (p. 260).

PERIPHERAL NERVES

Nearly all major peripheral nerves include fibers from several spinal nerves (p. 37). For example, the femoral nerve in the thigh is derived from the second, third, and fourth lumbar spinal nerves and supplies the skin over the anterior surface of the thigh and the extensor muscles of the leg. The obturator nerve is also derived from the second, third, and fourth lumbar nerves, but it supplies a different skin area and the adductor muscles of the thigh. Thus these lumbar nerves are distributed by way of different peripheral nerves. Furthermore, the fourth lumbar nerve contributes to the sciatic nerve.

When a spinal nerve is severed, therefore, the effects are found in parts of several peripheral nerve areas. A lesion of the second lumbar spinal nerve, for instance, is followed by involvement of part of the femoral and part of the obturator nerve supply. A lesion of a peripheral nerve, however, involves parts of several spinal nerves. These facts are of the utmost clinical value in determining the location of a lesion causing muscle paralyses are anesthesias, or both.

Peripheral nerve lesions are not uncommon in automobile and industrial accidents, as well as in wartime injuries. If a nerve is completely severed, all its fibers distal to the injury degenerate. The muscles supplied by the nerve undergo a sudden, complete, flaccid paralysis. Reflexes as well as sensation are lost. The anesthesia covers an area less than the anatomical distribution because of the overlap from neighboring peripheral nerves. Without proper care the muscles will atrophy before regeneration can occur, and atrophy will inevitably follow if there is no regeneration.

As nerve fibers begin to regenerate, spontaneous pains may occur in the area of distribution of the nerve. This results from an irritation at the growing ends, and the pain is of a projection type. When connections are re-established, the muscles slowly regain their tone, atrophic changes lessen, and the field of sensory impairment gradually narrows and disappears. Pain and temperature return first, partly because small fibers grow faster, and partly because nonmyelinated fibers from neighboring normal areas grow into the denervated skin. The regeneration of the larger peripheral nerves may take a year or two.

A description of a radial nerve injury suffices to illustrate. This nerve supplies the extensors of the forearm, wrist, and proximal phalanges, so that these muscles become paralyzed and a "wrist drop" results. The fingers tend to bend because the flexor muscles are unopposed. Sensory losses are slight because there is a considerable overlap; only a small area on the back of the hand between the thumb and first finger becomes anesthetic. If the cut ends are united, regeneration may occur in a year or less.

SUMMARY

The spinal cord retains, to a certain extent, the segmental character of the neural tube. The gray matter has a basic arrangement which is modified by local changes in character and number of contained neurons. The white matter is arranged in funiculi which are also modified locally. Tracts, such as the lateral spinothalamic, are not anatomically demonstrable in normal material.

In the spinal cord the basic reflexes are coordinated in local and general movement patterns. These, such as stepping or walking, are spinal mechanisms, but cannot function autonomously. Certain higher centers must be present before the spinal cord can function normally.

Transection of the cord in man is followed by spinal shock, with complete flaccid paralysis and loss of sensations. Autonomic functions, such as sweating and evacuation of the urinary bladder, are restricted to local reflexes operating over cord levels.

Spinal nerves contain general somatic afferent and general visceral afferent components, which enter dorsal roots; and somatic efferent and general visceral efferent fibers derived from motor neurons by way of ventral roots. The major peripheral nerves likewise contain these components.

Lesions of spinal and peripheral nerves differ in their effects because (1) a spinal nerve reaches its area of supply through several different peripheral nerves and composes only part of each, and (2) a major peripheral nerve contains parts of several spinal nerves.

REFERENCES

See the references on pages 6 and 319.

Austin, G.: The Spinal Cord. Springfield, Ill., Charles C Thomas, 1961.
Eccles, J. C., and Schadé, J. P., eds.: Organizatión of the Spinal Cord; Physiology of Spinal Neurons. (vols. 11 and 12, Progress in Brain Research). Amsterdam, Elsevier Publishing Company, 1964.
Kuhn, R. A.: Functional capacity of the isolated human spinal cord. Brain, 73:1-51, 1950. (A very thorough study, especially valuable because patients were observed for long periods of time, and cord transections were verified at surgery.)

Chapter 16

THE BRAIN STEM

Some of the morphological characteristics of the brain stem have been discussed previously (p. 8), and others with their functional correlations in chapters on motor and sensory paths. Because of the diversity of functions in these areas, further details must be added.

The brain stem differs from the spinal cord in a number of features. Most of the cranial nerves arise or terminate within the brain stem. The cerebellum forms massive connections throughout the whole region. The reticular formation contains neurons active in both visceral and somatic functions. The various motor and sensory pathways undergo rather marked rearrangements in their passage through the brain stem, to and from the spinal cord. The entire area may be considered a suprasegmental apparatus concerned with special senses, vital processes, and other visceral and somatic functions, all of which may be modified by impulses entering over the cranial nerves and from the cerebellum and forebrain.

GENERAL FEATURES OF THE BRAIN STEM

THE MEDULLA OBLONGATA

The change from spinal cord to medulla oblongata at the level of the foramen magnum is more evident microscopically than grossly. The lower limit of the pyramidal decussation marks the transition. The

256

nucleus gracilis and the nucleus cuneatus soon appear on each side, and above this level the medial lemnisci become more and more prominent (Fig. 135). The bilaterally placed *olivary nuclei*, characterized by their crumpled shape, begin at the approximate level at which the medial lemnisci appear, and extend upward to the pons.

In the dorsal part of the medulla oblongata, on each side of the midline, are the motor nuclei of the hypoglossal nerves. Lateral to each is the dorsal motor nucleus of the vagus. The nuclei of both nerves lie in the floor of the fourth ventricle (Fig. 135).

Dorsolaterally in the medulla oblongata on each side is an isolated

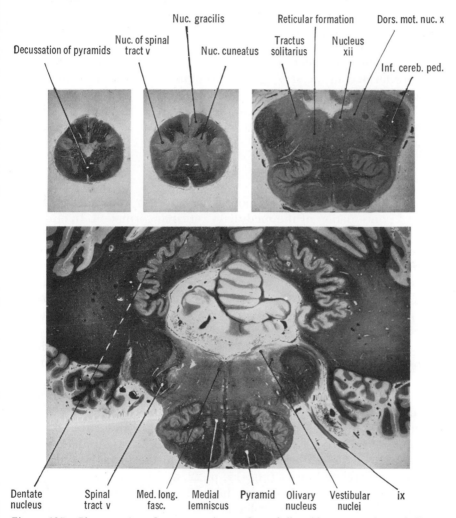

Figure 135. Photographs of cross sections of medulla oblongata and cerebellum. Weigert stain.

bundle of myelinated fibers, the *tractus solitarius*. The spinal tract of the trigeminal nerve lies on each dorsolateral surface of the lower part of the medulla oblongata, while at higher levels it lies ventral to the restiform body.

The reticular formation constitutes a large part of the medulla oblongata. It is a mixture of white and gray matter which contains many types of neurons, as well as myelinated and nonmyelinated fibers (Fig. 17, p. 23, and Fig. 135). Some of the functions of the reticular formation are discussed later (p. 272).

Cells subserving different functions may lie side by side. For example, the vagus, glossopharyngeal, and accessory nerves supply striated muscles by axons derived from large neurons in the medulla oblongata and upper cervical cord. These neurons form a nucleus in the reticular formation, but one in which the cells are so scattered that the nucleus is anything but prominent and is called the *nucleus ambiguus*. Other cells that are located in the same general region are involved in cardiovascular and respiratory mechanisms (p. 268).

The reticular formation near the point of entrance of the eighth nerve is specialized as several nuclei in which the vestibular nerve terminates (Fig. 135).

THE PONS AND MIDBRAIN

The dorsal portion of the pons is structurally and functionally an upward continuation of the medullary reticular formation. In addition, it contains the motor nuclei of the facial, abducent and trigeminal nerves, as well as the sensory nuclei of the trigeminal nerves. As the medial lemnisci enter the pons, they become oriented transversely instead of dorsoventrally, and they thereby separate the ventral from the dorsal pons (Fig. 136). With this rearrangement there appears on each side of the dorsal midline the *medial longitudinal fasciculus*, which can be traced into the midbrain.

The ventral pons contains masses of cells, the pontile nuclei, the axons of which project laterally and form the middle cerebellar peduncles. Corticospinal fibers descend through the pontile nuclei.

At the lower limit of the midbrain the fourth ventricle becomes continuous with the cerebral aqueduct. Dorsal to the aqueduct are the superior and inferior colliculi; ventral to it are the motor nuclei of the oculomotor and trochlear nerves. The red nuclei are landmarks in the upper part of the midbrain; ventral to them are the substantia nigra and the cerebral peduncles (Fig. 15, p. 22, and Fig. 137).

The inferior colliculi receive fibers from the ascending auditory paths. Cells in the inferior colliculi project to motor neurons of the brain stem by way of the *tectobulbar tracts* and to the spinal cord by way of

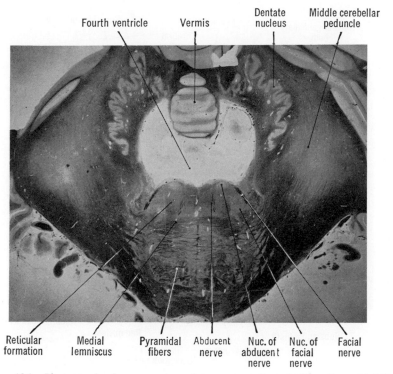

Fourth ventricle   Vermis   Dentate nucleus   Middle cerebellar peduncle

Reticular formation   Medial lemniscus   Pyramidal fibers   Abducent nerve   Nuc. of abducent nerve   Nuc. of facial nerve   Facial nerve

Figure 136. Photograph of cross section of the pons and cerebellum. Pyramidal fibers form small bundles in the ventral part of the pons. Weigert stain.

the *tectospinal tracts.* The term *tectum* refers to the roof of the midbrain; hence the name of any tract arising here carries the prefix *tecto.*

The superior colliculi and the area between them and the thalami receive fibers from the retinae by way of the optic nerves and tracts. These fibers are distinct from those which form the visual path to the cortex. Cells in the superior colliculi also project to the motor neurons of the brain stem and spinal cord by way of tectobulbar and tectospinal tracts.

The various cranial nerves and the upper cervical nerves are frequently coordinated in movement patterns. One of the important pathways in this connection is the bilaterally placed medial longitudinal fasciculus (Fig. 135), an association tract which appears early in the development of the nervous system. Each tract runs from the midbrain to the upper cervical cord and carries ascending and descending fibers which link the various motor nuclei.

The substantia nigra and the red nuclei probably represent specialized portions of the reticular formation. In connections and function they are associated with the basal ganglia of the forebrain, and the red

Lateral geniculate
body
Medial geniculate
body
Thalamus
Pineal body
Cerebral
aqueduct
Superior colliculus
Corpus callosum

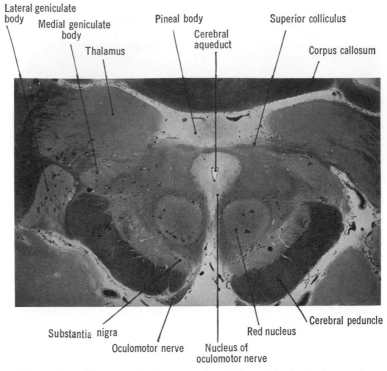

Substantia nigra
Oculomotor nerve
Nucleus of
oculomotor nerve
Red nucleus
Cerebral peduncle

Figure 137.   Photograph of cross section of the midbrain. Weigert stain.

nucleus is also associated with the cerebellum. The substantia nigra is present in man and perhaps in some of the other higher primates also. Its dark appearance is because its constituent cells contain melanin pigment. In lower animals the cells in corresponding regions lack this pigment.

The red nuclei are usually composed of large cells found chiefly in the caudal part, and small cells found chiefly in the rostral part. There is marked species variation in the proportion of large and small cells. Small cells are more numerous in primates and project to the spinal cord indirectly by way of rubroreticular and reticulospinal tracts (Fig. 143, p. 279). In subprimate vertebrates, the large cells tend to project directly to the spinal cord by way of *rubrospinal* tracts. It is likely that in man the rubrospinal tracts are either nonexistent or are functionally unimportant. In all animals, the chief afferent fibers are from the cerebellum by way of the superior cerebellar peduncles.

CRANIAL NERVE COMPONENTS

Some of the differences between cranial and spinal nerves have already been pointed out (p. 39), as have the functional components of the spinal nerves (p. 252). Figure 138 illustrates the fundamental arrangement of cranial nerve components and indicates certain ones not found in spinal nerves. This diagram represents the condition not only in the medulla oblongata, but also in most of the brain stem. For each component the cells of origin or termination form a column which extends longitudinally in the brain stem. If any particular column is interrupted in some levels where certain nerves may not have this component, the cells above and below are nevertheless found in the same positions relative to medial and lateral planes.

What are the reasons for these added components? The questions relating to them have for the most part been answered by studies of amphibian forms, and the available evidence indicates that the arrangement is fundamentally similar in man.

Gills do not develop in the human embryo, but *branchial arches* do, and occur in the neck region. The muscles derived from and associated with the arches are, therefore, said to be *branchiomeric*. The muscles of mastication arise from the first arches and are innervated by fibers from the motor nuclei of the trigeminal nerves. The facial muscles arise from the second arch and are supplied by the facial nerves. The muscles of the pharynx and larynx arise from the third, fourth, and fifth arches. They are supplied by the glossopharyngeal, vagus, and medullary portions of the accessory nerves; all of the nerve fibers concerned arise from cells in the columns formed by the nuclei ambigui. The spinal divisions of the accessory nerves supply those parts of the sternocleidomastoid and trapezius muscles which appear to be derived from branchial arches. Although the branchiomeric muscles are striated,

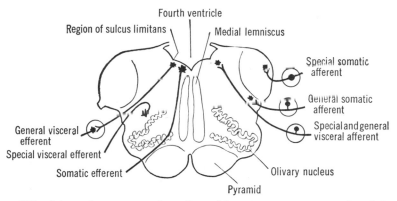

Figure 138. Schematic representation of cranial nerve components as found in the medulla oblongata. Afferent fibers are shown on the right, and efferent on the left. Also indicated are the approximate locations of the cells of origin and termination for the various components.

many are functionally associated with the respiratory and alimentary systems and others function in vocalization. Because of their association with visceral activities, the nerves supplying them have been designated *special visceral efferents.*

Taste is a special sense associated with visceral functions, and taste

Table 3.   Components of Cranial Nerves

CRANIAL NERVE	COMPONENT	FUNCTION
Olfactory	Special visceral afferent (Sometimes classified as special somatic afferent)	Smell
Optic	Special somatic afferent	Vision
Oculomotor	Somatic efferent	Movements of eyeball
	General somatic afferent	Proprioception from extrinsic eye muscles
	General visceral efferent (parasympathetic)	Accommodation and pupillary constriction
Trochlear	Somatic efferent	Movements of eyeball
	General somatic afferent	Proprioception from extrinsic eye muscle
Trigeminal	Special visceral efferent	Movements of mastication
	General somatic afferent	General sensations from face and head
Abducent	Somatic efferent	Movement of eyeball
	General somatic afferent	Proprioception from extrinsic eye muscle
Facial	Special visceral efferent	Facial expressions
	General visceral efferent (parasympathetic)	Salivation and lacrimation
	Special visceral afferent	Taste
Vestibulocochlear (or eighth nerve)	Special somatic afferent	Hearing and equilibrium
Glossopharyngeal	Special visceral efferent	Pharyngeal movements
	General visceral efferent (parasympathetic)	Salivation
	Special visceral afferent	Taste
	General visceral afferent	Visceral reflexes; sensation in tongue and pharynx
	General somatic afferent	Sensation from external ear
Vagus	Special visceral efferent	Pharyngeal and laryngeal movements
	General visceral efferent (parasympathetic)	Movements and secretion of thoracic and abdominal viscera
	Special visceral afferent	Taste
	General visceral afferent	Visceral reflexes; sensation in tongue and pharynx
	General somatic afferent	Sensation from external ear
Accessory	Special visceral efferent	Movements of pharynx, larynx, head, and shoulders
	General visceral efferent (parasympathetic)	Same as vagus
Hypoglossal	Somatic efferent	Movements of tongue

fibers are called *special visceral afferents.* The fibers travel centrally over the facial, glossopharyngeal, and vagus nerves and enter the tractus solitarius in the medulla oblongata. *General visceral afferent* fibers from abdominal and thoracic viscera and from the pharynx and larynx also enter this tract. These fibers convey impulses aroused by hunger, thirst, distention, changes in blood pressure, and so forth.

The *special somatic afferent* component refers to other special senses. The fibers in the vestibulocochlear and optic nerves are in this category.

Table 3 tabulates the cranial nerves according to their functional components.

MOTOR FUNCTIONS OF THE BRAIN STEM

The brain stem in Ambystoma, even in the adult, is the chief area that controls muscular activity. It acts in conjunction with the spinal cord, and its functions are modified by afferent impulses from the spinal cord, the inner ear, and the cerebellum. This type of arrangement is present in all vertebrates. In higher vertebrates, however, the brain stem is controlled by the basal ganglia and the cerebral cortex.

From work on the cat and other higher animals, as well as on Ambystoma and other lower forms, it has been shown that the brain stem cells concerned in the control of muscular activity are scattered throughout the reticular formation, particularly in the medulla oblongata and pons. Some of the cells, located chiefly in the medulla oblongata, constitute an inhibitory mechanism to extensor or antigravity muscles; when these cells discharge, they inhibit the motor neurons which supply the muscles. At the same time, they facilitate or excite the antagonistic muscles, that is, the flexors. If, for example, one stimulates this region of the brain stem while knee jerks are being elicited, one finds that the contraction of the leg extensor either decreases in amplitude or else stops, whereas the opposing flexor muscles are activated. Other regions of the nervous system, such as the cerebral cortex, may inhibit activity by causing the inhibitory brain stem mechanisms to act, or may increase activity by preventing the inhibitory brain stem level from discharging.

Other cells in the reticular formation, which are located more laterally and which are found in the midbrain and pons as well as in the medulla oblongata, constitute an excitatory mechanism to extensor or antigravity muscles; when these cells discharge, they facilitate or excite the motor neurons which supply the muscles. At the same time, they inhibit the antagonistic muscles, that is, the flexors. As in the case of the inhibitory mechanisms, other regions of the nervous system may either activate or block the excitatory system.

In lower forms, such as fishes, one of the principal mechanisms modifying brain stem functions is the inner ear. Impulses resulting from changes in position of the head reach the brain stem over the vestibular nerve. The fibers of this nerve terminate in the vestibular nuclei, which are specialized portions of the reticular formation. One of these nuclei, the lateral, gives rise to the vestibulospinal tract, which descends with the excitatory reticulospinal tract, mainly in the ventral part of the spinal cord. Functionally, this lateral vestibular nucleus and its tract are part of the excitatory mechanism of the brain stem. The other vestibular nuclei project to various cranial nerve nuclei. In higher animals, this basic arrangement is present, and in man, both vestibulospinal and reticulospinal tracts are to be found. One may consider therefore that in man, the extrapyramidal system mediates its effects upon the spinal cord by discharging through the reticular formation of the brain stem. Some of these effects result from the influence of descending impulses upon interneurons in the dorsal gray matter, others because of influence upon interneurons and motor cells in the ventral gray matter.

A number of brain stem functions concerned with posture and movement are carried out reflexly. For example, one can demonstrate some of these in a subject who is sitting in a chair which is being rotated. The rotation stimulates semicircular canals according to the manner discussed previously (p. 215). With the proper optical system, it can be seen that, when rotation begins, the eyes exhibit certain rhythmic movements called *nystagmus*. Nystagmus represents a reflex attempt to fix the eyes during movement. When the rotation reaches a steady state, the nystagmus stops. But when rotation stops, the nystagmus reappears and persists for 15 to 20 seconds or more. This is a reflex result of post-rotational pressure in the semicircular canals. One may see nystagmus in people in an elevator, or in people in a train watching telegraph poles.

Many other types of brain stem reflexes can also be demonstrated in normal subjects. Examples are the jaw jerk (reflex contraction of jaw-closing muscles in response to sudden stretch); the corneal reflex (blinking when a cornea is touched); blinking in response to objects appearing suddenly in the visual fields; and sudden muscular responses to noise.

Various types of reflexes can be studied in an animal in which the brain stem has been isolated from higher centers. It was pointed out previously (p. 247) that, after spinal cord transection in higher animals, the reflex extensor activity decreases. A different picture is presented, however, if the brain stem is transected at the level of the midbrain, thereby producing a *decerebrate animal*. In such an animal, the brain stem is superimposed on the spinal cord and can influence or modify its functions. Most of the cranial nerves and many of the cerebellar connections are still intact. A decerebrate cat exhibits strong, maintained contractions in extensor muscles, so much so that, if placed upright with the proper support, the limbs can support the body weight. The animal cannot, however, carry out any locomotor activity. If pushed over, it falls and cannot right itself. It must be fed and, since temperature control is lacking, it must be kept warm. Blood pressure is reflexly maintained, and respiration is slow and deep.

Why does a decerebrate animal differ from a spinal animal? Certainly the inhibitory and excitatory mechanisms of the brain stem have been added, but why should certain postural features predominate? A concept rather generally held today postulates that the brain stem mechanisms which activate extensor muscles exhibit autonomous activity when connections with higher centers are lost. In other words, the cells in the excitatory centers maintain a repetitive discharge to the spinal cord, whereas the cells in the center which inhibits extensor activity are silent, and are activated only when impulses from the proper sources reach them. In a decerebrate animal, then, impulses continually reach the motor cells supplying antigravity muscles, either stimulating them or so facilitating them as to make them more susceptible to afferent impulses from muscles. Impulses also reach the motor cells giving rise to gamma efferents. These impulses cause the spindle discharge rate to increase, thereby accentuating reflexes. The gamma system appears to be more easily influenced by impulses from the brain stem than are the large motor cells. Finally, the interneurons involved in reflexes may be influenced by descending impulses.

Decerebrate rigidity can be abolished or greatly diminished by cutting dorsal roots or the descending motor tracts. Inhibition of muscular activity can also be carried out in a coordinated manner by the spinal cord (p. 248). If, after decerebration, the spinal cord is transected in the thoracic region, the stretch reflexes and the rigidity of the forelimb become even more marked. Evidently the lumbar portion of the cord had been inhibiting motor cells of the cervical region.

Decerebrate rigidity is not often seen in man. When it does occur, it resembles in many respects the situation seen in lower animals. Less severe motor disorders are common, however, and certain aspects of them are similar to decerebrate rigidity. For example, it was pointed out (p. 168) that in an upper motor neuron lesion, exaggerated deep reflexes and spasticity were characteristic findings. If the causative lesion is in the internal capsule, the result is akin to decerebration in that some of the connections between higher centers and the brain stem are cut so that the excitatory mechanisms become autonomous and the inhibitory ones relatively inactive. The spasticity which is seen is therefore similar to rigidity. Spasticity will also result from a spinal cord lesion when such a lesion destroys the inhibitory paths in the lateral funiculi, leaving only the excitatory ones intact.

The predominance of extensor tone in a decerebrate cat makes fluidity of motion and walking impossible. These depend upon intact higher centers. Certain types of reflex responses can, however, be demonstrated in a decerebrate animal, including many of those demonstrable in normal animals. The reflexes are mainly of a static nature. Phasic types of reflexes are either not easily demonstrable in a decerebrate animal or else are fleeting in duration.

STATIC REFLEXES IN DECEREBRATE RIGIDITY

Local. If a limb of a decerebrate animal touches the ground, it stiffens enough to offer support. The intrinsic mechanisms are stretch reflexes operating locally, initiated by stretch of antigravity muscles and pressure upon the foot. The local reaction may be illustrated in a somewhat different manner. If the animal is supported off the ground and the foot is touched, or slightly pressed, the limb extends. The extension continues as the finger is slowly drawn away, the foot appearing to follow the finger like a magnet. This is the *positive supporting reaction.*

Segmental and Intersegmental. The classic example of the segmental reaction is the crossed extensor reflex (p. 248). This is obtained in a spinal as well as in a decerebrate cat. It may be accompanied by extension of the opposite forelimb, so that there is an intersegmental reaction forming a pattern resembling a phase of locomotion.

General. This includes the reactions to changes in position of the head and neck. These are (1) the tonic neck reflexes and (2) tonic labyrinthine reflexes.

Tonic neck reflexes are best demonstrated after the labyrinths are destroyed. If the head is turned to one side, the limbs on that side increase in extensor tone, thus providing a mechanism for supporting the body on the side to which the cat is looking. The reaction depends upon proprioceptive impulses from the neck muscles being stretched, and from joints between the cervical vertebrae. Long propriospinal fibers conduct the impulses to the ipsilateral motor neurons.

Tonic labyrinthine reflexes are best shown after the cervical dorsal roots are cut so as to eliminate tonic neck reflexes. Changes in the position of the head are again followed by maintained reactions. If the cat is placed on its back with the head somewhat elevated, a maximal tone appears in the limbs, which become fully extended. In intermediate head positions, the tone is less than maximal. In this particular plane the maculae utriculi are maximally stimulated by the effects of gravity. Impulses reach the vestibular areas and thence the motor neurons of the spinal cord. Although these are static and not acceleratory phenomena, there is considerable evidence that the semicircular canals subserve some functions in this matter. If the maculae are destroyed, tonic labyrinthine reflexes may yet be demonstrated. This leads to the concept that acceleratory reactions are predominantly but not entirely vested in the canals, and static reactions predominantly but not exclusively in maculae utriculi. Since extensor tone is maintained as long as the head occupies a position under these conditions, Magnus (p. 273) has termed these responses *attitudinal reflexes*. Under most circumstances the tonic neck and labyrinthine reflexes operate together, producing coordinated reactions.

FUNCTIONS OF THE MIDBRAIN

The midbrain is a complex region having many incompletely understood functions. The superior collicular area, for example, is the main visual area in lower animals, and in birds it overshadows the rest of the brain stem. But in mammals the process of cephalization becomes more and more evident, and in primates the occipital lobes carry out nearly all the visual functions. The superior colliculi are mainly centers for visual reflexes which are possible by means of the connections mentioned previously (p. 259). An example of a common type of reflex is blinking in response to an object that appears suddenly in the visual fields. More generalized muscular responses may also occur in response to such a stimulus. Pupillary constriction in response to light shining on the eyes is another example of a visual reflex, although, strictly speaking, this is carried out by the region between the colliculi and the thalami. The colliculi, together with centers in the pons, may under certain circumstances carry out reflex conjugate movements of the eyes even when voluntary pathways for such movements have been destroyed. The colliculi themselves appear to be particularly concerned in vertical conjugate movements. It should also be mentioned that careful studies indicate the possibility that the superior colliculi may have visual functions after removal of the striate (visual) cortex.

The inferior colliculi are centers for auditory reflexes. Thus a sudden noise may be followed by turning the eyes, the head, or the body to the sound, or by a general startle reaction. These responses ordinarily depend upon impulses reaching the interior colliculi by paths mentioned previously (p. 258).

Certain midbrain structures are functionally closely associated with the basal ganglia (see Chapter 18). These are the substantia nigra, the red nuclei, and probably certain tegmental nuclei as well. These structures, although relatively intact in a decerebrate animal, function mainly when their connections with higher centers are intact and are concerned in various phases of muscular activity. The red nuclei in addition are closely associated with the cerebellum.

AUTONOMIC FUNCTIONS OF THE BRAIN STEM

Many of the cells in the reticular formation are concerned with autonomic activities. These cells are smaller than somatic motor neurons, but, like them, are scattered throughout the pons and medulla, so that cells subserving somatic and autonomic functions may lie side by side. The autonomic cells receive projections from the hypothalamus and in turn project to various cranial nerve nuclei and to the spinal cord.

Some of the cells are concerned in relatively simple mechanisms. For instance, certain ones scattered in the upper medulla and lower pons *(salivatory nuclei)* project as parasympathetic fibers to salivary glands by way of the facial and glossopharyngeal nerves. These fibers mediate excitation, and, therefore, control secretory processes in these glands. The cells may be reflexly activated by impulses resulting from taste or smell, or psychically by impulses from the cerebral cortex. The psychic influence is usually inhibitory, as, for example, dryness of the mouth in many emotional states. The salivatory system was extensively used by Pavlov (p. 274) in his studies of conditioned responses.

Many of the autonomic cells function in more complex, integrated activities. Some of these, such as the control of blood pressure, were discussed previously (p. 238). Others are as follows:

CONTROL OF RESPIRATION

Although the muscles of respiration are skeletal in type, the respiratory process itself is reflexly controlled. No one can voluntarily hold his breath to the point of asphyxiation. The following brief account of respiratory mechanisms is based mainly upon the cat, but there is reason to suppose that similar mechanisms occur in man.

Scattered throughout the reticular formation, dorsal to the olivary nuclei, are small neurons which project to the spinal cord. Here they synapse with those motor neurons in the cervical part of the spinal cord which give rise to the phrenic nerves which supply the diaphragm. They also reach those cells in the thoracic part of the spinal cord which supply the intercostal and abdominal musculature.

If the cells in the medulla oblongata are stimulated with electric currents, two different functions can be demonstrated. More caudally placed stimuli are followed by an inspiration which is maintained for the duration of the stimulus. Since transection of the upper cervical cord prevents this, these cells apparently control the spinal supply of respiratory muscles. Collectively they form the bilateral *inspiratory centers.*

More cephalically placed stimuli cause an expiratory act, and the cells mediating this activity form *expiratory centers* which project to the same regions of the cord.

Inspiration is a fundamentally more important act than expiration, since, in the latter case, the intrinsic elasticity of the lungs is more significant than muscular action. This dominance is reflected in the medullary centers. If these are isolated from all afferent impulses, the inspiratory centers discharge continuously and the animal dies in a state of prolonged inspiration. Normal respiration is reflexly controlled by modifying the intrinsic activity of these centers.

Within the lungs are interoceptive receptors which are sensitive to the stretch resulting from the expansion of the lungs during inspiration. The nerve impulses which traverse the vagi increase in frequency as the expansion, and thereby the stimulus intensity, increases. The fibers carrying the impulses are of the general visceral afferent type. They enter the tractus solitarius of the medulla oblongata and are then relayed to the respiratory centers (Fig. 139). When the impulses reach a certain

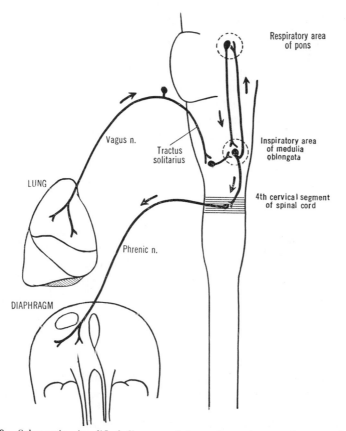

Figure 139. Schematic, simplified diagram of the pathways in a respiratory reflex. The terminals in the lung are stimulated by expansion during inspiration. See text for description.

frequency, they inhibit the inspiratory and stimulate the expiratory centers. The most important result is the lessening of discharges from the former center. Inspiration, therefore, lessens and stops; expiration supervenes. The stimulation of lung receptors naturally decreases in intensity. Below a certain frequency the inhibition of inspiratory centers lessens, and they again resume activity.

If the vagi are cut, however, so as to prevent the entrance of vagal impulses, respiration slows and deepens, but does not stop. It stops only when the brain stem is transected just above the centers. In the pons there is a bilaterally placed respiratory center which receives fibers from the medullary centers and in turn projects to them. These pontile centers, upon receipt of impulses at or above a certain frequency, discharge to and inhibit the inspiratory centers. Expiration thus intervenes. Either vagal impulses or pontile centers can produce fairly normal respiration, but, if both are absent, the animal dies in prolonged inspiration.

That the cervical cord is unable to maintain respiration automatically is shown as follows: If the cord is severed just below the fourth or fifth cervical segment, respiration continues because the control of the diaphragm is intact. But if the transection is above this level, the fibers descending from the medulla oblongata are severed. Death rapidly follows because of the asphyxia resulting from failure of respiration. This explains why transections of the cord high in the cervical levels are rapidly fatal in man. It also explains why medullary lesions may be fatal if they involve much of the reticular formation.

The respiratory centers receive impulses from higher centers, so that their activity may be considerably modified, either voluntarily or in emotional states, but in neither case can reflex functions be completely suppressed.

The respiratory centers are directly sensitive to gaseous tensions in the blood flowing through them. Thus an increase in carbon dioxide in the lungs is followed by an increase of carbon dioxide in the blood and, consequently, by an increase in the rate and depth of breathing. This blows off the excess carbon dioxide which had raised the blood level of this gas.

At the bifurcation of each common carotid artery is a small tissue mass, the carotid body, containing receptors which are likewise sensitive to changes in gaseous tensions of the blood flowing by them. The impulses traverse the glossopharyngeal nerves to the respiratory centers and result in reflex mechanisms similar to those cited in the preceding paragraph.

Respiration illustrates a coordination of somatic and visceral systems, a coordination of a type which may be carried out progressively and consecutively, from one organ to another, as described next in connection with the alimentary canal.

CONTROL OF MOVEMENTS IN THE ALIMENTARY CANAL

When food enters the mouth and is tasted and smelled, or even before it enters the mouth, saliva reflexly flows into the oral cavity. Its contained enzymes begin the digestion of certain constituents of the food.

Swallowing initiates other types of reflexes. The first part of swallowing is the voluntary thrusting of food into the oral pharynx by the tongue. The impact of the food upon the walls of the pharynx stimulates receptors in the walls. The nerve impulses reach the medulla oblongata over the vagus and glossopharyngeal nerves, and are distributed to special visceral efferent cells in the motor nuclei of these nerves. There is set into play a complex series of involuntary actions involving the branchiomeric muscles. The palate and upper part of the pharynx constrict so as to prevent food from entering the nasal cavity. The upper part of the larynx constricts so as to shut off the air passages to the lungs. The muscles just around the bolus of food contract, while those just ahead of it relax so as to receive it. The wave of contraction, preceded by a wave of relaxation, proceeds from the pharynx into the esophagus and thence to the stomach. The timing of this mechanism is even more intricate when one realizes that initially the activity involves striated muscle, but that in the middle of the esophagus the musculature becomes of the smooth type. Hence the impulses shift from the special visceral efferents of these nerves to the general visceral efferents of the vagus nerves (from the dorsal motor nuclei). Furthermore, sympathetic fibers are involved, because inhibition of the muscles, as evidenced by the wave of relaxation, is a function of the sympathetic system. Impulses descend from the medulla oblongata to the thoracic cord, then out to the sympathetic ganglia and eventually to the esophagus. This type of activity, in which there is a wave of relaxation preceding a wave of contraction, is known as *peristalsis,* and is one of the fundamental types of coordinated activity of the intestinal tract. The complexity of events is even more pronounced when one considers that secretory phenomena accompany intestinal movements, and in this the dorsal motor nuclei of the vagus nerves are important factors.

Gastrointestinal movements may be reversed in vomiting. This is accompanied by simultaneous contraction of the external abdominal muscles and descent of the diaphragm, thereby increasing the intra-abdominal pressure and forcing intestinal contents out orally. Whether or not vomiting results from activity of a special center is unknown. It may be reflexly induced by impulses resulting from irritation of gastric mucosa, from putrid odors, and so forth. There is a drug, *apomorphine,* which apparently acts directly on brain stem cells so that its administration induces vomiting. Likewise, increased intracranial pressure stimulates these cells so that otherwise unexplained vomiting is an important sign of such an increase.

RETICULAR FORMATION

A brief description of the reticular formation is appropriate here, and will serve to summarize the functions which have already been discussed. The reticular formation consists of nerve cells scattered throughout the brain stem. Some of the cells form well-defined nuclei. The formation receives impulses from the spinal cord, the cerebellum, and the cerebral hemispheres, and it sends impulses to these structures.

The cells of the reticular formation, which are concerned with the motor and autonomic functions already described, carry out their functions by way of pathways to the spinal cord.

Many cells of the reticular formation, however, project to higher centers. These cells receive collaterals from the ascending sensory pathways and, in turn, relay to the cerebral cortex by way of a diffuse system of relays through subcortical centers. Stimulation of these particular cells in unanesthetized animals leads to an arousal reaction, that is, a sleeping animal wakes. This arousal reaction is accompanied by a flattening of the waves in the electroencephalogram (p. 297). Thus, it appears that these cells play an important role in wakefulness, conscious states, and attention; they form what has been termed the *reticular activating system*. This system seems to be more easily affected by general anesthetics than are the long sensory pathways, and it has been postulated that one of the reasons for an anesthetic state is a depression of the reticular activating system.

Destruction of midbrain reticular formation can produce enduring loss of consciousness. Similar conditions have been reported for man. Otherwise, there is as yet little direct evidence regarding the reticular activating system in man.

What is also of importance, however, is the converse of wakefulness, namely sleep.

Sleep.   There is as yet no good definition of sleep, one that covers the marked species and individual variations, and indicates the causes. In spite of voluminous studies, the mechanisms of sleep are still poorly understood. There is increasing evidence that it is an active, that is, induced, process involving the cerebral cortex, limbic system, and brain stem, and depending upon sleep-inducing structures in the brain stem. There is also increasing evidence that the brain contains sleep-inducing substances.

Sleep is characterized by phase (the number and kind vary according to species), and by a variety of motor and behavioral activities. In general, light sleep with slow brain waves is followed by deep sleep with faster cortical activity. Furthermore, animals, including man, have periods of fidgeting. In man, these active periods of sleep are accompanied by rapid eye movements under closed eyelids and are associated with dreams and fairly characteristic brain wave patterns.

SUMMARY

The spinal cord becomes the medulla oblongata at the foramen magnum. Above this point the major tracts are topographically rearranged, and nuclei of cranial nerves appear. Functional components found in spinal nerves are also found in cranial nerves. In addition, there are others: special visceral efferent supplying branchiomeric muscles; special visceral afferent or taste; and special somatic afferent, including hearing, balance, and vision.

The reticular formation, including the vestibular nuclei, contains motor neurons, some of which are excitatory in function and others inhibitory. A decerebrate animal is one in which the brain stem is sectioned between the basal ganglia and the reticular formation. The excitatory mechanisms become active, the inhibitory mechanisms relatively silent, and the result is an increased, exaggerated postural activity termed decerebrate rigidity. The reticular formation mechanisms are modified by impulses from the labyrinths, the paleocerebellum, the midbrain and the cerebral hemispheres.

Many cells in the reticular formation of the brain stem subserve visceral functions. The most important of these are the control of blood pressure, cardiac activity, respiration, and alimentary movements. Still others project indirectly to the cerebral cortex and constitute the reticular activating system, which is concerned with consciousness and attention.

Within the midbrain there are also areas concerned in auditory and visual reflexes. The inferior colliculi subserve auditory reflexes, the superior, optic reflexes.

Names in Neurology

RUDOLPH MAGNUS (1873-1927)

For many years Magnus was Professor of Pharmacology at Utrecht. In 1908, shortly after a winter spent at Liverpool with Sherrington, he began the first of a series of investigations of postural mechanisms. In 1924 he published a classic monograph on animal posture in which he clearly described reactions in three dimensions.

IVAN PETROVICH PAVLOV (1849-1936)

Pavlov, a Russian physiologist, was director of the Institute for Experimental Medicine in Petrograd. He devised an operative procedure for gastric and pancreatic fistulas which left the nerve supply intact. In such animals, if the esophagus is severed, gastric reactions with and without food can be studied. Later he devised a fistula for salivary ducts and over many years carried out his famous experiments on conditioned responses. In 1904 he was awarded the Nobel Prize.

REFERENCES

See the references cited on pages 6 and 319.

The following are advanced reviews, monographs, or symposia, wth excellent bibliographies. Some are cited for their historical interest.

Adrian, F. D., Bremer, F., and Jasper, H. H., in Delafresnaye, J. F., ed.: Brain Mechanisms and Consciousness. Springfield, Ill., Charles C Thomas, 1954.
Bender, M. B.: The Oculomotor System. New York, Harper and Row, 1964.
Jouvet, M.: The states of sleep. Sci. Amer., *216*:62-72, 1967.
Jouvet, M.: Neurophysiology of the state of sleep. Physiol. Rev., *47*:117-177, 1967.
Kleitman, N.: Sleep and Wakefulness. Revised and enlarged edition, Chicago, University of Chicago Press, 1963.
Magoun, H. W.: Caudal and cephalic influences of the brain stem reticular formation. Physiol. Rev., *30*:459-474, 1950.
Magoun, H. W., and Rhines, R.: Spasticity: The Stretch Reflex and Extrapyramidal Systems. Springfield, Ill., Charles C Thomas, 1947.

CHAPTER 17

THE CEREBELLUM

The cerebellum is attached to the brain stem by the superior, middle, and inferior cerebellar peduncles on each side (p. 18). It is grossly divisible into two hemispheres and a midline connecting portion, the *vermis*. Fissures of varying depths subdivide the hemispheres and vermis. The cerebellum is connected with the spinal cord and cerebral hemispheres as well as the brain stem, and on the basis of these connections there has been devised a more functional subdivision, as follows: A small portion of the cerebellum, shown in Figure 140, is the *archi-*

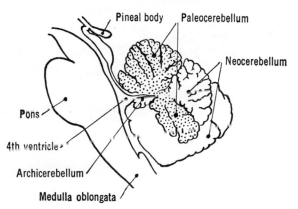

Figure 140. Outline sketch of a median section of the brain stem and cerebellum, after Figure 11 (p. 19). The neocerebellum, which forms the bulk of this organ, is only partially visible in this view (see Figure 6, p. 14).

275

cerebellum, which is closely associated with the vestibular nerve. Although a corresponding part is present and may be prominent in lower animals, the archicerebellum in man is relatively unimportant. Most of the vermis and certain parts of the cerebellar hemispheres form the *paleocerebellum*, which is present in vertebrates with limbs. The bulk of the cerebellum is the *neocerebellum*, so called because it is present and best developed in animals high in the evolutionary scale; it is most prominent

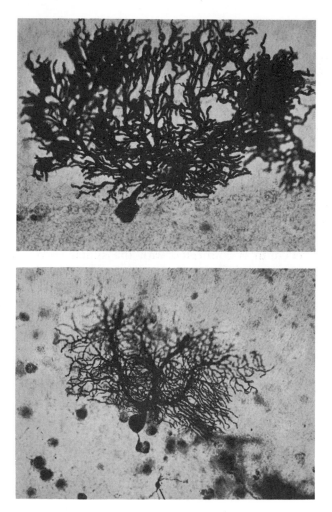

Granule cell

Figure 141. Photomicrographs of Purkinje cells, Golgi stain. In the lower photograph a thin axon is seen extending downward from the cell body. This cell is incompletely impregnated. Hence the larger dendrites are less obscured than in the upper cell.

in primates. These three subdivisions are rather arbitrary, but as an organization or basis for discussion they are useful.

The cerebellum, like the cerebral hemispheres, has a cortex of gray matter and an interior of both white and gray matter. The cortex has an inner or *granular layer* composed of many small neuroglial and nerve cells, a middle layer composed of a single row of large neurons called *Purkinje cells* (Fig. 141), and an outer or *molecular layer* consisting mainly of nerve cell processes, plus scattered nerve cells (Fig. 142).

The gray matter in the interior of each half of the cerebellum is composed of several nuclear masses, chief among which are the dentate nucleus and nucleus fastigius. The fastigial nuclei and several smaller ones form the so-called roof nuclei in the roof of the fourth ventricle.

The nerve fibers going to and from the cerebellum form the peduncles. The entering (afferent) fibers reach the cortex and end as

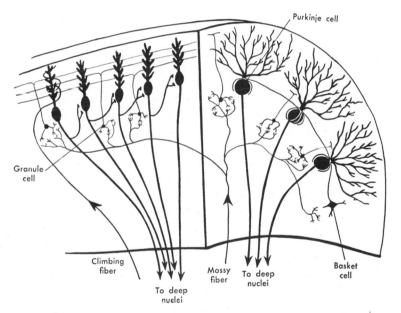

Figure 142. Diagram of cells in a folium of the cerebellum. The Purkinje cells have a very large dendritic tree across the plane of the follum, hence in this view are much more extensive than in the plane parallel to the length of the folium. Mossy fibers synapse with many granule cells, and these in turn with many Purkinje cells. The axons of granule cells enter the molecular layer and divide, each branch running lengthwise in the folium as a "parallel" fiber. These serve as afferents for and activate basket cells. Climbing fibers synapse directly with Purkinje cells. Axons of Purkinje cells have recurrent branches to adjacent Purkinje cells. The molecular layer contains granule cell axons, Purkinje cell dendrites, and basket cells. The axons of the basket cells link Purkinje cells. Thus the entire arrangement is such that a few afferent fibers can activate a wide extent of cerebellar cortex.

follows: Some fibers (mossy fibers) synapse with granule cells, whereas others (climbing fibers) end on dendrites of Purkinje fibers. The cerebellar cortex is organized for *avalanche conduction*, that is, widespread discharge following relatively limited afferent input (Fig. 142). The reasons are (1) a mossy fiber connects with many granule cells, and (2) a granule cell connects with many Purkinje and other cells. Basket cells in the molecular layer also provide for widespread connections through their afferents from parallel fibers and their efferents to Purkinje cells.

Purkinje cells are now known to be inhibitory. Also, their axons have recurrent collaterals which end on other Purkinje cells, and on basket cells and others termed Golgi cells (not shown in Fig. 142). These two types of cells are also inhibitory. Hence, their inhibition by Purkinje cells constitutes a double negative. The axons of Purkinje cells project chiefly to the deep cerebellar nuclei, which they inhibit. The axons of cells in these nuclei leave the cerebellum by way of the peduncles.

CONNECTIONS WITH THE CEREBRAL CORTEX

The cerebral cortex is closely connected with the cerebellum, particularly with that part known as the neocerebellum, although the latter has, in addition, many connections in the brain stem. The corticocerebellar connections are in the nature of a circular or closed route, in that impulses which leave the cerebral cortex may ultimately return by way of the cerebellum (Fig. 143). Fibers destined for the cerebellum arise mainly from motor and sensory areas and descend in the internal capsule to the pons. Some are specifically concerned with the cerebellum and end in the pons. Others are major tracts, such as corticospinal, and the fibers give off collaterals as they descend through the pons. The direct fibers and collaterals synapse with nerve cells scattered throughout the ventral part of the pons. The axons of these cells cross the midline and collect to form the middle cerebellar peduncle (brachium pontis). Since the cerebral cortex and neocerebellum are relatively large in man, the ventral portion of the pons is correspondingly well developed. The fibers in the peduncles radiate to the cortex of the cerebellar hemispheres. Impulses leaving the cortex do so over axons of Purkinje cells, which conduct them to the dentate nuclei. Axons from the cells in these nuclei then ascend as the superior cerebellar peduncle, most of the fibers crossing the midline on reaching the mesencephalon. Some of the fibers ascend to the thalamus, which then relays impulses back to the cerebral cortex. Other fibers end in the red nucleus, which relays impulses to the brain stem and spinal cord.

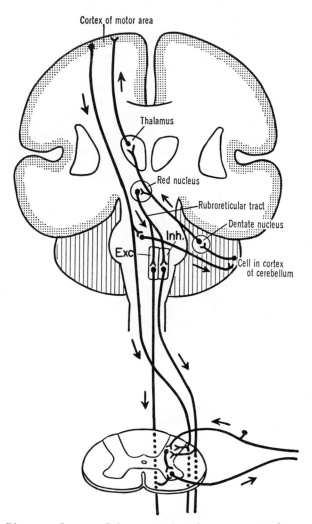

Figure 143. Diagram of some of the connections between cerebral cortex and cerebellum. Corticospinal fibers are represented as giving off collaterals in the pons. The cells with which they synapse give rise to the brachium pontis. The path ascending from the dentate nucleus is the superior cerebellar peduncle. In man, impulses from the red nucleus reach the spinal cord only by way of relays at brain stem levels.

CONNECTIONS WITH THE SPINAL CORD

The cerebellum has long been regarded as a "head ganglion" or "proprioceptive organ" because it was thought that impulses reaching it from the spinal cord originated in neuromuscular spindles. It is now known that impulses from skin, periosteum, joints and ligaments, as well as muscles and tendons, reach the cerebellum, and tactile projections are the most prominent. The impulses that enter the spinal cord ascend chiefly by *anterior* and *posterior spinocerebellar tracts* (Fig. 134, p. 246) that enter the cerebellum by the inferior cerebellar peduncle, and to a lesser extent by passing over the superior cerebellar peduncle. There are other ascending tracts that relay in the brain stem before reaching the cerebellum (Fig. 144). The various tracts are distributed

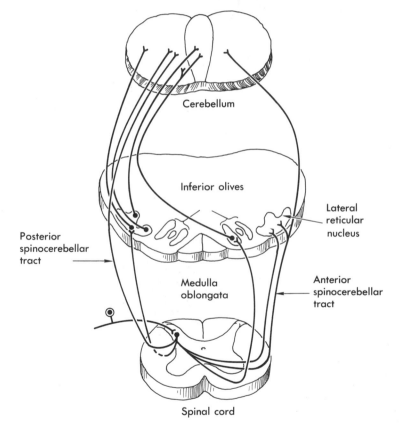

Figure 144. Schematic representation of a variety of pathways from the spinal cord to the cerebellum (anterior and posterior spinocerebellar tracts), including relays through the inferior olive and the lateral reticular nucleus. (Modified from Gardner, E.: Ciba Foundation Symposium on Myotatic, Kinesthetic and Vestibular Mechanisms. London, J. and A. Churchill Ltd., 1967.)

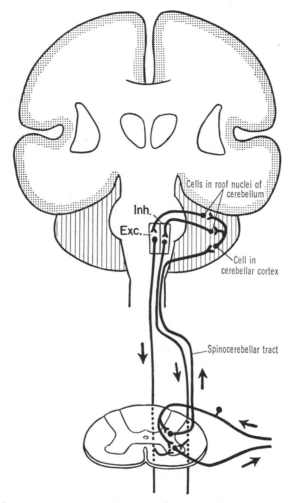

Figure 145. Connections of the cerebellum and spinal cord showing possible connections to descending paths.

mainly to the paleocerebellum. Axons of Purkinje cells then project to roof nuclei, and these in turn to the reticular formation of the brain stem. Accordingly, the functions of this part of the cerebellum are directed back to the spinal cord (Fig. 145).

CONNECTIONS WITH BRAIN STEM AND CRANIAL NERVES

That portion of the cerebellum known as the archicerebellum receives fibers from the vestibular nerve directly and also from vestibular

nuclei. Its efferent fibers reach the vestibular nuclei and reticular formation.

Fibers from other cranial nerves, such as the trigeminal, also reach
the cerebellum. These fibers are probably similar to those coming from
the spinal cord in that they carry impulses originating in various peripheral receptors. The cerebellum also receives impulses from tracts
carrying other special senses, such as hearing and vision.

The cerebellum is connected with other brain stem structures.
Figure 135 (p. 257) illustrates the striking similarity of the dentate
nuclei and the olivary nuclei. The latter are like the dentate nuclei and
neocerebellum in that they are relatively larger in man. The olivary
nuclei project to the cerebellar cortex by way of the inferior cerebellar
peduncles, probably mainly to the neocerebellum.

LOCALIZATION IN THE CEREBELLUM

There have been numerous attempts to correlate cerebellar and
body areas to determine, for instance, whether this or that part of the
cerebellum is concerned with the upper limb, and another part with
the lower limb. These efforts have been somewhat successful in lower
animals, but in man the only localization known with any certainty is
that relating a hemisphere to the same side of the body, and that the
arm is represented in the cerebellum to a greater extent than the leg.
Figure 143 illustrates that the right cerebellar hemisphere is concerned
with the right side of the body. This ipsilateral control is a characteristic
but not absolute feature of the cerebellum. This means that a lesion in
the *left* cerebellum will cause signs on the *left* side of the body, in contrast to a lesion in the *left* internal capsule which can cause a *right* hemiplegia. A confusing situation results when there is a lesion in a superior
cerebellar peduncle after it has crossed in its ascent, in which case there
are cerebellar signs contralateral to the side of the lesion. Thus it is not
unknown for cerebellar signs to follow lesions in the frontal lobe, so
that with a left-sided lesion the signs would be on the right side. The
signs may also be related to involvement of corticopontine fibers in
such instances.

FUNCTIONS OF THE CEREBELLUM

It has been difficult to analyze cerebellar functions, particularly
in man, because data are largely restricted to those obtained from clinical disorders. These data and those obtained from animal experimen-

tation indicate that the cerebellum has an important role in the co-ordination of muscular activity and that its functions are not at a conscious level.

This can be illustrated in the following manner. Suppose that in carrying out a movement such as flexion of the elbow, the flexor muscles contracted, but the extensors did not relax to a corresponding degree. This lack of relaxation would either prevent flexion or make it difficult to carry out smoothly. Suppose now that the extensors did relax, but not until flexor contraction had begun. The result would be a jerky type of movement.

These examples illustrate that an important part of muscular activity is timing, that even if muscle power and voluntary control are normal, if muscle groups do not contract in the proper time with respect to each other, movement will be jerky and awkward. The cerebellum seems to be largely responsible for coordinating and timing activity in various groups of muscles, both in static or postural and phasic or locomotor mechanisms. The functions of the cerebellum cannot be voluntarily modified. Actually, so far as is known, we are never directly conscious of the functions of the cerebellum, and defects resulting from cerebellar disorders cannot be voluntarily controlled or modified to any extent.

In order for the cerebellum to control or modify muscular activity, it needs information about position and movement. This information is derived from all receptors involved — skin, muscle, tendon, joint, labyrinth — and, since a very important feature of control of movement is visual, impulses from the retinae reach the cerebellum. Likewise, auditory impulses reach the cerebellum. It is very likely that those impulses from muscles which signal changes in muscle tension are mainly important at cord levels, but are less important than touch and vision at cerebellar levels. The cerebellum receives impulses from the cerebral cortex but, perhaps more important, its own discharges to the cerebral cortex serve to maintain or enhance the excitability of cortical neurons and thus facilitate and time discharges over motor tracts.

It is commonly stated that the paleocerebellum is primarily concerned in coordination of postural activity, and the neocerebellum in locomotor activity. This is based on the fact that in lower animals, such as the cat, it has been demonstrated experimentally that electrical stimulation of the anterior part of the cerebellum (paleocerebellum) may be followed by relaxation of antigravity muscles. Whether there is actually such a sharp distinction is open to question. For example, it is possible to obtain opposite effects merely by changing the frequency of the stimulating current.

Not much is known of the functions of the archicerebellum, and it is probably relatively unimportant in man. There is a malignant tumor, the *medulloblastoma*, composed of undifferentiated, rapidly growing cells, which occurs in children and frequently starts in this portion of the cerebellum. The earliest signs may be incoordination in trunk musculature. It has been deduced, therefore, that this part of the cerebellum is concerned in the coordination of the dorsal musculature of the trunk. The validity of these deductions is still uncertain.

So far as the deep nuclei of the cerebellum are concerned, little is known of the part they play in cerebellar functions.

The cerebellum is receiving increasing attention from experimenters and clinicians. With the knowledge that impulses from all types of receptors reach the cerebellum has come the realization that this structure is much more than a "head ganglion." It is undoubtedly implicated in a variety of nervous functions. For example, there is increasing evidence that the cerebellum is concerned in many visceral activities, such as respiration, the control of blood pressure, and others.

DISORDERS OF THE CEREBELLUM

In general, cerebellar defects are manifested as disorders in timing or coordination. This may result in jerky movements or *intention tremors*. The loss of timing may be particularly noticeable at the end of movement and result in *terminal tremor*. These defects may be elicited by asking the patient to put his finger to his nose. He may do so, but is often unable to stop his finger at his nose, or he may point much to one side of it. If elicited during walking, the resulting stumbling gait is known as *ataxia*. The defects may be pronounced during standing and may be elicited by having the patient put his feet close together, whereupon he sways severely and may fall over. Patients with lesions in the posterior funiculi of the spinal cord also have their difficulty, but mainly when the eyes are closed. They use vision to compensate for the loss of position sense. Cerebellar signs tend to be present whether the eyes are open or closed, although naturally much worse with the eyes closed. Cerebellar signs are compensated for rapidly, provided the lesion is not progressive. That is, symptoms may partially or completely disappear after several weeks or months. Perhaps vision is used to tell when muscular contractions reach the proper point, thus compensating for the loss of the more automatic mechanisms.

Another common cerebellar sign is *hypotonia*. This may be so great that the muscles are limp or actually flaccid, with decreased or even absent deep reflexes. This may be due to (1) decreased excitability of neurons in the cerebral cortex following loss of impulses from the cerebellum, and (2) decreased discharge from the red nucleus.

SUMMARY

The cerebellum is a fissured structure attached to the brain stem by three pairs of peduncles. It has a cortex, composed of an inner granular layer, a middle Purkinje layer and an outer molecular layer. Fibers to the cerebellum reach the cortex and establish various types of connections. Axons of Purkinje cells leave the cortex and connect with the cells which form the cerebellar nuclei. These cells in turn project to other regions of the nervous system.

The cerebellum has widespread reciprocal connections with the cerebral cortex, particularly the motor and sensory areas. It has many connections with the spinal cord, chiefly with paths derived from peripheral receptors, and there are many connections with cranial nerves, particularly the vestibular, auditory, trigeminal, and optic nerves.

The cerebellum is involved in timing or coordination of muscular activity. It receives information from peripheral receptors, and from motor and sensory regions of the cerebral cortex. It carries out its functions primarily through brain stem inhibitory and excitatory mechanisms, which it modifies, and also the motor cortex. The anatomical connections are such that each cerebellar hemisphere is concerned mainly with muscles on the ipsilateral or same side of the body.

Disorders of the cerebellum are manifested chiefly as defects in coordination of muscular activity.

Names in Neurology

JOHANNES PURKINJE (1787-1869)

Purkinje was a physician, born in Bohemia, who was the first to use a microtome in the preparation of microscopic slides and also developed many other aids for microtechnique. He was a man of widespread interests. In 1837, two years before formulation of the cell theory by Schleiden and Schwann, he pointed out the similarity of animal and vegetable cells. He studied nerve cells, glands, the heart, and other organs. He described the specialized conducting fibers of the heart and the large nerve cells of the cerebellar cortex. He did not confine his interests to anatomy, but studied fingerprints, noted that deaf mutes could in some cases hear through the bones of the skull, and investigated the effects of opium, belladonna, and other drugs.

REFERENCES

See the references cited on pages 6 and 319.

Fox, C. A., and Snyder, R. S.: The Cerebellum. Amsterdam, Elsevier Publishing Company, 1967.

Chapter 18

THE PROSENCEPHALON
OR FOREBRAIN

The forebrain is the primary brain vesicle from which the telencephalon or endbrain and the diencephalon or interbrain differentiate. In the present account, it is used as a general term to refer to the adult derivatives, such as the cerebral cortex, basal ganglia, thalamus, and hypothalamus. The term *cerebrum* (Latin, brain) is also in common use. Usually it means brain, as contrasted with spinal cord. It has also been used to mean specifically the forebrain and midbrain. The adjective *cerebral* is derived from it. By contrast, *encephalon* is of Greek origin *(enkapholos)*. Terms such as encephalitis, which means inflammation of the brain, are derived from it.

Human behavior is related to neurological structure and function just as is its counterpart in lower forms. Its infinite complexity is correlated with increasing development of the forebrain, particularly the cerebral cortex. Here reside the mechanisms governing language formation and use, emotional reactions, and intelligence. Although our understanding of these mechanisms is extremely limited, this does not mean that there are no physiological processes forming the bases for such complex functions as memory or intelligence. Instead, it implies that they are not visible to the naked eye or detectable with present-day instruments.

Behavior is modifiable even in such simple forms as amebae. An ameba will not enter a beam of strong sunlight, and any portion of the cell that does so is immediately withdrawn. This behavior is known as a *tropic reaction*. After a few such local experiences, the entire cell takes part in a general avoiding reaction. The ameba then changes its direction of movement. The stimulus has not changed, but the local response has been followed by a spread of activity which depends upon some intrinsic protoplasmic organization. This rudimentary modification, however, is short-lived.

A paramecium ordinarily swims in wide spirals. In a strong avoiding reaction it may swim backward, but still spirally. If, however, it is placed in a small capillary tube which is too narrow to permit spiraling, the paramecium swims forward by a rotary movement to the end of the tube. Here it reverses the movement several times and finally turns around by a series of quick jerks. This reaction is never seen in normal unconfined behavior. It is "learning by experience" in a primitive manner.

As the synaptic type of nervous system appears in higher groups of animals, behavior becomes more complex and more modifiable. Fixed types are nevertheless present in any one species, and these usually predominate. In insects, for instance, the nervous system is almost fully formed before it begins to function. Hence modifiability is at a minimum. Ant colonies, for example, are complex phenomena because of the various types of ants within them, each with its own specific and relatively nonmodifiable function within the group.

Vertebrates also have fixed or "instinctive" types of behavior, for the most part determined by highly differentiated local patterns of nerve tissue which, however, do not function spontaneously. Some environmental factor is always needed to activate them. In ascending the vertebrate scale, "intelligent behavior" becomes more and more pronounced, attaining its highest development in man. This is correlated with the appearance of labile areas which have a large capacity for growth and differentiation even after they have started to function.

The structural features relating to lability of behavior appear to be on a hereditary basis. They are evident before the nervous system assumes its functions as a conducting mechanism. Hence they may be termed *preneural changes*. For instance, cranially located neuroblasts develop processes which extend downward and link with other cells at spinal levels. Spinal neuroblasts develop growing tips which push through the external surface of the neural tube and grow into areas of developing muscle (p. 63). At the same time, multineuronal sensory chains are being formed dorsally which give branches to the surface of the body. The sensory and motor chains are not connected commissurally, even when they begin to conduct. Hence, experience due to influences of the external environment plays no part in exciting or influencing through nervous conduction the formation of these paths. The basic pattern of behavior is not determined by normal experience with the outside world.

Even after the longitudinal motor and sensory tracts take form and begin to function, there are preneural changes in higher areas. Neuroblast proliferation and differentiation becomes especially localized in forebrain areas. Optic centers differentiate before optic nerves enter them. The visual cortex is well defined in an 18 weeks' old human fetus at a time when body movements are simplest in form. Preneural and neural mechanisms thus overlap.

The characteristic feature of the cerebral cortex in primates is its tremendous early growth, even in the fetus. Long before it is needed or can be used, the adult pattern is formed. The cortex as well as the rest of the nervous system is composed of neurons, but the neuron concept as ordinarily presented creates the idea of rigid conducting patterns. It fails to account for the inherent capacity for change even after individual neurons are formed. Thus the adult pattern is unnecessary for the fetus at the moment, but provides a tremendous reserve for future learning. Growth is extensive even after conduction is possible. Neurons increase in length and size through fetal life, infancy, and childhood. Comparisons of pyramidal and Purkinje cells at birth and in the adult show that marked changes in numbers and arrangements of dendritic processes have taken place in the intervening period.

GENERAL FEATURES OF THE FOREBRAIN

The following brief account is intended to point out some morphological features of the forebrain in different vertebrates. The evolution of the nervous system has been characterized by the development of basal ganglia (most prominent in birds) and of a cerebral cortex (most prominent in mammals).

FISHES

Correlative mechanisms are not well developed in fishes. Most of the central nervous system is devoted to fixed fundamental patterns, although coordinating centers such as the cerebellum are prominent. Even the forebrain is dominated for the most part by the olfactory system, and but a small part of it resembles a correlation center, that is, an area receiving impulses from more than one sensory system. This small part lies at the base of the brain in the thalamic region and is apparently the forerunner of the thalamus, corpus striatum, and cerebral cortex of mammals. There is no true cerebral cortex in fishes.

The hypothalamic area of fishes is the dominant area for visceral mechanisms, while the midbrain subserves the same functions for somatic senses. Figure 146 *a* illustrates a primitive vertebrate forebrain.

AMPHIBIANS

In amphibians part of the forebrain is evaginated into cerebral hemispheres that are devoted almost entirely to olfactory functions. But even in these forms, two structural tendencies are evident. The cerebral hemispheres are complex because of (1) the local differentiation of functionally specific areas, and (2) the presence of functionally diffuse areas. The first are represented by the corpus striatum, the second by the cerebral cortex. Thus, in the frog, a specialized amphibian, one finds a corpus striatum and a rudimentary cerebral cortex.

Figure 146 *b* illustrates an amphibian forebrain.

REPTILES

Reptilian brains have fairly evident basal ganglia and a true cerebral cortex.

Figure 146 *c* illustrates the forebrain of a turtle.

BIRDS

The corpus striatum is relatively large and complex in birds, whereas the cerebral cortex is primitive and scanty. The cerebral hemispheres are larger than those of reptiles, because of large basal lobes. Olfaction is reduced, as evidenced by the small size of the olfactory bulbs. The exteroceptive senses are well developed and are represented by a large midbrain. Birds are capable of highly complex behavior, but this is cast in stereotyped forms and instinctive responses. For instance, certain complex behavior cycles are really composed of parts which must occur in a regular sequence. If these cycles are interrupted, they must be renewed from the beginning and not from the point at which interrupted.

Figure 146 *d* illustrates the forebrain of a bird.

MAMMALS

The development of cerebral cortex in mammals is associated with a relative reduction in basal ganglia. The cortex of the dorsolateral surfaces of the hemispheres is associated with somatic afferent and efferent mechanisms. Ventromedially, the cortex is linked with higher olfactory and visceral processes and is known as the *hippocampal area.* Just behind the olfactory bulbs is the *piriform area,* concerned with olfaction on a lower level. The last two areas are the phylogenetically older

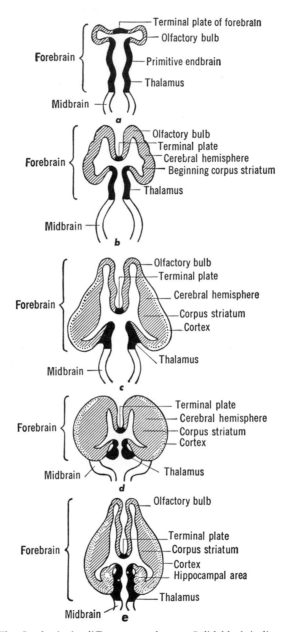

Figure 146. The forebrain in different vertebrates. Solid black indicates the primitive or unevaginated portion of the forebrain. *a,* Primitive vertebrate forebrain; *b,* frog; *c,* turtle; *d,* pigeon; *e,* rabbit. (Modified after Herrick.)

cortex or *archipallium* (see limbic system, p. 335), whereas the remainder is the newer or *neocortex* or *neopallium*. The olfactory areas in each hemisphere are connected by a number of commissures, chief of which is the *anterior commissure*. In most mammals the neocortex on each side is connected by massive bundles of association fibers which form the corpus callosum.

Figure 146 *e* illustrates the forebrain of a rabbit.

The neocortex throughout the mammalian scale becomes increasingly prominent and the archipallium relatively overshadowed, the latter having reached its maximal development in lower mammals. Olfaction is less important than vision in the arboreal habitat of primates. The progressive development of the neocortex in the latter forms is correlated, among other things, with the increasing importance of auditory, tactile, and visual mechanisms.

Vision is one of the most important of these senses. Objects near at hand or far away may be recognized. Their precise location in space, their color, texture, and form are discernible with great accuracy. The importance of these phenomena hardly needs emphasis. The development of the visual sense is accompanied by a reduction of the snout region, a lessening of the importance of smell, and by rotation of the eyes. In lower forms with pronounced noses, binocular or stereoscopic vision is not possible because the eyes look laterally, instead of forward. Even as the snout decreases and the eyes come to look forward, binocular vision is not possible until visual fields can overlap. This takes place when there is a concomitant change at the optic chiasma from a total to a partial decussation. Only with the latter can corresponding retinal points of two eyes project to one side of the brain. Finally there is a shift in visualization from the midbrain to the occipital lobes.

Upright posture in the primates is associated with skill in motor activities through the development of digital dexterity and an opposable thumb. The corticospinal tracts are most prominent in species with such digital facility. Cerebral dominance also becomes pronounced in the sense that most persons are right-handed, the handedness originating in the left cerebral cortex.

The facility of speech is associated with higher centers of the cerebral cortex and also with corticobulbar tracts to the motor nuclei concerned with speech. Likewise, binocular vision necessitates finer, more precise control of eye movements, associated with greater cortical control and with increasing complexity and differentiation in the oculomotor nuclei.

These functions are all related to the motor and sensory areas of the cerebral cortex which give rise to and receive projections. These areas are about the same size in man and in such lower primates as the great apes. Yet the brain of man is by far the larger because of the greater extent of association areas which are intimately connected with each other and with the motor and sensory regions.

BASAL GANGLIA

The term "basal ganglia" or "basal nuclei" refers to masses of gray matter in the interior of the cerebrum (p. 20). They include the *caudate nucleus* and the *putamen* which, together with the internal capsule which separates them, form the *corpus striatum*. The *globus pallidus*, an important member of the group, is sometimes included with the putamen under the term *lentiform nucleus*. Adjacent to and just below the thalamus is the *subthalamic nucleus*, which is separated from the globus pallidus by the internal capsule. The thalamus and hypothalamus, in terms of position, belong with the basal ganglia, but functionally are more closely associated with other systems. The amygdaloid body is sometimes

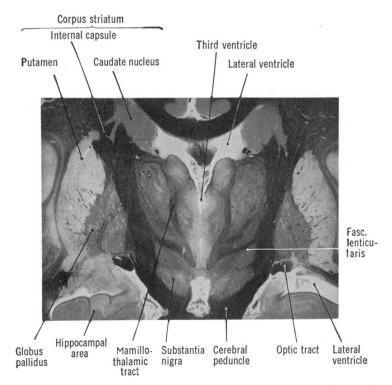

Figure 147. Photograph of a coronal section of the cerebrum. Weigert stain.

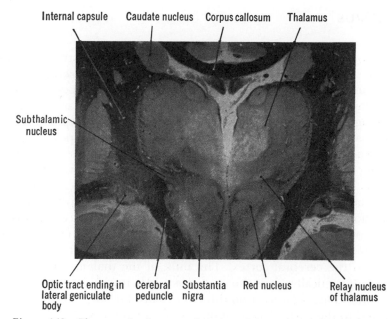

Internal capsule   Caudate nucleus   Corpus callosum   Thalamus

Subthalamic
nucleus

Optic tract ending in   Cerebral   Substantia   Red nucleus   Relay nucleus
lateral geniculate   peduncle   nigra   of thalamus
body

Figure 148.   Photograph of a coronal section of the cerebrum. Weigert stain.

grouped with the basal ganglia. The red nucleus and the substantia nigra, which are located in the midbrain, are in a sense a junctional region between the other basal ganglia and the more caudally placed reticular formation, and they are anatomically and functionally connected with both. The connections and functions of the basal ganglia are discussed below and on p. 308.

The term "subcortical" is in common use. In contrast to the term "basal ganglia," "subcortical" is a nonspecific term and is used to refer to any noncortical structure in the brain.

Connections of the Basal Ganglia. These are complex and still poorly understood. Most of the basal ganglia have connections with the sensory pathways by way of the thalamus, and they also receive fibers from the cerebral cortex, either directly or by relays through the caudate nucleus and putamen.

Various motor paths leave the basal ganglia, one of the most prominent being composed of fibers which leave the globus pallidus and form a tract called the fasciculus lenticularis (Fig. 147). This tract pierces the internal capsule (some fibers form the ansa lenticularis which loops around the capsule) and is distributed to the thalamus (Fig. 148), by which impulses are returned to the cerebral cortex, and to the reticular formation, by means of relays through the subthalamic nucleus and substantia nigra.

THALAMUS

Although the thalamus (plural, thalami) has been studied mainly from the standpoint of its importance in sensation, it is closely connected with the association areas of cerebral cortex, and is an important station in the projection of impulses from the cerebellum, reticular system, and basal ganglia to the cerebral cortex. It therefore has multiple functions.

The various nuclei of which each thalamus is composed may be grouped according to their connections with other parts of the brain. Many nuclei, found mainly next to the third ventricle, are termed *subcortical nuclei,* because they connect only with subcortical structures, such as the hypothalamus. Another group of nuclei comprises the ventral portion of the thalamus and is associated with afferent paths for special and general senses. These *cortical relay nuclei* relay impulses from these paths, as well as from cerebellum, reticular system, and basal ganglia, to the cerebral cortex. The bulk of the thalamus is relatively new phylogenetically—it is the *neothalamus.* Its nuclei receive no fibers from lower centers (at least no direct ones are known), but instead are connected to the cortical association areas, which themselves form most of the cerebral surface, and are termed *association nuclei.*

Many of the connections found by anatomical methods have been confirmed by physiological and pharmacological methods. These have dealt mainly with the classical afferent pathways and nuclei. Only in recent years have there been major attempts to decipher the connections of other nuclei.

Certain thalamic nuclei are called nonspecific, in the sense that although they project to cerebral cortex, they are not related solely to one cortical area. Stimulation of these nonspecific thalamic nuclei produces remarkable changes in the electrical activity of the brain, such that the record consists of large, relatively slow synchronized waves that in some instances resemble the petit mal discharges of epilepsy.

CEREBRAL CORTEX

In spite of the functional differences between species, extensive studies have led to the conclusion that the neurons of the cerebral cortex are arranged in a similar pattern in all animals that have a cortex. These conclusions are based on the fact that by studying sections stained for Nissl substance, the cell bodies of the cortical neurons appeared to be grouped into six layers.

By using stains for nerve fibers, it has been shown that nerve fibers projecting from the cerebral cortex (such as corticospinal) arise mainly

from cells in the fifth layer, that nerve fibers entering the cortex end
mainly in the fourth layer, and that the cortex is chiefly composed of
interneurons which provide for intracortical connections. The most
numerous interneuron in the fourth layer is the *granule cell;* hence the
first three layers are called *supragranular layers.*

The basic pattern of cortical connections (Fig. 149) is similar to
patterns of connections described for gray matter generally (p. 130).
Figure 149 is a gross oversimplification. The interneurons which link
the afferent and efferent fibers and also various units (not shown in
the figure) are numbered in the billions. Actually, our knowledge of
cortical structure is so fragmentary that any attempts to compare these
units to man-made electronic feedback circuits are purely speculative.

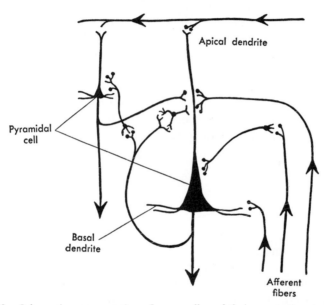

Apical dendrite

Pyramidal
cell

Basal
dendrite

Afferent
fibers

Figure 149. Schematic representation of some cells and their connections in the cerebral
cortex, based on Golgi staining. Microscopic studies using Nissl stains (thus showing only
cell bodies) do not reveal the connections of nerve cells. Some nerve fibers entering the
cortex relay through small cells to the body of the large pyramidal cell, activation of which
leads to a discharge over the axon with provision for reactivation through the recurrent
branch of the axon. Most synapses are with the dendrites of the pyramidal cell and not
the cell body. Dendritic activation is accompanied by large, slow potential changes, by lack
of an absolute refractory period, and by prolonged depolarization. The latter two factors
make it possible for successive impulses reaching dendrites to maintain them in a depolarized state. In turn, current flow from dendrites very likely can depolarize the cell
body and cause it to discharge. Thus, prolonged activity and repetitive discharges are
dependent not only on conduction through various chains of neurons (as shown in more
detail in Figure 73), but also on dendritic activation by connections shown above. Note
also that the apical dendrites of pyramidal cells can be linked together by axons in the
outer layer of cerebral cortex (cell body not shown). (Based on Clare and Bishop, Am.
J. Psychiat., *111*:818-825, 1955.)

The earliest studies of the cerebral cortex led to the naming of lobes, convolutions, gyri, fissures, and sulci. Subsequently, investigators of cortical lamination developed a system of numbering (also lettering), each area being given a number as it was studied, and each one supposedly structurally different from other numbered areas. As the studies continued, more and more numbered areas were delimited, several hundred now being described. Many of these studies are based on Nissl stains, which give no information about cell processes. Actually, few of the studies have established any objective criteria for critical distinctions between cortical areas, and few have taken any account of individual variations.

The naming and numbering of areas, and the use of diagrams, unfortunately, give the impression of clear-cut, sharp distinctions between areas. This is not so. Actually, except in a few instances, numbered and named areas are neither functionally nor structurally specific. The present tendency is toward a simplification of numbering, with more attention to physiological correlates in the intact organism. This does not mean that there are no structural or functional differences between different regions of the cerebral cortex. There probably are, but the criteria ordinarily used today do not demonstrate them satisfactorily. Some of the structural differences are mentioned later (p. 300) in connection with motor and sensory regions.

ELECTRICAL ACTIVITY

The electrical activity of the brain can be detected and recorded much in the same manner as electrical activity of the heart or a peripheral nerve is recorded. Electrodes are placed on the subject's scalp, and the voltages across the electrodes are magnified or amplified by means of a vacuum tube amplifier. Finally, the voltage changes are recorded with an ink writer or oscillograph. In normal subjects there is a characteristic pattern made up of waves of varying frequency and magnitude. Such a changing pattern represents the algebraic sum of the potentials of billions of cortical neurons. The record obtained is an *electroencephalogram* or *EEG*, and the oscillations recorded are popularly known as "brain waves." As pointed out previously (p. 109), the discharge of the initial segment of the axon is followed also by an electrotonic depolarizing invasion of the dendrites, and this in turn is followed by a long-lasting wave of hyperpolarization. It now seems clear that brain waves probably reflect the waxing and waning of electrotonic potentials in dendrites of cortical cells.

The electroencephalogram is obtained with the subject at rest, in

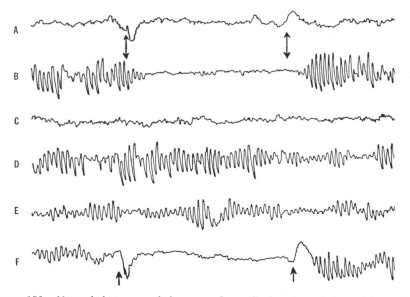

Figure 150. Normal electroencephalograms of a medical student. *A,* Record from right and left frontal regions and, *B,* from right and left occipital regions, taken simultaneously. The first arrow indicates opening the eyes. Note the subsequent deflection in the frontal record. This is an artifact due to the movement. Note that the activity in the occipital leads is suppressed. The second arrow indicates eye closing, again followed by an artifact, with a reappearance of occipital activity. *C* and *D,* Continuations of *A* and *B* to give an idea of variations in activity. The frontal records are mainly low voltage, relatively fast or *beta* activity. The occipital records are mainly higher voltage, 10 to 12 per second *alpha* activity. Alpha activity by definition decreases or disappears upon opening the eyes, as it did in *B.* *E,* Record between right occipital and right frontal, continued in *F,* in which the opening and closing of the eyes, indicated by arrows and blinking artifacts, is accompanied again by suppression of *alpha* activity.

a darkened room or with the eyes closed. Although the pattern of the electroencephalogram varies from one person to another, in many normal persons moderate deflections occurring 10 to 12 times a second are often visible. These are the *alpha waves* (Berger rhythm, p. 299).

Smaller, faster deflections, the *beta waves* (Fig. 150), may be superimposed on the alpha waves, especially when recording from frontal regions. Waves slower than five per second are frequently termed *delta waves;* these are not found in the normal person except during sleep.

Increased attention or sensory input, brought about by mental activity or by opening the eyes, causes the alpha waves to disappear (Fig. 150). Changes in the normal rhythm occur during sleep, especially during deep slumber, when slow waves of three a second or more duration appear. In moderately deep sleep there may be bursts of fast activity, the sleep *spindles,* superimposed upon the slow waves.

Anesthetics and metabolic changes frequently alter normal rhythm, this being correlated with variations in the excitability of the cerebral cortex. In certain disorders the wave form deviates from the normal.

The presence in an electroencephalogram of abnormal waves, especially if slow and large, often aids in the diagnosis of these disorders. The electroencephalogram has found its most useful clinical function in the localization of certain types of surface tumors or lesions and in studies of epilepsy (p. 316).

There are regional differences in the electroencephalogram, the alpha rhythm appearing to come mainly from the occipital cortex, while the frontal region shows mainly beta activity. The waves can be modified by various sensory and pharmacological procedures. Furthermore, there is considerable evidence that stimulation of brain stem reticular formation alters the brain wave pattern. The reticular activating system mediates the arousal reaction, with desynchronization or flattening of the EEG. There are also significant changes during sleep (p. 272). Also, reduction of afferent impulses to the cerebral cortex has a profound effect. For example, the cerebral cortex of a decerebrate animal, a cortex which receives impulses only from the olfactory and optic nerves, has a pattern resembling that of sleep. In certain paroxysmal states electrical patterns of the cortex may be "driven" by the thalamus. These examples give some idea of the complexity of events under study, and the section on volume conduction (p. 107) points out the difficulties involved in studying conducting tissue when the components of this tissue are not linear, parallel conductors.

Finally, recent years have seen significant advances from the study of electrical activity through the use of microelectrode recording from single cells. These studies have resulted in increased understanding of the codes by which information is transmitted to the brain. A peripheral stimulus results in features which may be roughly categorized according to intensity, duration, frequency, locus, and form. These may be modified or modulated at each synaptic level during transmission. It is becoming increasingly apparent that, in receiving such information, the brain may discriminate on a statistical basis, that is, on the probability that the information received is significantly different from that currently taking place or, on the basis of past experience, expected to take place.

SUMMARY

Instinctive behavior consists in stereotyped patterns which are mainly dependent upon highly differentiated local arrangements coordinated by spinal cord and brain stem centers. Intelligent behavior is related to labile, relatively nonspecific areas of the forebrain.

Forebrain arrangement in the vertebrate scale is in two general trends: (1) toward the appearance of basal ganglia, which in birds attain their maximal development relative to the rest of the brain; (2) toward the appearance of a cerebral cortex, which is maximally developed in mammals.

The cortex develops along olfactory and nonolfactory lines, the latter overshadowing the former with progression toward primate forms. In the latter, cortical development is correlated with the appearance of upright posture, opposable thumb, binocular vision, and higher mental processes.

Cortical structure can be illustrated by a fundamental vertical unit, but only a few regions of the cerebral cortex show consistent structural differences.

Electrical activity of the brain can be recorded and is a spontaneous type of activity known as brain waves or the electroencephalogram. This activity can be modified by various physiological and experimental procedures.

Names in Neurology

HANS BERGER (1873-1941)

Berger, a neurologist in Jena, was the first to record the electrical activity of the brain in the human subject. He studied the electroencephalogram extensively, and one of the basic patterns or rhythms bears his name.

REFERENCES

See references cited on pages 6 and 319.

Gibbs, F. A., and Gibbs, E. L.: Atlas of Electroencephalography. 2nd ed. Cambridge, Mass., Addison-Wesley Press, Inc., 3 vols., 1950, 1952, 1964. (This atlas presents representative records of normal subjects and of patients with various disorders.) See also Clinical Examinations in Neurology (cited on p. 154) for an excellent short chapter on electroencephalography.
Sholl, D. A.: The Organization of the Cerebral Cortex. New York, John Wiley and Sons, Inc., 1956.

CHAPTER 19

MOTOR AND SENSORY
FUNCTIONS OF
THE FOREBRAIN

The motor functions discussed in this chapter are those carried out by the regions of the cerebral cortex from which the motor paths arise, and by the basal ganglia. The sensory functions are those carried out by the thalami, and by the cortical regions in which the afferent paths end, that is, the primary receptive areas.

MOTOR FUNCTIONS

There are several regions of the cerebral cortex the electrical stimulation of which is followed by some type of muscular activity. These regions are the ones from which the descending motor paths arise. Most of those known at the present time lie anterior to the central sulcus and form the precentral motor cortex, a region which is usually subdivided into several numbered areas (Fig. 151). The cerebral cortex of this region is rather thick (Fig. 152). It receives many fibers from the thalamus, and these fibers end largely in the fourth layer. There are many pyramidal-shaped cells of various sizes in the fourth and fifth layers; as a consequence, the fourth layer is obscured, to the extent that motor

300

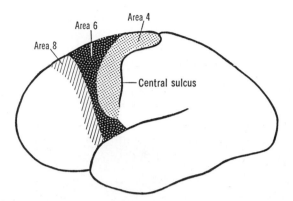

Figure 151. Diagram indicating the approximate locations of the motor areas on the lateral surface of the frontal lobe.

cortex is often spoken of as *agranular cortex.* These pyramidal cells contribute to the corticospinal and extrapyramidal tracts. There are no sharp lines of demarcation between the numbered subdivisions of the motor cortex, either grossly or microscopically. Figure 151 merely illustrates their approximate locations. In a brain exposed at operation it is very nearly impossible to know precisely what area is in the operating field. Arachnoid, pia mater, and blood vessels obscure surface landmarks, and there is great individual variation in the relation of surface landmarks to bony landmarks.

There are regions of the cerebral cortex other than the classical precentral which are also motor areas. Motor paths having to do with eye movements arise from the occipital cortex. A second motor area has been found on the medial surface of the hemisphere. Various parts of the frontal lobe, particularly medial and basal surfaces, give rise to paths having to do with visceral activities.

The cortical motor areas have little function at birth. A newborn infant shows little voluntary or coordinated activity and has reflex patterns ordinarily not seen in an adult. For example, a grasp reflex is easily demonstrated by placing one's finger in a baby's hand. A Babinski reflex is present and only gradually disappears when walking begins. One can argue that the withdrawal which a Babinski reflex represents would conflict with walking and that it consequently is inhibited when the cortex begins to function. At least it disappears and in an adult is elicited only in upper motor neuron disorders, in fatigue, or in deep sleep. The newborn infant also shows static and dynamic responses, reflex patterns much like those of a thalamic animal. Not until the child begins to walk does the fine coordination characteristic of more complete cortical functioning begin its development.

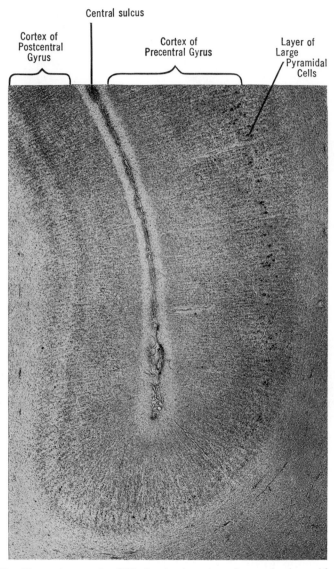

Figure 152. Photomicrograph of Nissl-stained section of central sulcus with the motor cortex (precentral gyrus) on the right and the sensory cortex (postcentral gyrus) on the left. Note large pyramidal cells in the motor cortex. The central fissure between the two is filled with pia mater and blood vessels.

STIMULATION

If the precentral motor cortex is explored with a stimulating electrode, an inverted representation of movements is found, such that movements in the lower limb follow stimulation of the upper or dorsal part of the region; movements in the upper limb when the middle of the region is stimulated; and movements in the head and neck muscles following stimulation of the lower or ventral part of the region. This is anything but a specific pattern, however. Figure 153 helps to illustrate what might be called overlap. For example, if one stimulates a spot on the motor cortex with a single electrical pulse, a muscle or a few muscles on the opposite side of the body will twitch. If the strength of the stimulus is increased, other muscles will also respond. And if the same spot is stimulated with 60-cycle current of the same strength, many more muscles contract. It is known that in the so-called arm region, nerve cells for the arm muscles have the lowest threshold, that is, are most excitable, other muscles in the body being represented by nerve cells with a higher threshold. Likewise, in the leg region, nerve cells to leg muscles have the lowest threshold.

One might suppose that contraction of a leg muscle when the arm area is stimulated is due to spread of the stimulus to the leg area. Actually, however, it is possible so to isolate the stimulated region surgically as to leave only connections to subcortical centers. Stimulation of just one spot can still yield multiple patterns of response. The results are

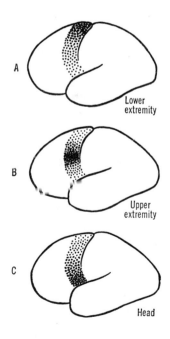

Figure 153. Diagram of the manner in which movements are represented in the cerebral cortex. *A*, Stimulation of the heavily shaded area usually, or most easily, elicits movements in the lower limb. Stimulation anywhere else in the motor cortex can also elicit movements in the lower limb, but less easily, and the degree of shading is some indication of the degree of response. *B*, Similar situation for upper limb and, *C*, for head and neck. If these three drawings were superimposed so as to represent the actual situation, then in any one region (even a very small region) of motor cortex, all types of movements would be represented, but some one type much more so than any other. Conversely, destruction of a part of the motor cortex would have its greatest effect on one type of movement, so that there might be weakness or paralysis of a muscle or group of muscles in this particular movement, but the same muscles might be used effectively in other movements.

Lower extremity

Upper extremity

Head

such that one can only conclude that even in very small parts of the motor cortex all types of movements all over the body are represented, and that some of them are predominantly represented, that is, more easily elicited by stimulation. Figure 153 simply illustrates predominant representation.

It must be emphasized that electrical stimulation is an artificial procedure, and that only by the merest chance would such a procedure activate a pattern of cells in the same manner as would a physiological stimulus. The results depend, not only upon the strength of the stimulus, but also upon the frequency. Contraction may occur in one group of muscles during stimulation at one frequency, and in another group during stimulation at another frequency.

The results also depend upon posture. That is, if a muscle or group of muscles is placed in a particular position, the result of stimulation may be different than if the muscles had been placed in another position.

Impulses from skin, muscles, and joints have a profound effect upon the result of cortical stimulation. The interpretation of cortical stimulation may be complicated by secondary movement. If one observes a pattern of activity in response to stimulation, one cannot assume that the entire pattern was a direct result of the stimulus. It is possible that some muscles contracted after stimulation, and that this contraction reflexly induced activity in still other muscles, independently of the cerebral cortex. Visual observation is extremely misleading in the study of muscular activity. Conscious human subjects on whom stimulation experiments are carried out report that any movements which result seem quite beyond their control and without any sense of being willed or initiated. It is interesting that stimulation of the precentral gyrus sometimes causes tingling or some other sensation rather than movement.

The multiplicity of representation is encountered clinically. A surface tumor may irritate a small part of the motor cortex and thereby cause involuntary movements or convulsions on the opposite side of the body. The convulsions start in those muscles which are predominantly represented in the affected area and then rapidly involve other muscles. These spreading seizures, without loss of consciousness, are often called *jacksonian* convulsions (p. 318).

The threshold, or excitable level, of the cerebral cortex varies greatly. For instance, after stimulation of a cortical focus there may be a long period during which no response can be obtained. This is a subnormal period. The threshold may also vary according to metabolic activities. A shift in hydrogen ion concentration toward the alkaline side is followed by an increase in excitability which may be recorded as fast activity in the electroencephalogram. The alkalinity can be produced by hyperventilation, during which carbon dioxide is blown off.

Even in normal subjects, continued overbreathing may be followed by such an increase in excitability that spontaneous involuntary twitchings or tremors appear.

The division of the precentral motor cortex into Areas 4, 6, and 8 has been made mainly on the basis of stimulation studies and to some extent on extirpation and on microscopic studies. Movements are most easily elicited by stimulation of Area 4, and the inverted representation of the body is most pronounced here. The area is practically coextensive with the precentral gyrus. Area 4 is often subdivided, the basis being the presence of large pyramidal cells within its fifth layer. Some are so large as to be called giant pyramidal cells. These large cells are most numerous in the upper part of the gyrus, that concerned primarily with the lower extremity. Their size is probably only a reflection of the distance which their axons travel (to the lumbar and sacral cord). Large pyramidal cells are often found in many other areas, including sensory cortex.

Stimulation of Area 6 is frequently without effect. It has been concluded that inhibitory fibers arise more strongly here than they do from Area 4, and it is known that fibers from this region reach the reticular formation of the brain stem by direct paths and by relays through basal ganglia. Area 8 is often called the frontal eye field, since its stimulation is often followed by conjugate eye movements as well as by various head and neck movements. It is quite similar to Area 6, and there is much doubt as to its distinctness.

Experimenters have reported that specific regions of the cerebral cortex are concerned with inhibitory mechanisms. These regions are said to be small and often form a strip of cortex. One, said to lie between Areas 4 and 6, is called Area 4S (a strip or suppressor area). This region is said to project by way of basal ganglia, and also by direct paths, to the brain stem. However, many investigators do not believe that such specific strips exist. One factor that has to be considered is that even minor trauma during study, or exposure of cerebral cortex to room temperature, often results in a spreading depression. This is characterized particularly by decreased electrical activity and decreased sensitivity to stimulation, and the spread is not dependent upon nervous pathways.

Visceral as well as somatic responses may follow cortical stimulation. Thus there is increased blood flow through muscles active in cortically induced movements, and the impulses mediating this vasomotor reaction probably originate in the cortex. Changes in systolic blood pressure and heart rate may also occur. Strong stimulation of Area 8 may be followed, not only by conjugate eye movements, but also by the formation and flow of tears, and by changes in pupillary diameter. There is a cortical zone anterior to Area 8, near the inferior surface of the frontal lobe, stimulation of which results in marked inhibition of many visceral activities.

Recent work indicates that motor responses may follow stimulation of a region on the medial surface of the hemisphere and that such responses may involve any muscle of the body. The significance of this second motor area is unknown.

EXTIRPATION

Many of the functions of the motor areas have been deduced by studying the loss of function following cortical destruction. If a small metal disk, heated to the proper temperature, is placed on part of the motor cortex, the first three or four cell layers will be destroyed, but stimulation of the area so treated is still followed by movements. However, if the temperature is such as to kill the first five layers, responses are no longer obtained, indicating that projections arise from the fifth cell layer. This again indicates the artificial nature of the electrical stimulus. The great numbers of small cells are undoubtedly of the greatest importance, yet removing them makes little difference in the response to stimulation.

With destruction of part or all of a motor area, either experimentally or by disease, upper motor neuron types of disorders occur. In general, the more widespread the destruction, the more pronounced and enduring is the weakness or paralysis. The degree to which functions can be assessed, however, is limited, because it is difficult to destroy one area precisely without affecting neighboring ones. This is especially true of pathological processes, which rarely limit themselves to one region.

Spasticity, hyperactive deep reflexes and pathological reflexes often accompany weakness, especially with widespread lesions. Complete paralysis is rare, once there is recovery from the sudden onset of a disorder. Weakness is only relative following cortical lesions, and this is clearly shown when such lesions are small. A muscle may, for all practical purposes, be paralyzed when attempts are made to use it in one type of movement pattern, and yet the same muscle may be used easily in another movement pattern. For example, with a loss of a part of the arm area, a patient may be unable to extend his wrist on command. Yet the wrist may extend when making a fist. This illustrates again the multiplicity of representation, that any one small part of the motor cortex deals with many movements, and that any one movement is represented in many parts of the motor cortex.

Weakness and even paralysis are also relative as to time, because with proper training, practice, and lapse of time, motor deficits from cortical lesions (and even subcortical ones) may diminish or disappear.

Certain types of pathological responses appear to be characteristic of large lesions of the motor cortex. For example, the grasp reflex and groping response seem to follow damage to large areas, especially when Area 6 or the supplemental motor area on the medial surface of the hemisphere are involved. The *grasp reflex,* seen normally in infants, is the reflex grasping of an object placed in the hand, a reflex initiated by the pressure of the object and carried out by the cerebral cortex. It has been postulated that Area 4 is responsible for carrying out this reflex and that Area 6 inhibits it in the adult. The *groping response* is more complex. Contact with an object by the fingers is followed by reflex reach toward and grasping of the object. Tactile, pressure, and proprioceptive afferents are necessary for the initiation of the response, which, like the grasp, is carried out by the cerebral cortex.

Comparable reactions in lower forms, such as the cat, are hopping and placing reactions. In the *placing reaction,* if the paw of a blindfolded cat is touched to the edge of a table, that paw is almost instantly placed upon the surface of the table. The initiating factors are tactile stimuli. The response is dependent upon the impulses reaching the sensory cortex, and then the motor cortex. Destruction of one motor cortex is followed by loss of the placing reaction in contralateral paws. *Hopping reactions* are similar. If the dorsal surface of a paw is dragged along the surface of a table, the animal makes repetitive placing movements, each of which is a pattern initiated by tactile impulses.

Removal of the motor cortex in man, either partially or completely, does not cause any memory loss. The patient still knows how to carry out even the most complex maneuvers he has ever learned and, if he has a usable extremity left, can attempt learned patterns with that extremity. In other words, the defects are just in the execution of motor activity.

RELATION TO SENSORY AREAS AND TO THE CEREBELLUM

Experimental work on lower animals has shown that motor and sensory cortices are interdependent, and clinical evidence indicates that this is also true in man. This was mentioned in connection with the hopping and placing reactions, which are initiated by tactile stimuli and are abolished by lesions of either the motor or sensory cortex.

As was pointed out previously, discharges from, or results of stimulation of, the motor cortex are modified, or even determined, by the state of contraction or activity in the muscle group supplied by the stimulated region. Even passive alteration of the position of a muscle may alter its subsequent response, or even abolish it. In other words, the proprioceptive impulses reaching the cerebral cortex condition the motor cortex.

The motor cortex is closely associated with the cerebellum, particularly as regards timing mechanisms. These relationships have already been discussed (p. 283).

BASAL GANGLIA

The motor areas of the cerebral cortex are connected with the various basal ganglia by pathways which are partially indicated in Figures 154 and 155. These connections constitute the highest and most important level of the extrapyramidal system. However, it is still not known with any degree of certainty how the functions of the basal ganglia are carried out. The basal ganglia are difficult to reach without destroying other parts of the nervous system. Electrical stimulation has on the whole yielded little information. Yet it is known that in lower forms, such as birds, well-coordinated behavior is carried out in the absence of cerebral cortex. Perhaps in mammals the functions of basal ganglia are obscured or overshadowed by the cerebral cortex.

Some facts appear fairly well established. Many of the so-called extrapyramidal functions of the cerebral cortex are mediated through the basal ganglia. This seems to be particularly true of inhibitory functions. Stimulation of certain regions of the cerebral cortex may be followed by suppression of electrical activity of neighboring motor cortex and of any active movement going on at the same time. These regions are associated with the circular routes through basal ganglia and with paths to the brain stem, some of which are illustrated in Figures 154 and 155. The fact that basal ganglia are involved in inhibitory mechanisms probably explains why direct stimulation of basal ganglia has often appeared to be ineffective. The basal ganglia are not, however, limited to inhibitory mechanisms. They are involved in much more complicated functions, as illustrated by the following discussion.

It was pointed out previously (p. 265) that a decerebrate animal is incapable of locomotor activity. If, instead of transecting the brain stem of a cat at the midbrain level, one severs it in the thalamic area in a manner which spares the midbrain and part or all of the thalamus and other basal ganglia, one has a *thalamic* or *midbrain* animal. *Dynamic* or *phasic reactions* can be demonstrated in such a cat. These consist in the ability to right itself or return to a standing position after changes in position and to carry out a fairly well-coordinated type of locomotion. In a normal animal the various reactions can be analyzed by excluding first one and then another of the various sensory and reflex fields. It must be emphasized that in the absence of cerebral cortex they can be carried out by the basal ganglia, together with the cerebellum, and perhaps with the hypothalamus also, and that practically nothing is known of the manner in which the necessary integration is carried out. The dynamic

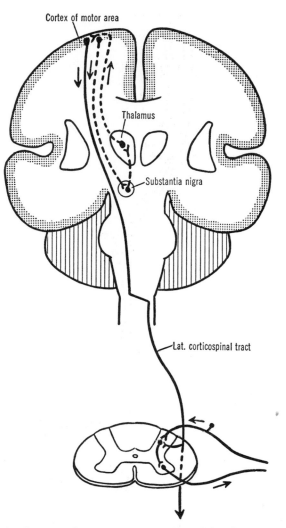

Figure 154. A circular route from motor cortex through basal ganglia and back to the cortex to the origin of corticospinal fibers.

reactions are also known as righting reflexes, of which there are five types, as follows.

Labyrinthine-Righting Reflexes. If an animal is blindfolded and placed in any position in space, the head returns to the normal horizontal position. The midbrain and the labyrinths appear to be essential for this reaction.

Body-Righting Reflexes Acting on the Head. The labyrinths must first be destroyed. If the blindfolded animal is then placed on its side,

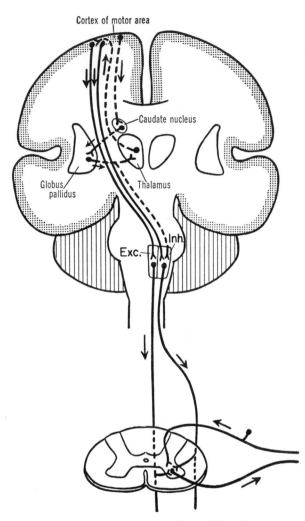

Figure 155. A circular route from motor cortex through basal ganglia and back to the origin of extrapyramidal fibers. The outflow from the globus pallidus is represented in part by the fasciculus lenticularis of Figure 147. In addition, projections to brain stem inhibitory levels are shown coming from the globus pallidus as well as directly from the cerebral cortex.

the head assumes a normal position. But this can be prevented if a board is placed on the upper surface of the body with enough pressure to equalize the pressure of the body weight exerted on that surface lying on the ground. The reflex depends then upon unequal stimulation of pressure receptors in the body.

Neck-Righting Reflexes. If the neck has once been turned in response to labyrinthine- or body-righting reflexes, proprioceptive receptors in the neck muscles are stimulated. This is followed by a reflex rotation which brings the body into line with the head and neck.

Body-Righting Reflexes Acting on the Body. In order to demonstrate these fully, the labyrinths must be destroyed and the animal blindfolded. If the forelimbs and shoulder are placed lateral to the ground, the hind-limbs tend to rotate to the horizontal position. This reaction can be prevented by equalizing the pressure with a board, as before.

Optic-Righting Reflexes. In the tests so far the animals are blind-folded to exclude optic-righting reflexes. These are important in the normal animal, but, since they depend upon the cerebral cortex, are absent in a midbrain animal. If the labyrinths are removed and cervical dorsal roots sectioned, the otherwise normal animal demonstrates right-ing reflexes with the eyes open, but not if blindfolded.

These reactions can be demonstrated in a thalamic cat or dog. In lower forms, such as birds, the basal ganglia are relatively much more important, and in the absence of cerebral cortex quite normal-appearing activity can still be carried out.

Primates differ from quadrupeds in that a midbrain primate, even though exhibiting righting reflexes, cannot stand. The cerebral cortex has become relatively much more important.

MOTOR DISORDERS

The basal ganglia, through their complex, reciprocal connections with the thalamus and the cerebral cortex, are involved in the control and regulation of posture and movement. Their effects upon motor cells are mediated indirectly by pathways that leave the globus pallidus and descend to the reticular formation of the brain stem. If the basal ganglia are damaged, normal motor functions are disorganized or lost, and spontaneous, abnormal movements appear. In their most complete, uncontrollable form, these movements are known as *dystonia*. There are two distinct types of basal ganglia disorders. In one, there is tremor, which can progress to dystonia, with a diffuse lesion of the globus pal-lidus. In the other, there is *athetosis*, which can progress to dystonia, with usually a lesion of the corpus striatum.

The tremors of the pallidal disorder are manifested as fine, rapid, involuntary contractions of digital and cranial muscles. These tremors disappear during sleep and tend to smooth out or disappear during a voluntarily induced movement. Hence they are frequently termed *tremors at rest*. The lay term is shaking palsy. The tremors are usually part of a disorder called *paralysis agitans*, frequently referred to as Parkinsonism (after James Parkinson, who first described it) (p. 319). Other signs are commonly present, including rigidity in all muscles, loss of such associated movements as arm swinging when walking, loss of emotional expression in the face, and often a propulsive gait. There is no true paralysis. Movements are difficult mainly because of the associated rigidity.

In the athetosis of the striatal disorder, the movements are slow in rate, writhing or twisting in nature, and are seen mainly in the limbs. In some instances, the involuntary movements are rapid, jerky, of wide range, and involve muscles all over the body. These movements are termed *chorea*. Chorea and athetosis may be combined as *choreoathetosis*. Violent choreiform movements are seen in *St. Vitus' dance* (Sydenham's chorea) (p. 319). This is a disease of children that is related to rheumatic fever, probably as an involvement of the nervous system by that disease. *Huntington's chorea* (p. 318) is a hereditary disorder which, however, does not appear until adult life. It is characterized, not only by chorea, but also by speech difficulties and progressive dementia.

Clinical studies have shown that destruction of the connections between the globus pallidus and the thalamus, by interrupting the blood supply, by injecting a chemical, or by killing the fibers by freezing, may relieve or abolish abnormal movements, in particular tremor, and sometimes rigidity also. The relief is contralateral; that is, for tremor on the right side the surgeon would destroy the left globus pallidus or its projections. These findings are in conflict with some of the commonly held ideas about the functions of basal ganglia, and it seems likely that they will stimulate research and necessitate revision of ideas. Destruction of the subthalamic nucleus on one side is followed by a most severe chorea of one half of the body (termed hemichorea or, more often, *hemiballismus*). Destruction of the outflow of impulses from the globus pallidus abolishes the hemiballismus.

SENSORY FUNCTIONS

In considering sensory functions, we may arbitrarily assign to certain portions of the cerebral cortex the function of initial perception of a primary modality of sensation; and to other regions, the localization, discrimination, and integration of the primary modalities and the integration of these mechanisms into learning. Such a method is useful in considering the symptoms resulting from destruction of different parts of the cortex, but so far as normal functions are concerned the various parts are so integrated that their separate functions are not subjectively recognized or differentiated. From the standpoint of organization it seems desirable to consider certain features of perception here and also in the next chapter.

The afferent pathways are relayed by the thalamus to the primary receptive areas, the cortex of which is generally thinner than that of the motor areas and has definite granular layers (Fig. 152). The afferent fibers that enter these areas form bands that are often visible to the naked eye, especially in the occipital cortex (Area 17) (Fig. 156). If a portion of cerebral cortex is destroyed, there is a characteristic reaction of the thalamus to cortical injury. The thalamic fibers ending in the injured cortex undergo retrograde degeneration to the extent that chromatolysis of the cells of origin is not reversed. The cells die, and the thalamic nuclei containing these cells atrophy. There is, therefore, no "pure" cortical lesion, because any cortical lesion is followed within a few months by death of some portion of the thalamus. This thalamic reaction to cortical injury has been widely used to determine anatomical relationships between the thalamus and the cerebral cortex.

The primary areas have been artificially stimulated, but the resulting sensations are not those normally experienced. Electrical stimulation of the visual cortex gives rise to sensations of flashes of light. One would not expect it to be otherwise, unless by chance the stimulation affected a group of neurons which would normally be activated by objects in the visual fields. Such stimulation is just as artificial as that which simultaneously activates all the fibers of a peripheral nerve.

Stimulation may also result from the actions of certain drugs. If, for example, strychnine is applied to the cortex of the postcentral gyrus of cats, the resulting excitation evidently is accompanied by subjective sensations, because the animal scratches, bites or licks those parts of the body which are represented in the stimulated part of the cortex. It is

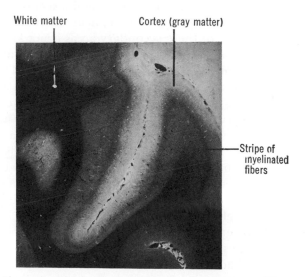

White matter   Cortex (gray matter)

Stripe of myelinated fibers

Figure 156. Photomicrograph of a section of occipital cortex. The entering visual fibers form a band or stripe as they end in the fourth cell layer. Weigert stain.

interesting that for cutaneous senses the subjective responses occur on both sides of the body. It should be emphasized that the cerebral cortex is insensitive. The sensations resulting from stimulation are projected sensations, perceived by the patient as if they were in some part of the body, and without any sensation directly referable to the surface of the brain.

Stimulation may also result from pathological processes. Tumors may stimulate sensory cortex much as they do motor cortex, and the patient experiences subjective sensations. The sensory cortex may also· be implicated in epilepsy (p. 316).

It is possible to record the electrical activity of sensory cortex in a manner that gives a clue to representation of different parts of the body. If brain waves are suppressed with a drug, such as a barbiturate, and a sense organ or a nerve is then stimulated, the arrival at the cerebral cortex of the resulting impulses is indicated by a well-defined, surface-positive spike potential. Studies of this kind on lower animals indicate that impulses from the lower limb enter the upper part of the gyrus; those from the face, the lower part of the gyrus. The available information, particularly that derived from clinical studies, indicates that a similar arrangement is present in man.

Recent studies indicate that there are secondary somatic areas, and perhaps tertiary, according to a terminology which lists the postcentral gyrus (and sensory cortex in lower animals) as Somatic Area I and the second somatic area as Somatic Area II. Impulses from sense organs all over the body reach the second somatic areas bilaterally. The location of Somatic Area II varies according to species, and it seems likely that one is present in man above the lateral fissure, near the foot of the central fissure. The significance of these secondary areas is not known.

Results indicate that for general senses, the thalamus and the postcentral gyrus are the primary receptive areas (Fig. 157). The interrelationships of these two are still uncertain. If the thalamus is destroyed, the effect is the same as if all the afferent pathways were severed. Lesions of the postcentral gyrus, however, are not followed by such marked losses. Position sense is severely affected, touch less so, and pain and temperature relatively little, at least as far as perception is concerned. But in such cases a patient may recognize that he has been touched and yet have difficulty in distinguishing degrees or intensities of stimulation. Furthermore, there is clinical evidence that a considerable degree of recovery from such defects is possible.

The primary receptive areas for vision are in the occipital lobes (Fig. 158). If both these areas are destroyed, the patient is as blind as if both optic nerves had been severed. There is evidence, however, that in other primates some visual function is retained in the superior colliculi.

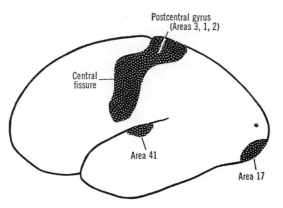

Figure 157.   Diagram indicating the approximate locations of primary receptive areas. The postcentral gyrus is often subdivided into Areas 3, 1 and 2, although no functional significance has been attributed to this subdivision.

The primary receptive areas for hearing are in the temporal lobes (Fig. 157), each receiving impulses from both ears, so that destruction of one such area will not produce total deafness.

Pain.   Pain, although but one of the general senses, is mentioned separately here because of its great clinical importance, and because of recent theories concerning its genesis (p. 179). These theories emphasize the importance of separating the physiological responses of certain receptors to noxious stimuli from the psychological reaction to the arrival of impulses in the brain. Pain is one of the most common presenting

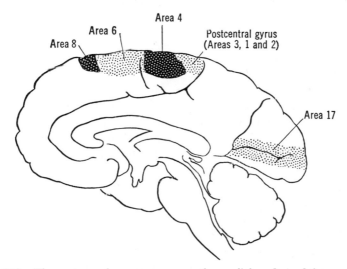

Figure 158.   The motor and sensory areas on the medial surface of the cerebral hemisphere.

complaints of patients. The amount and quality of perceived pain are determined by many psychological variants, and the alleviation of pain may be a major problem. The psychological, physiological, and pathological properties of this sensation constitute an extensive phase of neurophysiological research. It is still uncertain what level of the brain constitutes the primary receptive area. Little is known of the mechanisms that modify pain; removal of the hypophysis, for example, for advanced cancer may reduce or abolish the pain caused by the cancer. Some sensory qualities, such as itching, are related to pain, but the exact nature of itching is uncertain. The alleviation of pain by organic means may be carried out by a variety of methods, including surgery (Fig. 106, p. 182; see also p. 334). The advance of medicine has been possible in great part because a variety of chemical compounds can alleviate, abolish, or prevent pain, and one of the most important groups of this type is the anesthetics.

Anesthetics may be local in action—that is, they may block conduction in peripheral nerve fibers—or they may have central actions and in some way prevent subjective interpretation of afferent impulses reaching the brain, perhaps by affecting the reticular activating system (p. 272). Ether is a centrally acting drug, for example, that is given by inhalation, so that it reaches the nervous system by way of the blood. Anesthetic effects are proportional to the rate and length of administration and the concentration.

EPILEPSY AND THE CONVULSIVE STATES

The term "epilepsy" is applied to any disorder in which convulsions or fits occur, and of itself is not specific. Most epilepsies are associated with the motor or sensory cortex. For instance, tumors growing in or near the motor areas may so irritate the neurons that they discharge and thereby initiate jacksonian convulsions. Irritative phenomena resulting from inflammatory processes may likewise cause convulsions if the motor areas are affected. *Post-traumatic epilepsy*, a not infrequent complication of severe head injuries, may be the result of irritation by scar tissue formation in the region of the injury. Sensory fits may also occur if the irritative processes involve sensory cortex.

There is, however, a classic symptom complex of unknown etiology with which the term "epilepsy" has been associated. It is called *idiopathic epilepsy*, also known as the "falling sickness." In its most severe form there are convulsions preceded by periods of unconsciousness. These are known as *grand mal attacks*. The more common and less severe attacks with only momentary losses of consciousness are *petit mal attacks*.

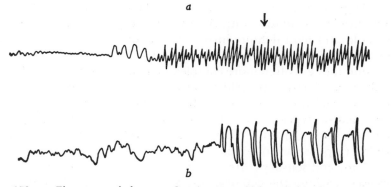

Figure 159. *a,* Electroencephalogram of a nine-year-old boy. Tonic-clonic seizure with fast, high voltage waves. Arrow indicates appearance of clinical evidence of seizure. *b,* Petit mal attack, with staring, blinking, and loss of consciousness. Characteristic wave and spike discharge in electroencephalogram. (Reproduced from Gibbs and Gibbs: Atlas of Electroencephalography, courtesy of Lew A. Cummings Co.)

There is no evidence that the cerebral cortex is primarily at fault in idiopathic epilepsy. It is possible that the cortex is "driven" by discharges from subcortical structures. The abnormal increase in excitability is not limited to the motor effects, because there may be epileptic fits of a sensory type; that is, instead of having muscular convulsions, the patient may experience peculiar or perverted sensations, such as itching or disagreeable odors.

The diagnosis can often be made from the history and from direct observation of attacks. In suspected cases, breathing deeply for a short time may initiate a convulsion. This hyperventilation decreases the amount of carbon dioxide in the lungs and leads to an alkalinity of the blood, so that the increased excitability may trigger an attack. Electroencephalograms taken during grand mal attacks show prominent high voltage waves (Fig. 159). At other times, and also during petit mal attacks, the records frequently show abnormal waves of the type pictured in Figure 159.

SUMMARY

The motor areas are those which give rise to the descending motor tracts. Most of them are found in the frontal lobes (precentral motor cortex). They are often called agranular cortex because of the large numbers of pyramidal cells in the granular layer. Electrical stimulation reveals an inverted, multiple representation of movements in different parts of the body. The type of motor response to stimulation depends upon the strength and frequency of stimulation.

The precentral motor cortex is divided into Areas 4, 6 and 8. Area 4 is practically coextensive with the precentral gyrus and has the lowest threshold and most definite inversion of body representation. Stimulation of Area 6 more often yields inhibitory responses. When movements do result, they are often more complex than in the case of Area 4. Area 8 is called the frontal eye field because stimulation primarily results in eye, head, and neck movements. Removal of motor cortex yields upper motor neuron types of disorders, the severity of which depends upon the extent of destruction. When Area 6 is involved, the grasp reflex and groping response are often characteristic signs in the adult.

Motor and sensory cortex are interdependent in function. Afferent impulses reaching the cerebral cortex, particularly tactile and proprioceptive impulses, condition the responses of the motor cortex.

Certain of the cortical motor areas project to the basal ganglia and, with them, constitute the highest level of the extrapyramidal system. Most of the basal ganglia are controlling or inhibitory in function; their destruction leads to positive signs, such as rigidity and involuntary movements. Destruction of the connections of the globus pallidus may abolish these signs.

The sensory cortex (primary receptive areas) includes those portions of the brain in which afferent paths end. These areas have to do with the perception of primary modalities of sensation, a function which is lost when a primary receptive area is destroyed. Electrical stimulation does not yield normal sensation. Recording of evoked electrical activity enables one to map out the termination of afferent paths.

The cerebral cortex is involved, although not necessarily primarily at fault, in various types of epilepsy. These are motor or sensory fits of various kinds, often characterized by an abnormal electroencephalogram.

Names in Neurology

GEORGE HUNTINGTON (1850-1916)

Huntington, an American physician, was the first to describe hereditary chorea.

JOHN HUGHLINGS JACKSON (1834-1911)

Jackson was an English physician and a clinical neurologist whose concepts of the nervous system were so far advanced for his time that to a large extent they were not appreciated. From clinical and postmortem studies of epilepsy, aphasia, and paralysis, he concluded that certain cortical areas were concerned in motor activities, sensory mechanisms, and language, and he accurately located the regions concerned. He pointed out that positive signs in neurological disorders are often the result of release of lower centers from the control of higher centers. His studies were the forerunner and often the basis of subsequent investigations of the brain.

JAMES PARKINSON (1755-1824)

Parkinson, an English physician, in 1812 described the first recognized cases of paralysis agitans. He was noted for his studies of fossil remains, being an able geologist and paleontologist, but was perhaps better known during his time as a radical reformer and political agitator.

THOMAS SYDENHAM (1624-1689)

Sydenham was an English physician who published first-hand accounts of many diseases, including gout, scarlatina, measles, bronchopneumonia, hysteria, chorea, and others. Some of his descriptions are unsurpassed classics.

REFERENCES

See the references cited on pages 6, 173 and 189.

Brutkowski, S.: Functions of prefrontal cortex in animals. Physiol. Rev., *45*:721-746, 1965.
Denny-Brown, D.: The Basal Ganglia. Oxford University Press, 1962. (An outstanding monograph on the relation of basal ganglia to disorders of movement.)
Martin, J. P.: The Basal Ganglia and Posture. Philadelphia, J. B. Lippincott Company, 1967.
Penfield, W., and Jasper, H. H.: Epilepsy and the Functional Anatomy of the Human Brain. Boston, Little, Brown and Company, 1954. (This is a valuable reference dealing with clinical research into the problems of epilepsy.)

The following three textbooks, which deal with clinical material, contain many sections that will be valuable to the advanced student.

Brain, R.: Clinical Neurology. 2nd ed., London, Oxford University Press, 1964.
Grinker, R., and Sahs, A. L.: Neurology. 6th ed., Springfield, Ill., Charles C Thomas, 1966.
Walshe, F.: Diseases of the Nervous System. 10th ed., Baltimore, Williams & Wilkins Company, 1963. (See also: On the interpretation of experimental studies of cortical motor function: with special reference to the "operational view" of experimental procedures. Brain, *74*:249-266, 1951: An attempted correlation of the diverse hypotheses of functional localization in the cerebral cortex. J. Neurol. Sci., *1*:111-128, 1964.)

CHAPTER 20

ASSOCIATIVE AND
INTEGRATIVE FUNCTIONS
OF THE FOREBRAIN

Mental and emotional events or processes form what may be termed the psychological level of the organism, that is to say, the "mind." Although one cannot consider the mind as substance, there is no doubt that it is resident in the nervous system. This is corroborated by the almost vegetable-like existence which follows complete decortication or decerebration, and by the effects on mental processes of various insults or damage to the cerebral cortex. In spite of the fact, then, that the mind is a concept, it is a concept which depends upon physical structures and, in that sense, is physical.

The most important parts of the nervous system as regards mental and emotional processes are those portions of the cerebral cortex known as association areas. As Figure 160 indicates, these regions occupy the greater part of the lateral surfaces of the occipital, parietal, and temporal lobes, and of the frontal lobes anterior to the motor areas. They are connected with each other and with the neothalamus by innumerable fibers passing through the corpus callosum and the white matter of the hemispheres.

There are several methods by which mental and emotional processes have been studied. The ability to learn and the retention of learned patterns of behavior have been investigated in normal subjects and have also been correlated with the destruction of part or all of the

320

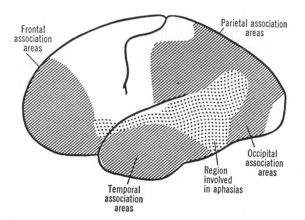

Figure 160. Diagram indicating the extent of association cortex on the lateral surface of the cerebral hemisphere. The stippled region is often involved in aphasic disorders, but there is no definite demarcation between it and the remaining association cortex.

cortex, both experimentally and in man after neurological disorders and surgical operations. The relation of learning to the conditioning of responses is another valuable approach, and there are many other psychological studies of normal subjects which may be carried out. The results of these investigations are often difficult to analyze because the occurrence of a defect following a cortical lesion does not necessarily indicate that the opposite of the defect is a function of the removed area. Furthermore, if no defect follows a cortical lesion, one cannot conclude that this area has no function. A brick can be removed from the foundation of a column; but if the column does not fall, one does not conclude that the brick served no purpose.

Mental and emotional events are extremely complex and cannot be broken down into a series of definite, separate performances. It follows that no separate, specific functions can be assigned to separate, specific parts of the association cortex. Rather, this cortex functions as a whole, and defects resulting from damage to it are complex. In many instances the severity of such defects is related to the extent or amount of cortex damaged and relatively little to the location of the lesion. In other words, the more cortex removed, the greater and more complex the defect. This does not mean that various parts of the association cortex do not function differently. They undoubtedly do in the sense that these parts contribute something different to performances carried out by the whole cortex. What should be emphasized is that different parts cannot be regarded as functioning in an isolated manner.

It should be made clear, however, that the brain consists of two halves (which are right and left mirror mates), which are connected by commissures, the largest and most important of which is the *corpus callosum.* In certain functional respects, the two halves differ. The left hemisphere, for example, is usually the major or dominant one (see below). However, if all the cross connections are cut, each of the halves behaves as an independent brain. Each has its own independent perceptual, learning, memory, and other higher functions, and neither half is aware of what is experienced in the other. Furthermore, each half can independently generate emotional reactions.

LEARNING

Learning is a general term used to indicate an attribute which is highly developed (relatively speaking) in man. The mechanisms involved in learning take years to develop, and the process as yet is beyond our comprehension. Learning includes, in the form of memory, relationships between neural processes which may last over scores of years. The time differential cannot be explained by any known physiological data or anatomical structure. It has been postulated that closed circuits of nerve cells, such as are illustrated in Figure 149, p. 295, are involved in memory, because of the possibility of continuous electrical activity. But electrical activity can be abolished completely, for example, by anesthetics, without impairing memory. It is much more likely that long-term processes in the nervous system will be found to depend upon chemical reactions and molecular arrangement in nerve cells. There is no specific region of the brain responsible for learning, no specific region which, when destroyed, results in inability to learn, and no specific anatomical or physiological characteristics of learning. What now seems clear is that there are two kinds of memory. One, which is immediate or short-term, is an active mechanism which may depend upon electrical changes. However, the memory trace of an experience is not laid down permanently either during or immediately after an experience. That is to say, the process of learning seems to differ from memory storage. The latter, also termed long-term memory, involves a structural change and seems to be dependent upon protein metabolism. The two kinds of memory can be selectively affected by brain damage or disease.

LEARNING AND SENSORIMOTOR FUNCTIONS

In this particular discussion certain features of afferent paths are included because of their importance in psychological mechanisms.

Motor. Although the movements resulting from electrical stimulation of motor cortex may give an idea of the functions of this part of the brain, the movements are, nevertheless, artificial. Stimulation may be followed by contractions of certain muscles, but not by patterns such as threading a needle, writing, or playing the piano. At present, the concept is that no one area of the brain specifically directs motor activities.

In spite of such nonspecificity, however, considerable information of clinical importance has been derived from the study of *apraxias*. Apraxias are defects in movement patterns or purposeful acts resulting from lesions of association cortex. A purposeful act may be an acquired automatism such as walking, or driving a car, or it may be threading a needle, lighting a cigaret, playing the piano, or operating a typewriter. In any event it is an arrangement of muscular activity into some meaningful or purposeful sequence. For any such pattern there is a period during which the component movements are laboriously learned. But finally all are arranged as a modal sequence which one thinks of as a total act. In driving a car there is usually no conscious awareness of component movements. In fact, if asked to describe just how all the necessary actions are carried out, one might be hard put to do so. What has been learned and retained is a total pattern.

The learning and performance of such types of motor behavior are related to handedness. In right-handed persons the left hemisphere is said to be the major one. In terms of neurological lesions this dominance is important for the following reasons: Lesions of association cortex in the major hemisphere may be followed by apraxias, whereas similar lesions in the minor hemisphere may cause no noticeable symptoms. There is no one specific part of association cortex which has to be involved in order to cause an apraxia. For example, destruction of the major supramarginal gyrus in one patient may cause an apraxia characterized by inability to play the piano (when such an ability had been present before), as well as difficulties with other movement patterns. Yet in other patients similar apraxias may follow lesions elsewhere, or lesions in this gyrus may cause other types of disorders.

There are various kinds of apraxias. In some the patient loses his concept of how to carry out a pattern. In others he may remember quite well, but be unable to perform it properly. It must be emphasized that these patients are *not* paralyzed unless the lesion has also involved motor areas or pathways. The muscles which cannot be used to light a cigaret properly may be used to thread a needle. The tongue which cannot be protruded on command may be used in talking.

Sensory. A typewriter is a familiar object because it has been seen and perhaps used. But it is not necessary to see it in order to revisualize it, either as an object or as a functioning mechanism. The sound of a typewriter in another room is sufficient to identify it as a typewriter. It can be recognized, if one is blindfolded, merely by handling it. By watching a typewriter in use, one might learn to operate it, though certainly not skillfully at first. The sensory phenomena involved are extremely complex. Although nearly all the senses may be involved in any one of the examples cited, the final result or experience is not a group of separately recognized senses, but a perception, the component factors of which are not consciously distinguished. One does not say, "Here is something which feels like this, looks like this, sounds like this, and is named a typewriter." It is simply a typewriter.

So it is with most sensory phenomena. Although it is true that the various senses may be individually detected or experienced under certain conditions, perception nevertheless depends upon quantitative differences in sensory fields. The stimulation of a single tactile spot is perceived because of differences in excitation of this and surrounding spots. Warmth is perceived only because of a difference in temperature from that of the body. An object may be colder than another object, yet both may be warmer than the body.

Nearly all environmental changes involve several modalities. When the base of a vibrating tuning fork is placed over a bony prominence, the resulting sensation is a combination of touch and pressure at a rather high mechanical frequency. A hot object is thought by many investigators to stimulate receptors of warmth and pain, a compound stimulation interpreted as hot. It is well known that if an object is very hot, only pain is felt. Likewise, cold is said to be compounded of pain and coolness. The fact that a subject whose eyes are closed can tell that two points of a compass are touching him (two-point or tactile discrimination) depends, not on the presence of special receptors and fibers for this quality, but upon the fact that impulses from tactile receptors in two different areas are recognized, localized and discriminated by the cerebral cortex.

This synthesis of modalities is given the general term *eugnosia*, and appears to be a function of association cortex. Those parts of the cortex adjacent to the primary receptive areas receive fibers from these areas and in turn are connected with each other and with the rest of the cerebral cortex.

If a lead pencil is examined manually, the average subject recognizes it even with his eyes closed. The individual modalities are integrated into factors of size, weight, shape, texture, and temperature. Past experience relates these qualities to a lead pencil. This *stereognosis* usually proceeds rapidly and, for familiar objects, is completed almost immediately without the conscious intervention of the component qualities.

The quality of rapid synthesis is especially marked in visual phenomena. If the picture of an airplane is flashed upon a screen, a certain time is necessary to determine its type, purpose, and nationality. If the time upon the screen is gradually reduced, it is not long before a fraction of a second suffices for identification. This is recognition of a total pattern and not a sequential recognition of individual qualities.

Similar functions obtain in regard to hearing. Dropping a lead pencil might or might not produce a characteristic sound, but dropping a coin on a hard surface certainly would. A subject could not only recognize that a coin produced the sound, but might very well be able to tell its denomination. For both vision and hearing, eugnostic mechanisms appear to be a function of the major hemisphere.

Agnosias may follow lesions of the association areas. Agnosia literally means "without knowledge." Here it is used in the sense that knowledge or recognition of objects is impaired or impossible. There are many grades and types of agnosias, and many of them cannot be related to specific cortical areas.

One type is *visual agnosia,* which often follows a lesion of the occipital cortex on the lateral surface of the major hemisphere. Previously familiar objects are seen but not recognized. A lead pencil may mean nothing unless the patient is allowed to handle it, recognition then being related to stereognosis. A bunch of keys is not recognized until they are shaken; their characteristic sounds are then the determining qualities.

Lesions of the parietal lobes may be followed by *astereognosis,* the loss of the normal quality of stereognosis. If the lead pencil is held in the hand opposite to the involved lobe, it is not identified, even though the primary modalities are relatively intact. If the eyes are open, recognition is possible because of visualization.

Afferent Paths and the Cerebral Cortex. Sensory functions are difficult to study because of the lack of objective responses which can be recorded, and because fluctuations at the cortical level may either enhance or depress subjective interpretation. It is well known that a painful injury received in the heat of play or some other activity may go unnoticed at the time it happens (part of this modulation may occur at the first synaptic level in the spinal cord; see p. 246). The concern of the brain with the activity of play enables it to ignore or suppress the afferent impulses reaching it. Yet if the same injury were deliberately inflicted upon someone with his foreknowledge, then the subjective interpretation of the afferent impulses is nearly always exaggerated.

A number of methods of investigation, however, have yielded considerable information. These include studies of receptors as regards their distribution and response to stimuli; the anatomical connections of the afferent paths; the recording of electrical activity in these paths and in the cortical areas; and the correlation of these with psychophysiological studies in the intact human subject.

The conventional diagrams of receptors and their afferent paths are useful in indicating anatomical configuration and location, but they are much too schematic to enable one to correlate structural and functional properties.

Let us first consider receptors, using the tactile type as an example. A dorsal root fiber does not enter a small skin area and there form but a single group of Meissner's corpuscles. If this were true, the simultaneous stimulation of adjacent tactile spots could not be differentiated, for there would be no unstimulated spot in between to form a neutral background. Perception always consists in the recognition of a figure against a background. The background may represent stimulation, but if its activity is generally less than that of some contained point or area, then a comparison is possible and configuration appears.

Anatomical studies have shown that a dorsal root fiber branches over a relatively wide area, probably hundreds of square millimeters or more. If such an area were supplied by but a single fiber (Fig. 161), one could detect differences in intensity of stimulation. An increase in intensity causes an increase in frequency of impulses traversing the afferent path and reaching the cerebral cortex (p. 142). Localization, however, is not possible, because stimulation of one side of the area causes impulses in the parent fiber similar to those resulting from excitation on the other side. So far as the cortex is concerned, the impulses might be arising anywhere in the area.

The actual situation is that any one skin area is supplied by several fibers, and in a single touch spot there are receptors derived from several parent fibers. The simplest possible arrangement which accounts for tactile localization is shown in Figure 161. Stimulation of a single touch spot results in impulses traversing two different fibers, thus allowing the cortex a comparison between these and nonlocalizable impulses from other parts of the area. But this arrangement does not correlate with the electrical activity recorded at the cortex under such conditions. Such activity is found over a relatively wide expanse and is of greater magnitude in the center of what might be called a field of activity. When even a small skin area is touched, there is not true point stimulation. The skin is bent or depressed, and the receptors in the center of the depression are more intensely stimulated than those at the periphery. Impulses starting here are therefore of a higher frequency. If, as shown in Figure 161, one fiber gives more receptors to a touch spot than another fiber, the result is a higher frequency of impulses following stimulation. Consequently, there arrives at the cerebral cortex a group of impulses which activates a field or region of cortex. Impulses in the central part of this group are more frequent; the resulting activity of the central part of the cortical field is therefore more intense. Localization of a stimulated spot is therefore a matter of intensity discrimination.

With a two-neuron arrangement, however, tactile or two-point discrimination is not possible. In order to account for two-point discrimination, at least five neurons are necessary, as indicated in Figure 161. Stimulation of two separate spots in their receptor pattern results in two

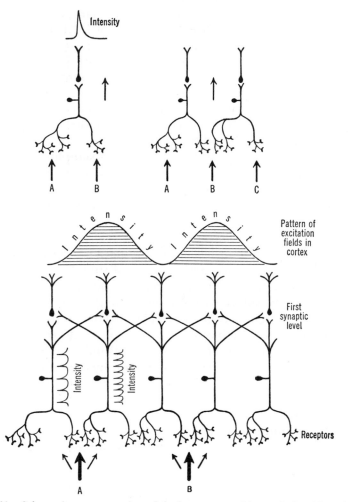

Figure 161. Schematic representation of the importance of interrelationships of peripheral receptors and their central connections. *Upper left:* The conventional scheme. Stimulation of a touch spot at *A* is not distinguishable from stimulation at *B*, since the impulses
traverse the same fiber. The electrical activity recorded on arrival at the cortex is represented as a spike of activity in a restricted field. *Upper right:* The touch spot at *B* is derived
from two dorsal root fibers. Stimulation here is localizable, but not distinguishable from
simultaneous stimulation of either *A* or *C*. In either case there would be a single field of
cortical activity. *Lower:* The simplest arrangement for two-point discrimination. Stimulation at *A* results in a higher frequency of impulses over the second neuron, since it contributes more endings to the touch spot and is therefore more intensely stimulated. The
same situation obtains for the fourth neuron giving endings to *B*. The interconnections
at the first and subsequent synaptic layers (omitted from the diagram) allow a spread of
excitation. The recorded cortical response is over a wide area and is a field of algebraic
summation of many spikes, more pronounced in the center because of the higher frequency of entering impulses. With two such fields, two-point discrimination is possible.

fields of cortical activity. Regional variations in sensitivity (two-point discrimination is more exact in the skin of the hand than in that of the back) appear then to be at least partially explained by differences in pattern and zonal distribution of fibers and receptors.

The appearance of fields of cortical activity in response to peripheral point stimulation is enhanced by interconnections at synaptic levels of the afferent paths (Fig. 161). At any level, cord, medullary, or thalamic, a single fiber may synapse with cells upon which other fibers of the same path impinge. Excitation, therefore, tends to spread laterally at synaptic levels and thus in the end activates a greater extent of cerebral cortex. The extent of spreading is exemplified in the visual system. With stimulation of a circular area in the fovea 5 microns in diameter, activity can be recorded from the occipital cortex in a region at least one hundred times as wide (0.5 mm.), the area being ten thousand times greater.

How may subjective interpretations be related to these facts? Can any correlation be made or law derived? There is a certain relationship between subjective sensation and intensity of stimulation. Suppose that to an object of a certain weight the arbitrary unit of 100 is assigned, and the same unit to the subjective sensation of weight. Then it is found that an object just enough heavier to be subjectively detected (101) has the weight of 110. The next subjective increase (to 102) necessitates an object of weight 121. These arbitrarily selected units indicate that the stimulus increases logarithmically while the sensation increases arithmetically — the *Weber-Fechner law* (p. 337). So far as peripheral receptors and afferent paths are concerned, increasing intensity of stimulation results in higher frequency of impulses. Frequency of impulses entering the cerebral cortex must therefore be of great importance in perception. The Weber-Fechner law, however, holds mainly for moderate intensities of stimulation.

LEARNING AND LANGUAGE MECHANISMS

The use of symbols is highly developed in man, but is also seen in other primates. Symbolization is the form of speech by which ideas are expressed verbally and manually; it is also a part of internal symbolization or thinking. The degree to which this is possible is directly related to the intellectual development of an individual. A person may be illiterate for a number of reasons, and yet be innately intelligent, that is, possess the capacity for development if given the opportunity. But the degree of symbolization nevertheless affords the best index of intelligence, so much so that it is difficult to estimate intelligence in the presence of illiteracy.

One can indicate the complexity of symbolization by tracing its formation and development from infancy. A baby hears certain sounds which gradually become associated with objects he sees, and, by trial and error, his first attempts at vocalization gradually evolve into spoken words. Subsequently, the acquisition of new words is by a process of conditioning, the words being associated with objects, situations, and the like. Soon he is able to put words together as phrases, and later as sentences. By these he can express wishes and, perhaps, have desires gratified. These visual and auditory functions are associated with increasingly complex movements: namely, the more and more precise coordination of muscles of the abdomen, thorax, larynx, pharynx, tongue, lips, and cheeks.

In other words, he learns that he can make different sounds by using these muscles in different ways. There is certainly no conscious selection of a particular muscle or muscles, but rather a trial and error method which, when successful, is facilitated by repetition and added to by conditioning.

At some time in his young life he becomes introduced to symbols in another form, that is, writing or printing. He may be shown the letters of the alphabet one by one and taught the sound of each. When he learns how letters are put together to form words, he identifies the printed words "mama" or "mother" with the sound of these words and with the person. Or he may be introduced to the word as a whole without any breakdown into component letters. After the visual introduction to letters and words the child can be taught to write these symbols. This introduces a new element of motor coordination—the use of digital muscles in symbolization.

In succeeding years these elements are gradually improved and expanded. More than this, he improves his phraseology and learns to group sentences so as to express emotions, ideas, and wishes. All his emotional and intellectual processes become colored by symbolization.

As can be seen, symbolization is a complex phenomenon or, rather, is a matter of complex phenomena. While one cannot say that speech is located in this or that part of the brain, there is a considerable body of information derived from the study of speech defects following cortical lesions. In such cases cerebral dominance is important, since, as a rule, defects only follow lesions of the major hemisphere. Furthermore, most such defects follow damage to a general area indicated in Figure 160.

These defects are called *aphasias*. Various kinds of aphasias have been described and classified, and in each, certain symptoms appear to predominate. However, rigid classifications in the past have hampered understanding; careful examination nearly always reveals widespread or generalized involvement of symbolization. This region functions as a whole in such a manner that interference with a part tends to disrupt the entire mechanism by interrupting connections.

The extent to which lesions of association cortex may disrupt symbolization may be illustrated by brief discussions of the resultant defects. Lesions may be the result of various neurological disorders. Thus a thrombosis of the left middle cerebral artery may be followed by softening and destruction of most of the cortex on the lateral surface of the hemisphere. Traumatic injuries, tumors, abscesses, and a number of other disorders often involve part or all of this general region.

The term "aphasia" literally means "without speech," but the term as used today refers to many different types of defects. The following is a general classification intended only to illustrate certain aspects of aphasias.

Expressive Disorders of Speech (Verbal, Motor or Broca's Aphasia) (p. 337).   The patient has difficulty in speaking or writing, or both, although he usually knows fairly well what he wants to say and may understand what is said to him. He may be able to use only a few words, and when he does speak he tends to repeat again and again those words which he does not wish to say. He is, according to Jackson, "not wordless, but speechless." Surprisingly enough, under the stress of emotional situations he may speak fluently, in some cases almost as well as before the injury. But when the emotion subsides, the inability to speak reappears.

The disorder is usually not restricted to the expressive side. Other phases suffer as well, though to a lesser extent. There may be diminution in understanding of written and spoken commands. Comprehension of situations may also deteriorate. This type of aphasia is said to follow lesions in the anterior portion of the region illustrated in Figure 160.

Receptive Disorders of Speech (Sensory, Auditory or Wernicke's Aphasia) (p. 338).   These are characterized by difficulty in understanding what is said or read. Symbols may be recognized as objects; words are heard as sounds. But to the patient they are a foreign language. If he is asked to do something, he cannot, because the directive words are meaningless. The lack of understanding prevents the patient from recognizing or knowing what he himself says. Consequently, what he speaks and writes is frequently a meaningless jargon. Other phases of symbolization suffer as well, but to a lesser extent. Receptive disorders often follow lesions in the temporal or parietal regions.

Expressive-Receptive Disorders (Total Aphasias).   With extensive lesions, there may be combinations of expressive and receptive disorders. These are incapacitating because patients cannot speak or write, or understand what they or anyone else reads or says. But there is no paralysis, no deafness, no blindness, and no loss of general sensations, unless other parts of the nervous system are affected.

Amnesic Aphasia (Nominal Aphasia).   The outstanding symptom is an inability to use words as nouns. Such a patient may know that the object with which he is confronted is "to write with," but cannot say "pen." The resulting speech disorder is, therefore, great. It is almost impossible to assign an involvement of a definite area in this aphasia, but the temporal lobe and even part of the parietal lobe are usually involved.

Aphasias on a Higher Level. In the previously discussed aphasias there is an inability to associate symbols with objects or acts. But in higher levels there is a loss of the *significance* of symbols. They may be recognized, but their meaning is not understood. This may constitute a *semantic aphasia,* or it may be combined with other aphasias as a semantic defect. In semantic aphasia, patients can understand and can read and write; but when one speaks to them, simple words must be used, and these must be spoken slowly. Often, in going from one sentence to the next, they lose the gist of what they are reading. Naturally, the inability to comprehend situations or ideas is present to a varying degree in all "normal" persons, so that, without a knowledge of previous intellectual level, the diagnosis of semantic aphasias and defects may be difficult, if not impossible.

The aphasias may be relatively easy to detect, but their analysis is often difficult. The intellectual level which a subject attains during life determines in part the degree of any aphasic disorder. Furthermore, just as in normal life, aphasic responses vary from day to day, and repeated examinations may be necessary.

Aphasias are not always the result of destructive lesions. There is hardly an element of agnosia, apraxia, or aphasia established as resulting from organic lesions that has not been noted in purely functional states.

The foregoing discussions have pointed out that aphasias are complex, variable defects, rather than clear-cut clinical syndromes. In most cases it is doubtful that the aphasia can be correlated with specific lesions in specific, small portions of the cortex. In the first place, lesions, even if surgically performed, are rarely sharp and clean. Usually they are diffuse, and their extent is seldom realized unless adequate microscopic examination is made at autopsy (many cases of aphasia do not come to autopsy until a long time after the defect occurred). Secondly, there is at present no way of assessing the function of the supposedly normal cortex remaining after damage to the brain In other words, the separation of aphasias into types is of great value in localizing a neurological disorder to a general region and, what is especially helpful, to one side of the brain. But it is doubtful that aphasias tell us much about the actual mechanisms of symbolization.

The supposedly silent side or minor hemisphere is of clinical importance in the recovery from aphasic defects. Positive training may lead to partial or complete recovery. The minor hemisphere and the cortex remaining in the major hemisphere are probably both important in this matter.

LEARNING AND CONDITIONED RESPONSES

The modification of behavior on the basis of past experiences is primarily a function of the cerebral cortex. Everyone is familiar with the fact that the sight or smell of food may be just as potent a stimulus for salivation as taste. The objective response—salivation—is mediated by a nervous pattern already established at birth. The newborn infant salivates in response to the taste of food. Only later do visual and olfactory stimuli induce salivation. Salivation in response to taste is an *unconditioned reflex,* just as is the knee jerk, which may be elicited in an infant.

Many unconditioned reflexes may be modified by, or adapted to, new stimuli. Pavlov (p. 274) made use of this fact in extensive studies of behavior. The sound of a bell is not ordinarily followed by salivation. Pavlov showed that, if an animal is given food, or acid is placed in its mouth, so that salivation occurs, and if this is accompanied or shortly preceded by another stimulus, such as the sound of a bell, after repeated trials the sound alone may induce salivation. This is a *conditioned response*—a salivatory reaction to an auditory stimulus. It may be that the nervous connections which make this possible are established at birth, but they are not innately functional as are those in the unconditioned reflex arc. This further exemplifies the functional reserve and plasticity of nervous systems of higher forms.

Although Pavlov used salivation as an objective index, more recent techniques have turned to striated muscle because of the rapidity of its response and the greater ease with which such response can be recorded. Thus the blinking of an eye to a puff of air can be conditioned to a light flashed in the eye. These studies have definitely established that conditioned responses are not completely identical with unconditioned reflexes. Conditioned responses are, instead, more of an anticipatory reaction, somewhat akin in latency of response to voluntary activity, and form part of a general pattern.

The neurophysiological factors in conditioning are not definitely established. It has been shown, however, that responses resulting from electrical stimulation of motor pathways cannot be conditioned by simultaneous sensory stimuli of an auditory or visual type. On the other hand, conditioned responses to visual stimuli may be obtained when the conditioned responses result from electrical stimulation of afferent pathways. This indicates that there is a mechanism for forming the pattern or association of conditioning, and that it resides in the central nervous system elsewhere than in the longitudinal pathways. The association areas are the most likely locations.

Removal of part or all of the cortex does not abolish conditioned responses or the ability to form new ones, but these are never as precise as in a normal animal. Whereas flexion of a limb might be the normal conditioned response, general escape movements of a diffuse type constitute the response in a decorticate animal. Subcortical areas thus appear to be able to function in this regard, but for precise or discrete activity the association areas are indispensable.

Conditioned responses, once established, are not invariable. They may gradually disappear if continually elicited without periodic reinforcement by the unconditioned stimulus, or if associated with extraneous stimuli. For a more extensive discussion of these variations, see the references at the end of the chapter.

It is important to note that the so-called involuntary processes may be easily conditioned. Marked changes in salivation, blood pressure, respiration, and many other visceral activities may become associated with many types of stimuli. The devastating effects of stage fright may well be conditioning of this type. Of interest is the *psychogalvanic reflex*, which can be conditioned. This is an increase in sweating during emotional states. In parts where it occurs, such as the hands, the resistance to the flow of an electric current decreases and can be measured, thus furnishing objective data of such changes.

It is also important to note that conditions resembling neuroses may be produced in animals by eliciting in them a conditioned response to a stimulus such as a circle which must be differentiated from an ellipse. If the ellipse is gradually changed until it resembles a circle, the animal is confronted with an impossible situation. In one of Pavlov's experiments a dog thus trained exhibited the symptoms of an acute neurosis.

The ultimate explanation of conditioning is lacking, just as it is in other types of learning, in memory, and in intelligent behavior. The fundamental difficulty is this: The time scale is too great to be adequately explained by present data. Our scanty knowledge is insufficient to explain the months and years over which these conditions last.

FRONTAL ASSOCIATION AREAS

These areas form a rather wide expanse of cortex anterior to motor areas, and various functions have been attributed to them. They are intimately connected with the thalami and probably with the hypothalamus as well. The frontal areas, like the rest of the brain, exhibit the property of functioning as a whole. They are dealt with specifically here because in recent years they have been vigorously attacked surgically, for a variety of reasons.

Removal of these areas in animals is followed by definite signs. Among these is *hyperactivity*, the appearance of which is separated from the operative period by a short-lived depressed state. This hyperactivity is a maintained or driven state of muscular activity, such as walking which has no immediate purpose and which appears almost maniacal. This may be the result of release of diencephalic levels from cortical control.

Another result of such lesions is an interference with temporally arranged acts. Animals cannot learn problems which demand a retention of facts for more than a few seconds, such as remembering in which of two cups food has been placed. "Immediate" or "recent" memory is lost, but abilities which the animal has as a result of previous training are not. The latter are performed or regained shortly after the operation. This indicates both the diffuseness of cortical function and the distinction between short-term and long-term memory.

Another factor in the inability to learn temporally arranged patterns is a *distractibility,* which may be so pronounced that an animal can be deviated from any line of activity by extraneous stimuli.

At present it appears that intelligence is not markedly deranged in frontal lobe disorders, either in man or in lower animals.

THE AFFECTIVE COMPONENT OF BEHAVIOR

It has been observed, especially in man, that frontal lobe lesions are characterized by alterations in emotional reactions. Such changes have been most extensively studied in connection with surgery of the frontal lobes.

Certain severe neurotic and psychotic states have been treated by cutting the connections between the frontal association areas and other regions, such as the thalamus and hypothalamus. Emotional states may be so altered that the result has been somewhat inaccurately termed a reversal of personality. The results are actually much more complex, and so variable from one patient to the next that no prediction of results should ever be made. The most striking changes or characteristics are lack of self-consciousness, and ease and freedom in social relationships, often to an aggressive or embarrassing degree.

Similar operations have been carried out for relief of intractable pain and are sometimes successful. Pain is not actually lost; the patients still feel pinpricks but the pain no longer bothers them.

EMOTIONAL AND VISCERAL FUNCTIONS OF SUBCORTICAL CENTERS

An emotion is difficult to define. It may be expressed in terms of a way of acting and a way of feeling. Emotional behavior may be determined by early social experiences and by mother-infant behavior. All bodily activities may be involved in emotional states. Fear is an emotion. In it, respiration may increase, blood pressure rise, sweating may occur.

The skin may pale, muscles tense, blood sugar may rise, and intestinal movements stop. Yet the same reactions may be present in anger, and an observer may find it difficult to distinguish the two states. It is also becoming clear that biogenic amines in the central nervous system play a role in affective or behavioral states. For example, drugs that deplete or inactivate central norepinephrine produce sedation or depression, whereas drugs that increase or potentiate norepinephrine excite or have an antidepressant action (see also p. 120).

Facial muscles are extremely important in the expression of emotion. It is known that upper motor neuron lesions may interfere with or destroy voluntary control of facial muscles, yet not affect reflex facial movements. In such instances it is not uncommon to find that all types of facial expressions occur during emotional states, in spite of the paralysis of voluntary movement. Conversely, subcortical lesions in the region of the thalamus may abolish facial movements in emotions, although voluntary control is retained. In other words, the arrangement of motor responses in affective behavior seems to be a function of regions other than the cortical motor areas. For instance, emotional speech may occur voluntarily in a patient with motor aphasia (p. 330).

The fact that stimulation of the hypothalamus is followed by responses similar to those seen in emotional states has led to a concept that the hypothalamus is concerned with motor components of emotion. An animal with its cerebral cortex removed may fly into *sham rages*, and these may be reproduced by electrical stimulation of the hypothalamic region. These rages subside when the stimulus stops, and there is no indication that they are accompanied by changes in affective tone. Patients deprived of objective emotional responses because of hypothalamic lesions may nevertheless subjectively experience the emotions. The feeling of an emotion is a function of other parts of the nervous system, including the cortex of the frontal lobe.

A single sense or group of senses cannot be identified with affective tone. Pain is a definite sense. But considered subjectively, it may be associated with pleasure. For example, some people gain pleasure from having pain inflicted on them *(masochism)*, whereas others may derive satisfaction in inflicting it *(sadism)*.

Limbic System. The limbic system consists of the limbic lobe (hippocampus and associated areas of gray matter, plus the cingulate gyrus), certain parts of the temporal and frontal cortex adjacent to the lateral sulcus, certain thalamic and hypothalamic nuclei, and parts of the basal ganglia, including the amygdaloid bodies. The limbic system constitutes what is sometimes termed the visceral brain and is concerned with various aspects of emotion and behavior. A part of the limbic system, namely the hippocampus and associated areas of gray matter, is distinguished by a three-layered, primitive type of cortex termed *archicortex*. This part of the limbic system is also termed the rhinencephalon, owing to the fact it was thought to be concerned primarily with the sense of smell.

In man, lesions of the temporal lobe, particularly lesions involving the medial, basal cortex, cause emotional disturbances. Symptoms may include hallucinations, disordered recognition and memory, disturbances of reality, dream states, clouding of consciousness, sensory fits (sudden, subjective smell or taste, often unpleasant), and psychomotor epilepsy. Surgical removal of part of the temporal lobe has been performed for psychomotor epilepsy. Surgical lesions in the temporal lobes of wild or otherwise unmanageable animals may tame them. Bilateral removal of temporal lobes may result in complete absence of emotion and, interestingly enough, may also result in increased sexual activity. The amygdaloid bodies consist of a number of nuclear masses, the connections and functions of which are still uncertain. It has been suggested that the amygdaloid bodies are involved in the mechanisms concerned with feeding, although it has also been reported that lesions of these bodies may lead to hypersexuality or abnormal sexual behavior. It has also been suggested that the hippocampus and related structures are involved in the emotional and other reactions incident to copulation and reproduction. Finally, it seems quite clear that the limbic system is involved in many outward expressions of emotion that are mediated by the autonomic nervous system.

It has been possible in man and experimental animals to insert electrodes into the brain and leave them there, so arranged as to be able either to stimulate with or record from these electrodes in the conscious, unanesthetized state. Some of the information mentioned above has been obtained with such methods. For example, stimulation of some regions (especially hippocampus and its connections) may cause widespread electrical convulsive activity in the cerebral hemispheres.

It has also been shown that electrical stimulation of some subcortical regions in animals affects these animals in a way such that they appear to be gaining pleasure from it. In such instances, on being trained to activate the electrical circuit and thus to stimulate themselves, the animals may keep up the self-stimulation for hours or days.

The importance of the various subcortical centers, and especially their possible importance in psychiatric disorders, is now generally realized. But our knowledge of these regions is still quite fragmentary.

SUMMARY

Cephalization in evolutionary processes is especially characterized by the increase in amount of association cortex, which in man makes up the bulk of cerebral cortex, and by an increasing complexity of cortical structure and function. This cortex functions as a whole in those complex mental and emotional processes which we conceive of as mind.

Learning is a process for which there is no physiological and anatomical basis, other than that it is a function of the nervous system. It is a process which, with symbolization, is one of the most characteristic attributes of the human brain and which can be altered by disorders affecting the brain. There are no specific regions of the brain which carry out specific phases of learning. The brain tends to function as a whole.

Names in Neurology

Paul Broca (1824-1880)

Broca is considered to be the founder of modern brain surgery in France. In a famous case study he postulated that the third left frontal convolution was concerned in speech, a theory previously advanced by Gall. Broca's patient was later shown to have a lesion involving much of the left side of the brain. He was the first to trephine the skull for a cerebral abscess located by symptoms relating to his theory of localization of function.

Gustav Theodor Fechner (1801-1887)

Fechner was a professor of physics at Leipzig who wrote the first treatise on psychophysics. He carried out extended experiments on cutaneous and muscle senses and restated Weber's law in its logarithmic form.

Ernst Heinrich Weber (1795-1878)

Weber was a distinguished professor of anatomy and physiology at Leipzig (1812-1866) and professor of anatomy until 1871. In 1825, he collaborated with his brother, Eduard Friedrich Weber (1806-1871), on the hydrodynamics of wave motion and showed the velocity of the pulse wave. In 1845 he discovered the inhibitory effects of the vagus nerve. He studied sensory phenomena and stated that the just detectable increment in the intensity of a sensation is some constant proportion of the stimulus intensity itself. A third brother, Wilhelm Eduard Weber (1804-1891), a professor of physics at Göttingen, collaborated with Eduard in a study of the mechanics of human locomotion.

CARL WERNICKE (1848-1905)

Wernicke was a German physician who studied sensory aphasias and clearly described a variety of these defects. He also studied diseases of the internal capsule and other portions of the nervous system.

REFERENCES

The following references are intended to cover a wide variety of special phases of investigation of the nervous system. Nearly all of them contain extensive bibliographies which should aid in more detailed studies of specific phases. See also references cited on p. 6.

Agranoff, B. W.: Memory and protein synthesis. Sci. Amer., *216*:115-122, 1967.
Bargmann, W., and Schadé, J. P.: The Rhinencephalon and Related Structures. Progress in Brain Research, vol. 3. Amsterdam, Elsevier Publishing Company, 1963.
Brain, R.: Speech Disorders. 2nd ed. Washington, D.C., Butterworths, 1965.
Gazzaniga, M. S.: The split brain in man. Sci. Amer., *217*:24-29, 1967.
Gellhorn, E., and Loofbourrow, G. N.: Emotions and Emotional Disorders. New York, Harper & Row, 1963.
Green, J. D.: The Hippocampus. Physiol. Rev., *44*:561-608, 1964.
Hebb, D. O.: A Textbook of Psychology. 2nd ed. Philadelphia, W. B. Saunders Company, 1966.
Hilgard, E. R., and Marquis, D. G.: Conditioning and Learning. Revised by G. A. Kimble. 2nd ed. New York, Appleton-Century-Crofts, 1961.
Lashley, K. S.: Brain Mechanisms and Intelligence. Chicago, University of Chicago Press, 1929.
McGaugh, J. L.: Time-dependent processes in memory storage. Science, *153*:1351-1358, 1966.
Morgan, C. T.: Physiological Psychology. 3rd ed. New York, McGraw-Hill Book Company, 1965.
Pavlov, I. P.: Conditioned Reflexes, translated by G. V. Anrep. London, Oxford University Press, 1927.
Peterson, L.: Short-term memory. Sci. Amer., *215*:90-95, 1966.
Sperry, R. W.: Cerebral organization and behavior. Science, *133*:1749-1757, 1961.
Stevens, S. S., ed.: Handbook of Experimental Psychology. New York, John Wiley and Sons, Inc., 1951.
Weisenberg, W., and McBride, K.: Aphasia. New York, Commonwealth Fund, 1935.

GLOSSARY OF NEW TERMS

Many of the terms used are listed here to show their derivation from the Greek or Latin and to indicate how they apply to the particular structure or function.

Abducent: L., *abducere,* to draw outward, away from the median axis. The muscle which the abducent nerve supplies turns the eyeball outward, that is, abducts it.

Acoustic: Gr., *akoustikos,* relating to hearing, from *akouein,* to hear.

Afferent: L., *ad,* to, plus *ferre,* to bear or to carry. In physiology, bearing or conducting inward to a part or organ.

Agnosia: Gr., ignorance, from *a,* without, plus *gnosis,* a knowing, denoting cognition or recognition. Loss of ability to recognize familiar objects.

Anatomy: Gr., *anatemnein,* to cut up. The science or branch of morphology which treats of the structure of animals.

Anesthesia: Gr., *an,* not, plus *aisthesis,* feeling. Loss of feeling or sensation.

Anterior: L., comparative of *ante,* before. Before or toward the front.

Aphakia: Gr., *a,* without, plus *phakos,* seed of a lentil (referring to lens). Absence of lens, as by surgery.

Aphasia: Gr., from *aphatos,* speechlessness, or not spoken, from *a,* not, plus *phanai,* to speak. Impairment of symbolization.

Apraxia: Gr., *a,* without, plus *praxis,* a doing. Therefore, inactivity; impaired ability to perform purposeful acts.

Arachnoid: Gr., *arachnoeides,* like a cobweb, from *arachne,* spider or spider's web. One of the meninges is so called because the delicate network of the tissue resembles a spider's web.

Archicerebellum: Gr., *archein,* to be first, plus *cerebellum.* The oldest part of the cerebellum, that is the part appearing first in the evolutionary scale.

Archipallium: Gr., *archein,* plus *pallium.* The first or oldest portion of the cerebral cortex.

Artery: Gr., *arteria,* air containing. So called because the Greeks saw arteries after death when contractions had forced blood into the veins. Hence, they supposed them to contain air.

Asphyxia: Gr., *a,* without, plus *sphyxia,* pulse, throb. Deprived of blood (pulseless) and therefore of oxygen.

Astrocyte: Gr., *aster,* from *astron,* star, plus *kytos,* cell. A neuroglial cell so named because of its star shape.

Ataxia: Gr., *ataktos,* out of order, from *a,* not, plus *taktos,* ordered. Absence of arrangement or orderliness; ataxic movements are disordered.

Atherosclerosis: L., from Gr., *atheroma,* groats, meal, plus *sklerosis,* hardness. A degenerative process of arteries with fatty degeneration of the inner coats which in later stages may harden because of calcification.

Athetosis: Gr., *athetos,* set aside, not fixed, from *a,* not, plus *tithenai,* to place.

Atrophy: Gr., *atrophia,* from *a,* not, plus *trephein,* to nourish. A wasting away from want of nourishment.

339

Autonomic: Gr., *autos*, self, plus *nomos*, law; acting independently. So named because that part of the nervous system is concerned with visceral (involuntary) processes.

Axon: Gr., *axon*, axis or vertebra. An axon is long, slender and relatively unbranched.

Brachial: L., *brachium*, from Gr., *brachion*, arm. The region between the shoulder and elbow.

Brachium Conjunctivum: L., from Gr., *brachion*, plus L., *conjunctivus*, connective. A connecting arm. So called because the two peduncles cross each other.

Brachium Pontis: L., from Gr., *brachion*, plus L., *pons*, a bridge. So called because these two peduncles resemble a bridge between the cerebellar hemispheres.

Branchiomeric: Gr., *branchia*, gills, plus *meros*, part or portion. Relating to the visceral arches.

Calvaria: L., *calvaria*, a bare skull, from *calvus*, bald. Refers to the skull cap.

Capillary: L., *capillus*, a hair or minute tube. So called because of the minute size of these vessels.

Carotid: Gr., *karotides*, from *karos*, heavy sleep. Named because of the supposition that pressure and obliteration of the carotid arteries interfere with the blood supply of the brain and produce unconsciousness.

Cauda Equina: L., *cauda*, tail, plus *equus*, horse. The lumbar and sacral spinal roots form a cluster in the lower spinal canal which resembles the tail of a horse.

Caudal: L., *cauda*, tail. Toward the tail or posterior end (in man, inferior).

Cerebellum: L., diminutive of *cerebrum*, brain; therefore, little brain.

Cerebrum: L., *cerebrum*, from Gr., *kara*, head. All the central nervous system above the line separating the midbrain from the hindbrain is referred to as cerebrum.

Chiasma: Gr., *chiasma*. Two lines placed crosswise, from *chiasein*, to make a mark with a *chi* or χ.

Chorea: L., *choreia*, a choral dance. So named because of the fancied resemblance of the involuntary, choreic movements to those of a dance.

Choroid: Gr., *chorion*, a delicate membrane, plus *eidos*, form. Therefore, like or resembling a delicate membrane.

Chromatolysis: Gr., *chroma*, color, plus *lysis*, solution. To lose or dissolve color, and in neurology refers to the loss of Nissl substance.

Chronaxie: Gr., *chronos*, time, plus *axia*, value. A value of time.

Clonic: Gr., *klonos*, violent, confused motion. A forced series of alternating contractions and partial relaxations of the same muscle or muscles.

Cochlea: L., *cochlea*, from Gr., *kochlias*, snail, from Gr., *kochlos*, a shellfish with a spiral shell. So named because of the coiled or spiral arrangement of the cochlea of the internal ear.

Colliculus: L., *colliculus*, mound, diminutive of *collis*, hill. Therefore, little hill. So called because each colliculus forms a small, rounded eminence or hill.

Congenital: L., *congenitus*, present at or dating from birth.

Conjugate: L., *conjugare*, to unite. In physiology, refers to muscles working in unison, as the eye muscles.

Cornea: L., *corneus*, horny.

Coronal: L., *coronalis*, of or pertaining to the crown or corona. In the plane of the coronal suture of the skull, the frontal plane.

Corpus Callosum: L., *corporis*, body, plus *callosum*, hard or indurated.

Cortex: L., *cortex*, bark of a tree, akin to *corium*, leather. Anatomically the term applies to the outer or superficial part of an organ, as the outer layer of gray matter of the cerebrum.

Cranial: Gr., *kranion*, the skull, akin to *kara*, head. Pertaining to or toward the skull or head.

Crista: L., *crista*, crest or cock's comb or ridge. So called because the crista of the semicircular canals are in the form of elevations or ridges.

Cuneatus: L., from *cuneus*, wedge. The fasciculus cuneatus is so named because it is short and wedge-shaped.

Cytoplasm: Gr., *kytos*, a hollow (cell), plus *plasma*, thing formed.

Dendrite: Gr., *dendrites*, of a tree, from *dendron*, tree. Dendrites are nerve processes which are numerous and branch repeatedly near the cell, forming a tree-like arborization.

Diabetes: Gr., *diabainein*, to pass through. Refers to the persistent and excessive discharge of urine in this disease.

Diastole: Gr., *diastellein*, to put asunder, from *dia*, through, plus *stellein*, to set or place. The expansion or dilatation of the heart cavities as they fill with blood.

Diencephalon: Gr., *dia*, through or between, plus *enkephalos*, brain; the between-brain.

Diplopia: Gr., *diploos*, double, plus *ops*, eye. Double vision.

Distal: L., *distare*, be separate or distant from. Away from the center of the body.

Dorsal: L., *dorsum*, back. Pertaining to or situated near the back of an animal or one of its parts.

Dura Mater: L., *durus*, hard, plus *mater*, mother. In ancient times the meninges were thought to give rise to all the membranes of the body; it is the tough, outer meningeal layer.

Ectoderm: Gr., *ektos*, outside, plus *derma*, skin. The outer, investing cellular membrane of multicellular animals; applies especially to the outer germ layer of embryos.

Efferent: L., *effere*, to bear or carry out or away from. In physiology, conveying outward or discharging.

Electrode: Gr., *elektro*, from *elektron*, amber (rubbing or friction of which produces static electricity), plus *hodos*, way. Either terminal of an electric source.

Embryo: Gr., *embryon*, to swell in or teem in, from *en*, in, plus *bryein*, to swell, teem. In the human being, the period of development up to the third month *in utero*.

Encephalon: Gr., *enkephalos*, from *en*, in, plus *kephalos*, head. Refers to the brain.

Endocrine: Gr., *endon*, within, plus *krinein*, to separate. Secreting internally.

Entoderm: Gr., *entos*, within, plus *derma*, skin. The inner germ layer.

Ependyma: Gr., *ependyma*, an upper garment. Refers to the cloak or lining of the ventricles.

Epilepsy: Gr., *epilepsia*, a seizure, from *epi*, upon or beside, plus *lambanein*, to take.

Exteroceptive: L., *exterus*, outside, plus *capere*, to take. To receive from the outside.

Facial: L., *facies*, the face. Of or pertaining to the face or facial nerve (so called because of its distribution to the facial muscles).

Fasciculus: L., diminutive of *fascis*, bundle. Therefore, a little bundle. Commonly applied to a slender bundle of fibers, either nerve or muscle.

Fetus: L., *fetus*, fruitful, offspring. In the human being, the child in that period of development from the third month *in utero*, until birth.

Flaccid: L., *flaccidus*, flabby, from *flaccus*, lack of firmness or stiffness.

Foramen: L., *forare*, to bore or pierce. An aperture or opening.

Fovea: L., *fovea*, a small pit; probably akin to Gr., *cheie*, a hole.

Frontal: L., *frontale*, a forehead ornament. Of or pertaining to the region of the forehead.

Funiculus: L., *funiculus*, diminutive of *funis*, cord. Therefore, a little cord, band or bundle of fibers. As applied to nerves, is less specific functionally than a fasciculus.

Ganglion: Gr., *ganglion*, swelling or enlargement. An enlargement or mass of nerve tissue containing nerve cells, usually outside the central nervous system.

Geniculate: L., *geniculum*, diminutive of *genu*, knee. That which means knee or bend. So called because the lateral geniculate body is bent or angled like a knee.

Glossopharyngeal: Gr., *glossa*, tongue, plus *pharynx*, chasm or throat. The ninth cranial nerve, so called because of its distribution to these structures.

Gracilis: L., *gracilis*, slender, thin. The fasciculus gracilis is so named because it is long and slender, extending throughout the length of the spinal cord. Likewise, the gracilis muscle in the thigh is long and slender.

Grand Mal: Fr., *grand*, large or great, plus Fr., *mal*, from L., *malum*, an evil. The convulsive episode of epilepsy.

Gyrus: L., *gyrus*, from Gr., *gyros*, circle, circular or spinal form. On the surface of the brain, a convoluted ridge between grooves.

Hemianopia: Gr., *hemi,* half, plus *a,* without, plus *ops,* eye. Loss of vision in half of each eye.

Hemiplegia: Gr., *hemi,* half, plus *plege,* stroke. Paralysis or weakness of one side of the body.

Hippocampus: Gr., *hippos,* horse, plus *kampos,* sea monster. A part of the brain next to the temporal horn of the lateral ventricle.

Histology: Gr., *histos,* web (denotes tissue), plus *logia,* discourse. The science which treats of the structure of tissues.

Homeostasis: Gr., *homoios,* like or similar, plus *stasis,* a standing still. A state of dynamic equilibrium in bodily processes.

Hydrocephalus: Gr., *hydor,* water, plus *kephale,* head. Excessive amount or pressure of cerebrospinal fluid.

Hypesthesia: Gr., *hypo,* beneath or less than, plus *aisthesis,* feeling. Lessened or diminished sensation.

Hypoglossal: Gr., *hypo,* below, plus *glossa,* tongue. So named because the nerve courses below the tongue to reach the muscles it supplies.

Hypothalamus: Gr., *hypo,* below, plus *thalamos,* thalamus.

Idiopathic: Gr., *idios,* individual, plus *pathos,* suffering. A peculiar or individual characteristic or affection; a primary disease of unknown cause.

Incus: L., *incus,* anvil. One of the three ear ossicles which in shape resembles an anvil.

Inhibition: L., *inhibere,* to restrain or check.

Interoceptive: L., *inter,* between or within, plus *capere,* to take. To receive stimuli from within.

Labyrinth: Gr., *labyrinthos,* an intricate passageway or maze. Refers to the inner ear because of the intricacy of structure of this region.

Lateral: L., *lateris,* side or flank, akin to *latus,* broad or wide. In a direction or position opposed to median.

Lemniscus: L., *lemniscus,* a ribbon hanging down, from Gr., *lemniskos,* fillet. A band of nerve fibers; usually applied to a collection of fibers of second order neurons.

Lesion: L., *laesus* or *laedere,* to hurt or injure. Any morbid change in tissues due to disease or injury.

Limbic: L., *limbus,* a border or hem. The limbic lobe forms a border or rim around the upper end of the brain stem.

Macula: L., *macula,* a spot or stain. Any structure forming a spot, as the macula of the utricle or of the retina.

Malleus: L., *malleus,* hammer. The ear ossicle whose shape resembles that of a hammer.

Median: L., *medius,* middle. Situated in the middle.

Medulla Oblongata: L., *medulla,* marrow or essence, plus *oblongata,* oblong. The most caudal part of the brain stem.

Meninges: L., *meninges,* from Gr. *meninx,* membrane. A general term for any of the membranes covering the brain.

Mesencephalon: Gr., *mesos,* middle, plus *enkephalos,* brain. Therefore, midbrain.

Metencephalon: Gr., *meta,* after, plus *enkephalos,* brain. The afterbrain, part of the hindbrain.

Microglia: Gr., *mikros,* small, plus *glia,* glue. A small neuroglial cell.

Micron: Gr., *mikros,* small, petty. Also 10^{-6}, or one millionth of standard units of measurements, and by itself is one millionth of a meter.

Microtome: Gr., *mikros,* plus *tomos,* cutting. An instrument to cut thin sections.

Microvolt: Gr., *mikros,* plus volt, the unit of electrical force. One millionth of a volt.

Millivolt: L., *mille,* thousand, plus volt. One thousandth of a volt.

Monoplegia: Gr., *monos,* one, plus *plege,* stroke. Paralysis of a single limb or part.

Morphology: Gr., *morphe,* form, plus *logia,* science. Science of form and structure of animals.

Muscle: L., *musculus,* diminutive of *mus,* mouse. Therefore, little mouse. So called because of the fancied resemblance of movements of the biceps brachii to the movements of a mouse.

Myasthenia Gravis: Gr., *mys* or *myos*, muscle, plus *aistheneia*, weakness, plus L., *gravis*, heavy. A disease of the muscles causing fatigue and eventually paralysis.

Myelencephalon: Gr., *myelos*, marrow, plus *enkephalos*, brain. The marrowbrain; refers especially to the medulla oblongata.

Myofibril: Gr., *mys*, muscle, plus L., *fibrilla*, a little fiber. Therefore, a little fiber within a muscle.

Myotatic: Gr., *mys*, muscle, plus *tasis*, stretching. Refers to stretch reflex.

Neocerebellum: Gr., *neos*, new, plus *cerebellum*, little brain. The newest or latest portion of the cerebellum in evolutionary processes.

Neopallium: Gr., *neos*, new, plus L., *pallium*, cloak or mantle (refers to cortex). The newest portion of the cerebral cortex in evolutionary processes.

Nerve: L., *nervus*, akin to Gr., *neuron*, sinew or nerve.

Neurilemma: Gr., *neuron*, nerve, plus *lemma*, skin or peel. The outer skin or cell layer around a nerve fiber.

Neuroblast: Gr., *neuron*, nerve, plus *blastos*, germ. Means nerve forming and refers to embryonic cells which give rise to nerve cells.

Neuroglia: Gr., *neuron*, nerve, plus *glia*, glue. Means nerve glue and refers to the cells which support or hold nervous tissue together.

Neurology: Gr., *neuron*, nerve, plus *logia*, science. The science which treats of the nervous system in all its aspects. In a more restricted sense it is often used to refer to disorders of the nervous system.

Nucleolus: L., diminutive of *nucleus*, from *nucis*, nut. Therefore, a little nut. A rounded, often conspicuous body within a nucleus.

Nucleus: L., *nucleus*, kernel, from *nucis*, nut. A central mass or point, as the nucleus of a cell.

Occipital: L., *occipitus*, back of head, as opposed to forehead.

Oculomotor: L., *oculus*, eye, plus *motor*, motion. Moving the eyeball. The nerve supplies muscles which move the eyeball.

Olfactory: L., *olfacere*, to smell. Refers to the sense of smell or to structures subserving this function.

Oligodendroglia: Gr., *oligos*, small or few, plus *dendron*, tree, plus *glia*, glue. A neuroglial cell with a few small branches.

Optic: Gr., *optikos*, akin to *opsis*, vision. Of or pertaining to vision and the structures subserving this function.

Orbital: L., *orbita*, track or circuit. Pertaining to the skull cavity in which the eye and appendages are located.

Ossicle: L., *ossiculum*, diminutive of *os*, bone. Therefore, little bone.

Paleocerebellum: Gr., *palaios*, old or ancient, plus cerebellum. A phylogenetically older portion of the cerebellum.

Paralysis: Gr., *para*, beside, plus *lyein*, to loosen, dissolve or disable. Hence, to disable on a side.

Paresis: Gr., *paresis* or *parienae*, to let go. In neurology, means weakness or incomplete paralysis and is also used to indicate the involvement of the cerebral cortex in syphilis.

Parietal: L., *paries*, a wall or plate of a part or cavity. The parietal bones of the skull form part of the sides and roof of the calvarium

Pathology: Gr., *pathos*, suffering or disease, plus *logia*. The science treating of diseases, their nature, causes, development, and changes.

Peduncle: L., *pedunculus*, diminutive of *pes*, foot. Therefore, little foot. A stem or narrow part by which some part is attached to another, as the cerebellum to the brain stem.

Peristalsis: Gr., *peristaltikos*, clasping and compressing, as in the peculiar wavelike motions of the intestines.

Petit Mal: Fr., *petit*, small, plus *mal*. The less violent of the episodes of epilepsy.

Phagocyte: Gr., *phago*, I eat, plus *kytos*, cell. Phagocytic cells ingest and destroy other materials, including cells.

Physiology: Gr., *physis*, nature, plus *logia*. The branch of biology dealing with the processes and activities of living organisms.

Pia Mater: L., *pius*, tender or kind, plus *mater*, mother. The more delicate and closely investing of the three meningeal layers.

Pineal: L., *pineus*, a pine cone. The pineal body in shape and attachment resembles a pine cone.

Plexus: L., *plexus*, a turning or braid. Refers to the interweaving of nerves as they form a plexus.

Pons: L., *pons*, a bridge. The pons consist of fibers which bridge across the brain stem to the cerebellum on either side.

Posterior: L., *posterus*, from *post*, behind or after. At or toward the hind end of the body; in a tailward or caudal direction (in man, behind or dorsal rather than below).

Proprioceptive: L., *proprius*, one's own, plus *capere*, to take. Receiving stimuli produced by tension in tissues, as muscles.

Prosencephalon: Gr., *pros*, toward or near, plus *enkephalos*. The first or foremost of the primary brain vesicles.

Protoplasm: Gr., *protos*, first, plus *plasma*, thing formed. Originally designated formative material of young animal embryos. Now refers to the essential substance of cell body and nucleus.

Proximal: L., *proximare*, to come near. Next to or nearest, as to the point of attachment of a limb to the body.

Psychiatry: Gr., *psyche*, the mind, plus *iatreia*, healing. Although literally meaning mind-healing, it is really the science of behavior, including behavior disorders.

Psychology: Gr., *psyche*, mind, plus *logia*. The science which treats of mental and behavioral processes.

Pudendal: L., *pudendus*, that of which one ought to be ashamed, from *pudere*, to be ashamed. Anatomically, refers to the region of the external sex organs.

Reflex: L., *re*, back, plus *flectere*, to bend. To turn or refer back.

Restiform: L., *restis*, rope, plus *forma*, form. Ropelike; these peduncles are so named because of their ropelike or cordlike shape.

Retina: L., *rete*, a net. The light-sensitive membrane of the eye.

Rheobase: Gr., *rheos*, current, plus *basis*, base or foundation. The basic or minimal current required to excite.

Rhinencephalon: Gr., *rhis*, nose, plus *enkephalos*. The olfactory or smellbrain.

Rhombencephalon: Gr., *rhombos*, equilateral parallelogram with oblique angles, plus *enkephalos*. The hindbrain, so named because of its shape.

Saccule: L., diminutive of *saccus*, sac. Therefore, a little sac. A small membranous bag in the inner ear.

Sagittal: L., *sagitta*, an arrow. Of or pertaining to the sagittal or midline suture of the skull and any plane parallel to this suture.

Spastic: Gr., *spastikos*, from *span*, to draw. To cause convulsions.

Sphygmomanometer: Gr., *sphygmos*, pulse, plus *manometer*, an instrument for measuring pressure. An instrument for measuring blood pressure.

Substantia Nigra: L., *substantis*, substance, plus *nigra*, black. So called because of the dark or black appearance of this area, resulting from the presence of melanin-containing cells.

Sulcus: L., *sulcus*, a groove or furrow.

Synapse: Gr., *synapsis*, a conjunction or union.

Syncytium: Gr., *syn*, with, plus *kytos*, cell. A multinuclear cell or aggregation of imperfectly separated cells.

Systole: Gr., *systellein*, to contract. Refers to the contraction of the heart.

Tactile: L., *tactilis*, tangible, from *tactum*, to touch.

Telencephalon: Gr., *telos*, end, plus *enkephalos*. The far or endbrain.

Temporal: L., *temporalis*, or *temporal*, the temples. Of or pertaining to the region of the temples.

Thalamus: Gr., *thalos* or *thalamos*, inner chamber or anteroom.

Thrombosis: Gr., *thrombosis*, coagulation or curdling. Refers to the clotting of blood.

Tonic: Gr., *tonikos, tonos*, tone. To stretch or strain.

Transverse: L., *transvertere*, to turn or direct across.

Trigeminal: L., *trigeminus*, born three together, from *tri*, three, plus *geminus*, twin. Pertaining to the trigeminal nerve with its three branches.

Trochlear: L., *trochlea*, block or pulley. So called because the muscle which this nerve supplies has a pulley for its tendon.

Tympanum: L., *tympanum*, drum. This membrane is stretched tightly across the end of the external ear canal, like the skin of a drum.

Utricle: L., *utriculus*, diminutive of *uter*, sac or vesicle; a skin bag.

Vagus: L., *vagari*, wandering. So called because of the long and extensive course of this nerve.

Vein: L., *vena*, akin to *vehere*, to convey.

Ventral: L., *ventralis*, from *venter*, belly. Anything pertaining to or toward this part of the body, as opposed to dorsal.

Ventricle: L., *ventriculus*, diminutive of *venter*, belly. A chamber or cavity.

Venule: L., diminutive of *vena*, vein. Therefore, a little vein.

Vermis: L., *vermis*, a worm. So called because of the narrow, wormlike appearance of the midpart of the cerebellum.

Vestibular: L., *vestibulum*, passage, hall or chamber.

Viscera: L., *viscus*, to turn or wind, as the internal organs.

INDEX

ABDUCENT nerve, 15, 17, 31
Abramson, D. I., 55
Absolute refractory period, 102
Absorption maxima of visual pigments, 198
Accessory nerve, 17, 31, 166, 231, 258, 261
Accommodation, of eye, 193
of nerve, 109
Acetylcholine, 111, 120, 149, 150, 233-234
formula of, 120
muscarine action of, 234
nicotinic effect of, 234
Acetylcholinesterase, 149
Achilles, 133
tendon of, 133
Acid, deoxyribonucleic, 73, 119
osmic, 76
ribonucleic, 72, 118, 119
Acoustic nerve. See *Vestibulocochlear nerve*.
Action potential, 100
Acts, purposeful, 323
defects in (apraxias), 323
Acuity, visual, 202-203
Adaptation, 143
dark and light, 199-201
of receptors, 143-144
Adenohypophysis, 229, 237-238
Adenosine diphosphate (ADP), 116
Adenosine triphosphate (ATP), 115-116, 120
Adrenal gland, 64
cortical hormones of, 241 242
medulla of, 64, 150, 234
Adrenaline, 120, 150, 234
formula of, 120
Adrenergic fibers, 150, 234
Adrian, E. D., 113
Adrian, F. D., 274
Affective component of behavior, 334
Afferent fiber, 28, 252
general somatic, 253, 262
general visceral, 253, 262-263
special somatic, 262-263
special visceral, 262-263

Afferent paths, and cerebral cortex, 325-328
lesions of, 185-187
Afterbrain, 59
Afterdischarge and reflexes, 129
After-potentials, 100, 103-104
Agnosis, 325
visual, 325
Agranoff, B. W., 121, 338
Agranular cortex, 301
Alar plate, 58
Alimentary canal, control of, 271-272
All-or-none law, 107
Alpha fibers, 147
Alpha waves of EEG (Berger rhythm), 297
Ambystoma punctatum, 131
Amino acids, 117
γ-Aminobutyric acid, 112
Amnesic aphasia (nominal aphasia), 330-331
Amphetamine, 121
Amphibians, forebrain of, 289
Amygdaloid body, 292, 335, 336
Anatomical planes, 3
terms, 3
Anatomy, terminology in, 1, 2
Andrew, B. L., 154
Anesthetics, 118
Angiography, 49
Angle, minimal visual, 202
Ankle jerk, 132
Anode, 109
Ansa lenticularis, 293
Anterior cerebral artery, 44
Anterior commissure, 291
Anterior corticospinal tract, 160
Anterior funiculus, 162
Anterior lateral sulcus, 17
Anterior median fissure, 17, 24
Anterior spinal artery, 24, 46
Anterior spinothalamic tract, 175, 177, 187
Aorticorenal ganglia, 40
Aperture, lateral, of fourth ventricle, 19
median, of fourth ventricle, 19
Aphakia (cataract), 200

Aphasias, 329-331, 335
  amnesic, 330-331
  expressive, 330
  expressive-receptive, 330
  higher level, 331
  receptive, 330
  semantic, 331
Apical dendrite, 71, 295
Apomorphine, 271
Apoplexy, 48
Apraxias, 323
Aqueduct (of Sylvius), 19, 258
Aqueous fluid (humor), 193
Arachnoid, 10
  villi, 51
Arc, reflex, general properties of, 122-133
Arches, branchial, 261
Archicerebellum, 275-276, 281, 283
Archicortex, 335
Archipallium, 291
Area(s), association. See *Association areas.*
  cortical, naming and numbering of, 296
  hippocampal, 289
  motor. See *Motor areas.*
  piriform, 289
  primary receptive. See *Sensory areas.*
  rhinencephalic, 222
Arey, L. B., 66
Argininosuccinaciduria, 117
Arterial circle (of Willis), 15, 45
Arterioles, 43
Arteriolosclerosis, 48
Arteriovenous anastomoses, 43
Artery(ies), anterior cerebral, 44
  anterior spinal, 24, 46
  basilar, 18, 45
  carotid, common, 44
    external, 44
    internal, 15, 44
  cerebellar, 14
  lumbar, 47
  medullary, 46, 47
  middle cerebral, 45
  middle meningeal, 46
  posterior cerebral, 18, 45
  posterior intercostal, 47
  posterior spinal, 24, 47
  radicular, 47
  retinal, 194
  sacral, 47
  vertebral, 18, 44-47
Association areas, 188, 320-322
  and conditioned responses, 332-333
  and language mechanisms, 328-331
  and learning, 322-333
  frontal, 333-334
Astereognosis, 325
Astrocytes, 84

Ataxia, 284
Atherosclerosis, 48, 194
Athetosis, 311
Atrioventricular node, 148
Atropine, 234
Atrophy of muscles, 170-172
Attacks, grand mal, 316
  petit mal, 316
Audiogram, 212
Auditory aphasia (receptive, sensory or Wernicke's), 330
Auditory connections, 213-214
Auditory nerve. See *Vestibulocochlear nerve.*
Auditory strings, 211
Auditory system, 208-214
  lesions of, 214-215
Auditory tube, 211
Austin, G., 255
Autonomic nervous system, 40, 227-235, 336
  functions of levels, 236-240
  general functions, 235, 241-242
  levels of organization, 228-230
  levels of outflow, 230-235
Avalanche conduction, 278
Axis, cylinder, 73
  visual, 194
Axo-axonal contact, 82, 112
Axodendritic contact, 82
Axon(s), 61, 73
  and chromatolysis, 85-91
  development of, 61
  hillock, 74
  in central nervous system, 78
  motor units and, 146-147
  myelinated, 76
  nonmyelinated, 77
  outside central nervous system, 77
  postganglionic, 148, 150, 230
  preganglionic, 148, 230
  staining of, 77
  structure of, 74
  synapses and, 82
Axoplasm, 100
Axosomatic contact, 82

BABINSKI, J., 133
  reflex (response), 132, 168, 170, 250, 301
Balance, 215-219
Balinsky, B. I., 66
Band (stripe) of Gennari, 206
Bargmann, W., 338
Barrier, blood-brain, 51
  blood-cerebrospinal fluid, 51
Bartelmez, G. W., 66

Basal ganglia, 20, 159, 267, 292-293, 308-311, 335
  and dynamic reactions, 308-309
  connections of, 293
  disorders of, 311-312
  functions of, 308-311
Basal plate, 58
Basilar artery, 18, 45
Basilar membrane, 211, 213
Basket cells, 278
Basmajian, J. V., 173
Beevor, C., 173
Behavior, affective component of, 334
  and chemistry, 120
  instinctive type, 287
  reflexes and, 130-131
Beidler, L. M., 225
Békésy, G. von, 224
Bel, unit of power, 212
Bell, A. G., 212
Bender, M. B., 274
Berger, H., 299
  rhythm (alpha waves of EEG), 297
Bernard, C., 243
Best, C. H., 6
Beta waves of EEG, 297
Biceps jerk, 132
Binocular vision, 205
Bipolar cells, 63, 73
  of cochlea (spiral ganglion), 211
  of olfactory mucous membrane, 221
  of retina, 195
  of vestibular ganglia, 216
Birds, forebrain of, 289
Bishop, G. H., 113, 154
Bitter, as primary taste quality, 220
Bladder, urinary, in spinal man, 251-252
Blind spot of eye, 195
Blindness, 314
  color, 204-205
Blood, 43
Blood-brain barrier, 51
Blood-cerebrospinal fluid barrier, 51
Blood flow, and body temperature, 226
  to brain, 48
Blood pressure, control of, 238-240
  diastolic, 239
  systolic, 238
Blood supply, 43-50
  clinical importance of, 48-50
  of brain, 44-46
  of meninges, 46
  of peripheral nerves, 47
  of spinal cord, nerves, and roots, 46
Bloom, W., 94
Body(ies), amygdaloid, 292, 335, 336
  carotid, 270
  geniculate, lateral, 205
    medial, 214

Body(ies) (*Continued*)
  Golgi (Golgi apparatus), 72, 119
  mamillary, 14
  pineal, 16
  vitreous, 194
Body-righting reflexes, 309-310, 311
Body temperature, and blood flow, 226
  control of, 226-227, 236-237
Bouton de passage, 82
Boutons terminaux, 82
Boyd, J. D., 66
Brachial plexus, 33
Brachium pontis, 278
Brain, 10-24
  blood supply of, 44-46
  electrical activity of, 296-298
  inorganic constituents of, 118-119
  metabolism of, 114-121
Brain, R., 319, 338
Brain stem, 12, 256-274
  and autonomic nervous system, 230, 238-240
  association paths of, 259
  cerebellar connections of, 281-282
  excitatory mechanisms, 264
  functions of, 263-272
    autonomic 238, 268-272
    motor, 263-266
    visceral, 268-272
  general features of, 256-263
  inhibitory mechanisms of, 263
  reflexes of, 264
  reticular formation of, 159
Brain waves (EEG), 107, 272, 296-297
Branched chain ketonuria, 117
Branchial arches, 261
Branchiomeric muscles, 166-167, 261, 271
Brazier, M. A. B., 113
Bremer, F., 274
Brightness of color, 203
Broca, P., 337
Broca's aphasia (expressive, motor, or verbal), 330
Brown-Séquard, C.-E., 188
  syndrome, 187
Brutkowski, S., 319
Buds, taste, 220
Bulbs, end, of Krause, 137
  olfactory, 14, 29, 222
Bunge, R. P., 94
Butyrate, 114

CALCARINE fissure, 206
Calne, D. B., 189
Canal, alimentary, 271
  central, 19, 59
  optic, 15

Canal *(Continued)*
  semicircular, 215
  vertebral, 9
Cannon, W. B., 243
Capillaries, 43
  of pituitary, 228
Capsule, internal, 21, 170, 278, 292
Carbohydrates, 115-116
Carbon dioxide, 48
  and respiration, 270
Cardiac centers, 238, 239
Cardiac muscle, 145
Carotid artery, common, 44
  external, 44
  internal, 15, 44
Carotid body, 270
Cat, decerebrate, 264-265
  spinal, 248
Cataract (aphakia), 200
Cathode as a stimulating electrode, 104, 108
Cauda equina, 24
Caudate nucleus, 21, 292
Causy, G., 94
Celiac ganglia, 40
Cell(s), 67
  basket, 278
  bipolar, 63, 73
    of olfactory mucous membrane, 221
    of retina, 195
    of spiral ganglion, 211
    of vestibular ganglion, 216
  ependymal, 59
  ganglion, of retina, 195
    parasympathetic, 64
    sympathetic, 64
  Golgi, 70, 278
  granule, of cerebellar cortex, 277, 278
    of cerebral cortex, 295
  hair, 216
  membrane of, 70-72
  multipolar, 61, 73
  nerve. See *Neuron(s)*.
  neural crest, 58
  neurilemmal (of Schwann), 64, 78
  neuroglial, 61, 83-85
  Purkinje, 277-278, 281
  pyramidal, 159, 305
  Renshaw, 126, 246
  satellite, 78
  unipolar, 64, 73
Cell bodies, electrical activity of, 109
Center(s), cardiac, 238, 239
  for conjugate (vertical) gaze, 166
  for lateral gaze, 164
  respiratory, 238, 268-270
  subcortical, 334-336
  vasomotor, 238, 239
Central canal, 19, 59

Central nervous system, 8-26, 58, 114
  metabolism of, 114-115
Central sulcus, 12, 300
Cephalin (phosphatidyl ethanolamine), 116
Cerebellar branches, 46
Cerebellum, 12, 18, 275-285
  connections with brain stem and cranial nerves, 281-282
    with cerebral cortex, 278-279
    with spinal cord, 280-281
  cortex of, 277
  disorders of, 284
  functions of, 282-284
  localization in, 282
Cerebral artery, anterior, 44
  middle, 45
  posterior, 18, 45
Cerebrosides, 119
Cerebroside lipidosis (Gaucher's disease), 117
Cerebrospinal fluid, 19
  clinical importance of, 52-54
  examination, 52
  formation and circulation of, 50-52
Cerebrum. See *Brain.*
  definition of, 286
Ceruloplasmin, 119
Chemistry of nervous system, 114-121
Chemoreceptors, 136
Chiasma, optic, 15, 29, 205
Child, C. M., 66
Choked disk, 194
Cholesterol, 116, 119
Cholinergic fibers, 150, 234
Cholinesterase, 234
Chorea, 312
Choreoathetosis, 312
Choroid layer of eye, 192
Choroid plexuses, 20, 51
Chromatin, 73
Chromatolysis, 85, 119
Chronaxie, 109
  and strength-duration curves, 151
Ciba Foundation Symposia, 189
Ciliary muscle, 192
Cingulate gyrus, 335
Cingulate sulcus, 20
Circle, arterial (of Willis), 15, 45
Circulation, portal, of pituitary, 228
Citric acid cycle, 116, 120
Citrullinemia, 117
Clare, M., 295
Clark, S. L., 6
Cochlea, 208, 211-214
Cochlear division of vestibulocochlear nerve, 31
Cochlear duct, 211
  nuclei, 214

Coghill, G. E., 134
Colliculus(i), inferior, 16, 258, 267
    superior, 16, 258, 267, 314
Color, blindness, 204-205
    factors influencing sensation of, 203
    properties of, 203-204
    vision, 198, 203-204
        Ciba Symposium on, 225
Commissure, anterior, 291
Common carotid artery, 44
Components of cranial nerves, 260-263
    of peripheral nerves, 78, 253
    of spinal nerves, 82, 252-253
Compound sensations, 324
Conditioned responses, 332-333
Conduction, avalanche, 278
    in dendrites, 109
    in unipolar and bipolar cells, 110
    rates, 102
    saltatory, 102
    volume, 107
Cones, of retina, 195-198
Congenital defects of nervous system, 65
Conjugate gaze, lateral, 164
    vertical, 166
Connections, auditory, 213-214
    central, of retina, 205-207
        vestibular, 217-219
    of basal ganglia, 293
    of cerebellum, 278-282
    of hypothalamus, 228-230
Contractions, postural, 125
    tetanic, 148
Convulsions, and epilepsy, 316-317
    jacksonian, 304
Cord bladder, 251-252
Cord, spinal. See *Spinal cord.*
Cornea, 191
Corneal reflex, 264
Corpus callosum, 13, 321-322
Corpus striatum, 21, 289, 292
Corpuscles, Meissner's, 136
    pacinian, 137, 138, 181, 183
Cortex, agranular, 301
    cerebellar, 277
    cerebral, 20, 159, 228, 236, 294-296
        areas of, 296
        layers of, 294-295
        motor functions of, 300-312
        sensory functions of, 312-316
        visceral functions of, 305
    frontal, 335
    occipital, 301, 313, 328
    precentral motor, 162, 164, 300-307
    temporal, 335
    visual, 313
Corti, organ of, 211
Corticobulbar tract, 164

Corticomesencephalic tract, 164
Corticopontine tract, 164, 282
Corticospinal tracts, 160, 162, 187, 247,
    258, 278, 294, 301
    anterior, 160
Cranial nerves, 29-32, 39
    components, 260-263
    development of, 63
Creatine phosphate, 116
Crest, neural, 58, 63-64
Cristae of semicircular canals, 216
Critical fusion frequency for flicker, 203
Crosby, E. C., 6
Crystalline lens, 191
Curare, 150
Current, 100
Curve(s), photopic, 201
    scotopic, 200
    strength-duration, 108
Cystathioninuria, 117
Cytoplasm, 67, 72, 119

DARK adaptation, 199-200
Davis, H., 224, 225
Davson, H., 55
Deafness, middle ear, 214-215
    nerve, 215
DeBois, J. (Sylvius), 26
Decerebrate animal, 238, 264-265
Decerebrate rigidity, 265
Decibel, 212
Decussation of pyramids, 160, 256
Deep touch (pressure), 138, 181
Defects, congenital, of nervous system, 65
Degeneration, after peripheral nerve le-
    sions, 87-91
    hepatolenticular, 118-119
    in nervous system, 85-91
    Marchi method and, 87
    retrograde, 87
    Wallerian, 87
Dekaban, A. S., 66
Delta waves in EEG, 297
Dendrites, 61
    apical, 71, 295
    conduction in, 109
    development of, 61
    structure of, 74
Dendrodentritic functions, 82
Denny-Brown, D., 319
Dentate nucleus, 24, 277, 282
Deoxyribonucleic acid (DNA), 73, 119
Depolarization, 97, 98
Depression, spreading, 305
Deuteranomaly, 204
Deuteranopia, 205
Diabetes insipidus, 237

Diaphragm, nerve supply of, 268
  referred pain and, 184
Diastole, 239
Dichromats, 205
Diencephalon, 12, 13, 59
Diplopia, 205
Dipole, 100
Discrimination, two-point, 326-328
Disk, optic, 194
  choked, 194
  tactile, 136
Distractibility in frontal lobe lesions, 334
Dominance, cerebral, 321, 329
Dopamine, 120, 234
Dorsal rami, 33
Dorsal root(s), 24, 78, 172, 252
Douglas, W. W., 113, 189
Drugs, parasympathetic and sympathetic,
  234
Duchenne, G. B., 173
Duct, cochlear, 211
  semicircular, 215, 216-217
Dura mater, 10
  blood supply of, 46
  sinuses of, 10
Dystonia, 311

EAR, external, 209-211
  inner, 211-214, 264
  middle, 209-211
Eccles, J. C., 113, 255
Ectoderm, 57
EEG. See *Electroencephalogram.*
Effectors, 123, 136, 144-146
  dependence on nerve supply, 151-153
  structure of, 144-146
Efferent fibers (motor), 28
  alpha, 147
  gamma, 139, 140, 144, 162
  general visceral, 253, 262
  somatic, 253, 262
  special visceral, 261-262
Electric organs, 136
Electrical activity, of brain, 296-298
  of cell bodies, 109
Electrocardiogram, 107
Electroencephalogram (EEG), 107, 272,
  296-297
  in epilepsy, 298
Electromyography, 150, 157, 173
Electroretinogram (ERG), 198
Embden-Meyerhof glycolytic pathway,
  115
Embryo segment, 62
  nerve growth into, 63
Emotions, 334-335
  facial movements, 335
  hypothalamus and, 335

Emotions *(Continued)*
  prefrontal lobotomy and, 334
  subcortical centers and, 334-336
End bulbs of Krause, 137
End plate, motor, 146
  potential, 111, 149
Endbrain, 12, 59
Endings. See also *Neuroeffector junc-
  tions* and *Receptors.*
  Ruffini, 138, 183
Endocrine glands, 146
Endoneurium, 81
Endoplasmic reticulum, 72
Entoderm, 57
Enzymes, 115-116, 117-118
Ependyma, 51
  cells, 59
Ependymal (germinal) layer of neural
  tube, 59
Epidural hemorrhage, 46
Epidural space, 10
Epilepsy, 316-317
  brain waves in, 298
  idiopathic, 316
  post-traumatic, 316
  psychomotor, 336
Epinephrine. See *Adrenaline.*
Epineurium, 81
Epiphysis. See *Pineal body.*
Equilibrium, 215-219
Ergotamine, 234
Ergotoxine, 234
Erlanger, J., 113
Eserine, 149, 234
Esophagus, 271
Ether, 118, 316
Eugnosia, 324
Euler, U. S. von, 243
Excitation, conduction, and transmis-
  sion, 95
  methods of study, 97
Excitation time, 109
Excitatory mechanisms of brain stem, 263
Excitatory postsynaptic potential, 111
Exocrine glands, 146
Expiratory centers, 268
Expressive-receptive (total) aphasia, 330
External carotid artery, 44
Extrapyramidal system, 264
  lesions of, 168-169
Eye(s), 191-205
  blind spot of, 195
  development of, 193
  movements of, 164-166

FABRY'S disease (glycolipid lipidosis),
  117
Facial nerve, 17, 31, 166, 220, 231, 261,
  268

Facilitation, 109, 130
Factors, passive, in steady potential, 97, 98
Falx cerebri, 12
Fasciculi of spinal cord, 25, 175
Fasciculus, cuneatus, 20, 25, 175
  gracilis, 20, 25, 175
  lenticularis, 293
  medial longitudinal, 165, 217, 258, 259
Fawcett, D. W., 94
Fechner, G. T., 337
Femoral nerve, 253
Fertilization and early development, 56-57
Fever and hypothalamus, 236-237
Fiber(s), adrenergic, 150, 234
  afferent (sensory), 252
    general somatic, 253, 262
    general visceral, 253, 262-263
    special somatic, 262-263
    special visceral, 262-263
  alpha, 147
  cholinergic, 150, 234
  climbing, 278
  efferent (motor), 28, 252
    general visceral, 253, 262
    somatic, 253, 262
    special visceral, 261, 262
  gamma efferent, 144, 162, 170
  intrafusal, 138
  mossy, 278
  muscle, 150
  myelinated, 74-82
  nerve, 28, 74-77
  nonmyelinated, 74-82
  postganglionic, 148, 150, 230
  preganglionic, 148, 230
  propriospinal, 247
  Purkinje, 148, 278
  spinospinal, 247
Fibrillary twitchings, 172
Filum terminale, 24
Final common path, 158
Fishes, forebrain of, 288-289
Fissure(s), anterior median, 17, 24
  calcarine, 206
  of brain, 12
  of cerebellum, 18, 275
Fits, sensory, 317
Flaccid paralysis, 172, 250, 254
Flicker, critical fusion frequency of, 203
Fluid, aqueous, 193
  cerebrospinal. See *Cerebrospinal fluid.*
Fluid balance, control of, 241
Foramen (foramina), in base of skull, 9
  interventricular, 19
  intervertebral, 10
  magnum, 9
  vertebral, 10

Ford, D. H., 94
Forebrain, 12, 159, 286-299
  associative functions of, 320-337
  basal ganglia of, 292-293
  cortex of, 294-296
  derivatives of, 60
  development of, 59
  electrical activity of, 296-298
  general features, 288-292
  motor functions of, 291, 300-312
  of amphibians, 289
  of birds, 289
  of fishes, 288-289
  of mammals, 289-292
  of reptiles, 289
  sensory functions, 291, 312-316
  thalamus of, 294
Formation, reticular, 24, 159, 217, 258, 259, 268, 272-273, 280, 293
Fourth ventricle, 19
  median sulcus of, 20
Fovea, 194
Fox, C. A., 285
Fredrickson, D. S., 121
Free nerve endings, 136, 138
Frequency, critical fusion, for flicker, 203
  range of hearing, 213
Frontal association areas, 333-334
Frontal eye field, 305
Frontal lobe, 13, 305, 320, 335
  lesions of, 334
Frozen sections, 4
Fulton, J. F., 6
Funiculus of spinal cord, 25, 162, 170, 187, 246-247

GABA, 112
Galen, 6
  vein of, 1
Gamma efferent fibers, 139, 140, 144, 162
Ganglion(a), 29
  aorticorenal, 40
  autonomic, 230
  basal, 20, 159, 267, 292-293, 308-311, 335
  celiac, 40
  cells, of retina, 195
  geniculate, 31
  inferior, of glossopharyngeal and vagus nerves, 31
  mesenteric, 40
  parasympathetic, 64
  phrenic, 40
  renal, 40
  semilunar, 30
  spinal, 32
  spiral, 31, 211

Ganglion(a) *(Continued)*
  splanchnic, 40
  superior, of glossopharyngeal and vagus
    nerves, 31
  sympathetic, 40, 64, 231
  trigeminal, 30
  vestibular, 31, 216
  visceral, 240
Ganglioside lipidosis (Tay-Sachs' dis-
    ease), 117
Gardner, E., 6
Garland, H., 173
Gasser, H. S., 113
Gaucher's disease (cerebroside lipidosis),
    117
Gaze, conjugate (vertical), 166
  horizontal (lateral), 164
Gazzaniga, M. S., 338
Gellhorn, E., 338
General senses, 174-189
  and primary receptive areas, 187-188
Geniculate body, lateral, 205
  medial, 214
Geniculate ganglion, 31
Gennari, stripe (band) of, 206
Germ layer formation and differentiation,
    57
Gibbs, E. L., 299
Gibbs, F. A., 299
Gilman, A., 243
Glands, 146, 150
  adrenal, 64, 234
  endocrine, 146
  exocrine, 146
  hypophysis (pituitary), 15
  lacrimal, 231
  multicellular, 146
  neuroeffector junctions in, 148
  salivary, 31, 231, 268
  sweat, 233
  unicellular, 146
Glees, P., 94
Gliosis, 87
Globus pallidus, 21, 292
Glossopharyngeal nerve, 17, 31, 166, 220,
    231, 258, 261, 268, 271
Glucose, 114
Glycogen, 115
Glycolipid lipidosis (Fabry's disease), 117
Glycolipids, 119
Golgi apparatus (bodies), 72, 119
Golgi, C., 92
Golgi cells, 278
  type 1 cells, 70
  type 2 cells, 70
Golgi tendon organs, 140
Goodman, L., 243
Grand mal attacks, 316

Granule cells, of cerebellar cortex, 277,
    278
  of cerebral cortex, 295
Grasp reflex, 301, 307
Gray, D. J., 6
Gray matter, 20
  composition of, 76
  of spinal cord, 24
Green, J. D., 338
Grinker, R., 319
Groove, neural, 58
Groping response, 307
Growth of nervous system after birth, 65
Guth, L., 94
Guyton, A. C., 6
Gyrus(i), 12
  cingulate, 335
  postcentral, 177, 188, 220, 313
  precentral, 160, 300, 304
  supramarginal, 323
  temporal, 214

HAIR cells, 216
Ham, A. W., 94
Hamburger, V., 134
Hamilton, W. J., 66
Harris, G. W., 243
Haymaker, W., 7
Hearing, 208-214
Heart, nodes of, 148
  Purkinje fibers of, 148
  referred pain from, 184
Hebb, D. O., 338
Helmholtz, H. von, 223
  resonance theory, 213
Hemianopia, 207
Hemiballismus, 312
Hemichorea, 312
Hemiparesis, 170
Hemiplegia, 170
Hemisphere(s), cerebral, 12
  major, 322, 329
  minor, 331
Hemorrhage, epidural (extradural), 46
  intracerebral, 49
Hepatolenticular degeneration (Wilson's),
    118-119
Hilgard, E. R., 338
Hillock, axon, 74
Hindbrain, 12, 59
Hippocampal area, 289
Hippocampus, 1, 335, 336
Hirst, R. J., 189
Histidinemia, 117
Hodgkin, A. L., 113
Homeostasis, 241

Homocystinuria, 117
Hopping reaction, 307
Horizontal (lateral) gaze, 164
Hormones, adrenocorticotrophic, 241-242
  antidiuretic, 237
  of adenohypophysis, 237-238
  of hypothalamus, 120, 237
Horns of spinal cord gray matter, 24
Hoyle, G., 154
Hues of color, 203
Humor, aqueous, 193
Humphrey, T., 6
Huntington, G., 318
Huntington's chorea, 312
Hydrocephalus, 54
Hydroxyprolinemia, 117
Hyperactivity after frontal lobe lesions,
  333-334
Hyperammonemia, 117
Hyperlysinemia, 117
Hyperpolarization, 97
Hyperprolinemia, 117
Hypertension, 48
Hypervalinemia, 117
Hyperventilation and cortical excitability,
  304-305, 317
Hypesthesia, 252
Hypoglossal nerve, 17, 32, 166
Hypophysis (pituitary), 15
  and autonomic nervous system, 228
  hormones of, 237-238
  portal circulation of, 228
  relation to hypothalamus, 237-238
Hypothalamus, 13, 21, 292
  and autonomic nervous system, 228-
    230
  emotions and, 335
  fever and, 236-237
  functions of, 236-238
  relation to pituitary, 237-238
Hypotonia, in cerebellar lesions, 284
  in corticospinal tract lesions, 168
  in lower motor neuron lesions, 172

IDIOPATHIC epilepsy, 316
Impulse nerve, 28, 102, 107-110
  types, 28
Inclusions, 67
Infants, motor areas of, 301
Inferior cerebellar peduncle, 17, 18, 282
Inferior colliculi, 16, 258, 267
Inhibition, presynaptic, 112
  Sherrington's (reciprocal), 126
Inhibitory mechanisms and cerebral
  cortex, 305
Inhibitory nerve impulses, 112

Inhibitory postsynaptic potential, 112
Inner ear, 211-214
Inspiratory centers, 268
Intensity, of light, 203
  of sound, 212
Intention tremor, 284
Interbrain. See *Diencephalon.*
Intercostal artery, posterior, 47
  nerve, 37
Internal capsule, 21, 170, 278, 292
Internal carotid artery, 15, 44
Interneuronal pool, 184
Interoceptive receptors, 135, 142, 239
Interventricular foramen, 19
Intervertebral foramen, 10
Intracerebral hemorrhage, 49
Intracranial pressure, 52, 54
  choked disk and, 194
Intrafusal fibers, 138
Iodopsin, 199
Iris, 192

JACKSON, J. H., 318-319, 330
Jacksonian convulsions, 304, 316
Jasper, H. H., 274, 319
Jaw jerk, 264
Jerk, ankle, 132
  biceps, 132
  jaw, 264
  knee, 123, 124, 162, 248
  triceps, 132
Joints, nerve endings in, 138
Joseph, J., 173
Jouvet, M., 274
Junctions, neuroeffector, 136, 146-151

KETY, S. S., 121
Kidney stone and referred pain, 184
Kimble, G. A., 338
Kinesthetic sense (position sense), 182-
  183
King, B. G., 7
Kleitman, N., 274
Knee jerk, 123, 124, 162, 248
Krause, W., 153
  end bulbs of, 137
Kuffler, S. W., 94
Kuhn, R. A., 255

LABYRINTH, 208
  canals of, 208
  cochlea of, 208, 211-214
  utricle and saccule of, 215
  vestibule of, 215

Labyrinthine righting reflexes, 309
Lacrimal gland, 231
Lactate, 114
Langman, J., 66
Language mechanisms, and association
    areas, 329-330
    and learning, 328-331
    defects of (aphasias), 329-331, 335
Larynx, 31, 271
Lashley, K. S., 338
Lateral corticospinal tract, 160, 162, 247
Lateral geniculate body, 205
Lateral lemniscus, 214
Lateral spinothalamic tract, 179, 180, 183,
    187, 249
Lateral sulcus, 13
Lateral ventricle, 19, 51
Lateral vestibular nucleus, 264
Lauer, E. W., 6
Law, all-or-none, 107
    Weber-Fechner, 328
Layers of neural tube, 59-61
Learning, 322-333
    conditioned responses and, 332-333
    language mechanisms and, 328-331
    sensorimotor functions and, 322-328
Lecithin (phosphatidyl choline), 16
Lemniscus, lateral, 214
    medial, 177, 181, 183, 187, 220, 258
Lens, crystalline, 191
    yellow, 205
Lentiform nucleus, 21, 292
Lesions, lower motor neuron, 170-172
    of auditory system, 215-216
    of temporal lobe, 336
    of visual system, 207-208
    pyramidal, 170
    subcortical, 335
    upper motor neuron, 167-170, 335
Light adaptation, 199-201
    color of, 203
    reflex, 240
    refraction of in eye, 192
Limb, phantom, 185
Limbic system, 335-336
Lipids, 116-117
Lipochondria, 72, 119
Lipochrome pigment, 73
Lobes, of brain, 13
    frontal, 13, 305, 320
    limbic, 335
    occipital, 13, 314, 320
    parietal, 13, 320
    temporal, 13, 315, 320, 336
Localization, tactile, 326
Logarithmic scale in sound intensity, 212
Loofbourrow, G. N., 338
Loudness as a quality of sound, 212

Lower motor neuron lesion, 170-172
Lumbar arteries, 47
Lumbar plexus, 37
Lumbar puncture, 51
Luminescent organs, 136
Lungs, receptors in, 142, 269
Lysergic acid diethylamide (LSD), 117,
    121

MACULA lutea, 194
Maculae of utricle and saccule, 215
Magnus, R., 273
Magoun, H. W., 274
Major hemisphere, 322, 329
Mamillary bodies, 14
Mammals, forebrain of, 289-292
Mantle layer of neural tube, 61
Marchi, V., 92
    method of staining, 87
Marginal layer of neural tube, 61
Marquis, D. G., 338
Marrowbrain, 59
Martin, J. P., 319
Masochism, 335
Mass extension, 251
    flexion, 250
Mastication, muscles of, 166, 261
McBride, K., 338
McGaugh, J. L., 338
McIlwain, H., 121
Meatus, external acoustic, 209
Mechanoreceptors, 136, 138
Medial geniculate body, 214
Medial lemniscus, 177, 181, 183, 187,
    220, 258
Medial longitudinal fasciculus, 165, 217,
    258, 259
Median eminence, 228
Medulla oblongata, 12, 17, 256-258
Medulla of adrenal gland, 64, 150, 234
Medullary sheath. See *Myelin sheath.*
Medulloblastoma, 284
Meissner, G., 153
    corpuscles, 136
Melanin pigment, 73
Melatonin, 117
Melzack, R., 189
Membrane, basilar, 211, 213
    cell, 70
    potential, 97
    tectorial, 211
    theory (core theory), 100
    tympanic, 209
Memory, long term, 322
    recent, 334
    short term, 322

Meninges, 10
    blood supply of, 46
Mesencephalon (midbrain), 12, 15, 59, 258-260
    animal, 308
    functions of, 267
Mesenteric ganglion, 40
Mesoderm, 57
Metabolic gradient, 57
Metabolism, 114-118
    general, of nervous system, 114-115
    intermediary, of nervous system, 115-118
Metachromatic leukodystrophy (sulfatide lipidosis), 117
Metencephalon, 59
Microglia, 64, 84
Microphonic potential, 211
Microtome, 4
Microvesicles, 72
Midbrain. See *Mesencephalon.*
Middle cerebellar peduncle, 18, 258, 278
Middle cerebral artery, 45
    thrombosis of, 330
Middle ear, 209-211
    deafness, 214-215
Milieu intérieur, 241
Millen, J.W., 55
Minor hemisphere, 331
Mitochondria, 72, 119
Monochromats, 205
Monoplegia, 170
Monro, A., 26
Morgan, C. T., 338
Mossman, H. W., 66
Motor aphasia (expressive, verbal, or Broca's), 330
Motor areas, clinical importance of, 167-172
    extirpation of, 306-307
    relation to sensory areas and cerebellum, 307-308
    representation of movements in, 300-307
    stimulation of, 303-306
Motor end plate (myoneural junction), 146
Motor fibers. See *Efferent fibers.*
Motor functions of forebrain, 291, 300-312
Motor neurons. See *Neurons.*
Motor pathways, 155-173
    clinical importance of, 167-172
Motor units, 146
Moulton, D. G., 225
Multipolar cells, 61
Muscarine, 234

Muscle(s), 144-146
    antagonists, 156
    antigravity, 158
    atrophy of, 170-172
    branchiomeric, 166-167, 261, 271
    cardiac, 145, 150
    ciliary, 192
    control of, 155-172, 234-235, 283
    dependence on nerve supply, 151-153
    facial, 166, 168, 261, 335
    fixation, 156
    hypotonia of, 168, 172, 284
    motor units of, 146
    neuroeffector junctions of, 146-151
    nonstriated (smooth), 144
    of expression, 335
    of eye, 164-166, 231
    of head and neck, 164
    of iris, 240
    of larynx, 261, 271
    of mastication, 166, 261
    of pharynx, 261, 271
    of respiration, 268
    of swallowing, 166, 271
    of tongue, 166
    of vocalizing, 166
    paradoxical action of (negative work), 157
    prime movers, 156
    receptors of, 146-151
    segmental supply of, 37-39
    skeletal, 144, 151, 170
    smooth, 144, 150
    sternocleidomastoid, 32, 166, 261
    strength-duration curves of, 151-153
    striated, 144, 145
    synergists, 156
    tetanic contractions of (tetanus), 148
    trapezius, 32, 166, 261
Myasthenia gravis, 150
Myelencephalon, 59
Myelin sheath, 74, 79
    composition of, 119
    conduction rates and, 102
    degeneration and regeneration of, 87-91
    staining of, 76
Myelinated fibers, 76
Myofibrils, 144
Myoneural junctions, 146-148
Myotatic reflexes, 124, 248, 266

NECK reflexes, tonic, 266
Neck righting reflexes, 310
Negative after-potential, 103
Neocerebellum, 276, 282, 283

Neocortex (neopallium), 291
Neothalamus, 294
Nerve(s), 28
  abducent, 15, 17, 31
  accessory, 17, 31, 166, 231, 258, 261
  acoustic, auditory. See *Vestibulococh-
    lear nerve.*
  cochlear, 31, 211
  components of, 252-253, 260-263
  cranial, 29-32, 39, 164, 168
  deafness, 215
  facial, 17, 31, 166, 220, 231, 261, 268
  femoral, 253
  glossopharyngeal, 17, 31, 166, 220, 231,
    258, 261, 268, 271
  hypoglossal, 17, 32, 166
  intercostal, 37
  obturator, 253
  oculomotor, 15, 29, 240
  olfactory, 14, 29, 222
  optic, 15, 29, 205, 240, 259
  peripheral, 28, 47, 78, 172, 253-254
  phrenic, 268
  radial, 254
  sciatic, 253
  spinal, 32-40, 82, 172, 252-253
  subcostal, 37
  trigeminal, 17, 29, 166, 177, 282
  trochlear, 15, 29
  ulnar, 185
  vagus, 17, 31, 166, 220, 231, 239, 258,
    261, 271
  vestibular, 31, 258, 264, 281
  vestibulocochlear, 17, 31, 211, 258
Nerve cells. See *Neurons.*
Nerve endings. See *Neuroeffector junctions* and *Receptors.*
Nerve fibers, 28, 74-77
Nerve growth factor, 64
Nerve impulses, 107, 142
Nervous system
  autonomic, 40, 151, 227-242
  central, 8-26, 58, 114
  chemical composition of, 119-120
  chemistry of, 114
    behavior and, 120
  congenital defects of, 65
  degeneration in, 85
  development of, 57-65
  effects of drugs on, 150-151
  general metabolism of, 114
  growth and differentiation of after
    birth, 65
  inorganic constituents of, 118-119
  intermediary metabolism of, 115-118
  methods of study, 3-6
  microscopic anatomy of, 67-94
  peripheral, 28-42, 115

Nervous system *(Continued)*
  regeneration in, 85, 90-91
  tumors of, 84
Nervus terminalis, 29
Neural crest, 58
  adrenal medullae from, 64
  bipolar cells and, 63
  migration and differentiation of, 63-64
  neurilemmal cells from, 64
  parasympathetic ganglia and, 64
  sympathetic ganglia and, 64
  unipolar cells and, 64
Neural groove, 58
Neural tube, 58
  cell changes in, 59
  formation of, 57-63
  layers of, 59
  subdivisions of, 58-59
Neurilemma, 64, 74-75, 78-79
  in degeneration and regeneration, 87-
    91
  origin of, 64
Neuroblasts, 61, 287
Neurocele, 59
Neuroeffector junctions, 122-123, 146-
    151, 233-235
  in cardiac muscle, 148
  in glands, 148
  in skeletal muscle, 146-148
  in smooth muscle, 148
  physiology of, 148-151
  structure of, 120
Neuroendocrinology, 237
Neurofibrils, 72
Neuroglia, 61, 83-85
Neurohypophysis, 229, 237
Neurokeratins, 119
Neuroma, 91
Neuromuscular junctions, 111
Neuromuscular spindles, 124, 138-140
  alteration of excitability of, 144
Neuron(s), 28, 67-82
  bipolar, 63, 73
    of olfactory mucous membrane, 221-
      222
    of retina, 196
    of spiral ganglion, 211
    of vestibular ganglion, 215
  cytoplasmic and nuclear constituents,
    72-73
  Golgi, 70
  intercalated (internuncial, interneuron),
    123
  motor, 124
  multipolar, 61, 73
  Nissl substance of, 72
  processes of, 73-78
  reaction to injury, 85-91

Neuron(s) *(Continued)*
  steady or resting potential of, 97
  theory, 91
  unipolar, 64, 73
Neurosecretion, 120
Neurotendinous endings (spindle, Golgi
    tendon organs), 140
Nicholls, J. G., 94
Nicotine, 150, 234
Niemann-Pick disease (sphingomyelin
    lipidosis), 117
Night blindness, 201
Nissl, F., 93
  method of staining, 93
  substance, 69, 72, 74, 119, 294
    in degeneration and regeneration,
      85-86, 90
Nociceptors, 136
Node(s), atrioventricular, 148
  of Ranvier, 77
    and conduction rates, 102
  sinoatrial, 148
Nomina Anatomica, 7
Nominal aphasia (amnesic aphasia), 330-
    331
Nonmyelinated fibers, 74-82
Noradrenaline (norepinephrine),   111,
    150, 233-234
  formula of, 120
Nuclear layer of neural tube, 61
Nucleolar satellite, 73
Nucleolus(i), 73
Nucleoproteins, 119
Nucleus(i), 67
  abducent, 164, 258
  ambiguus, 258, 261
  association, 294
  basal, 20. See *Basal ganglia.*
  caudate, 21, 292
  cochlear, 214
  cortical relay, 294
  cuneatus, 175, 177
  dentate, 24, 277, 282
  dorsal motor, of vagus, 257
  facial, 166, 258
  fastigius, 277
  gracilis, 175, 177
  hypothalamic, 335
  lateral cervical, 177
  lentiform, 21, 292
  main sensory (pons), 177
  of hypoglossal nerve, 166, 257
  of oculomotor nerve, 165, 166, 231, 258
  of origin of cranial nerves, 164
  of trigeminal nerve, 258, 261
  olivary, 257, 282
  paraventricular, 237
  pontile, 258

Nucleus(i) *(Continued)*
  red, 23, 258, 259-260, 267, 284, 293
  roof, of cerebellum, 24, 277, 281
  salivatory, 268
  subcortical, 294
  subthalamic, 21, 292, 293
  supraoptic, 237
  thalamic, 335
  trochlear, 166, 258
  vestibular, 164, 217, 264, 281
Nystagmus, 264

Obturator nerve, 253
Occipital lobe, 13, 34, 320
  area 17 of, 206, 315
  association areas of, 324-325
Occlusion, 49
Ochs, S., 113
Oculomotor nerve, 15, 29, 240
Olfactory bulb, 14, 29, 222
Olfactory nerves, 14, 29, 222
Olfactory rods, 222
Olfactory tracts, 14, 29, 222
Oligodendroglia, 84
Olive and olivary nuclei, 17, 257, 282
Ophthalmoscope, 194
Optic canal, 15
Optic chiasma, 15, 29, 205
Optic disk, 194
  choked, 194
Optic nerves, 15, 29, 205, 240, 259
Optic righting reflex, 311
Optic tracts, 15, 29, 205, 259
O'Rahilly, R., 6
Organ(s), electric, 136
  Golgi tendon, 140
  luminescent, 136
  spiral (of Corti), 211
Organelles, 67
Osmic acid, 76
Ossicles, ear, 209
Otoliths, 217
Ovum, 56
Oxygen, 43
  consumption, 114
Oxytocin, 237

Pacini, F., 154
Pacinian corpuscles, 137, 138, 181, 183
Pain, 136-137, 179-180, 181-182, 183-185,
    315-316
  delayed, 179
  pathways, 179-180, 181-182
  projected, 183-185

Pain *(Continued)*
  receptors, 136-137, 142
  referred, 183-185
  surgery for, 179
  visceral, 183
Paleocerebellum, 276, 281, 283
Pallis, C. A., 189
Palsy, shaking, 311
Paralysis, flaccid, 172, 250, 254
  spastic, 170, 306
Paralysis agitans, 311
Paramecium, 287
Parasympathetic ganglion cells, 64
Parasympathetic system, 230-235
  general functions of, 241
Paravertebral sympathetic trunk, 40
Paresis, 168
Parietal lobe, 13, 188, 320
  areas 1, 2, 3 of, 314
Parkinson, J., 319
Parkinsonism, 311
Path(s), afferent, 322
    and cerebral cortex, 325-328
    clinical importance of, 185-187
    general senses and, 174-188
    special senses and, 190-222
  final common, 158, 252
  motor, 158-166
    clinical importance of, 167-172
    levels of control, 158-160
  naming of, 158
  reflex, 122
  sensory, 175-183
    ascending auditory, 258
    pain, 179-180, 181-182, 183
    position (kinesthetic), 182-183
    pressure, 181
    smell, 221-222
    taste, 219-220
    temperature, 180
    touch, 175-179
    vestibular, 217-219
    vibration, 181
    visual, 205-207
Patterns, receptor, 326
Pavlov, I. P., 268, 274, 332, 338
Pease, D. C., 55
Peduncles, cerebellar, 18, 277
    inferior, 17, 18, 282
    middle, 18, 258, 278
    superior, 18, 260, 278
  cerebral, 14, 15, 258
Peele, T. L., 6
Penfield, W., 319
Pentose monophosphate pathway, 115
Perineurium, 81
Period, absolute refractory, 102
  relative refractory, 102

Peripheral nerves, 28, 47, 78, 172
  blood supply of, 47
  components of, 78, 253-254
  lesions of, 254
  regeneration of, 90-91
  respiratory quotient of, 115
Peripheral nervous system, 28-42
  metabolism of, 115
Peristalsis, 271
Peterson, L., 338
Petit mal attacks, 316
Pfaffman, C., 225
Phagocytes (phagocytosis), 84, 87
Phantom limb, 185
Pharynx, 31, 271
Phase, subnormal, 102
  supernormal, 102
Phenylalanine, 117
Phenylketonuria, 117
Phosphatidyl choline (lecithin), 116
Phosphatidyl ethanolamine (cephalin), 116
Phosphatidyl inositol, 117
Phosphatidyl serine, 117
Phosphocreatine, 115
Phosphofructokinase, 115
Phospholipids, 116, 119
Photophobia, 205
Photopic curve, 201
Phrenic ganglia, 40
Phrenic nerve, 268
Pia mater, 10
Pickford, R. W., 189
Pigment, lipochrome, 73
  melanin, 73
  of eye, 196
Pineal body, 16
Piriform area, 289
Pitch of sound, 212
Pituitary gland. See *Hypophysis.*
Place theory, 213
Placing reaction, 307
Planes, anatomical, 3
Plasmalemma, 70
Plasmalogens, 117
Plate, alar, 58
  basal, 58
Plexus(es), 33
  autonomic, 40
  brachial, 33
  choroid, 20, 51
  lumbar, 37
  pudendal, 37
  sacral, 37
Pneumoencephalography, 52
Polarization, 97
Polyak, S. L., 224
Pons, 12, 16, 258-260

Pool, interneuronal, 184
Porphyropsins, 198
Portal circulation of pituitary, 228
Position, anatomical, 3
Position sense (kinesthetic sense), 182-183
Positive after-potential, 103
Positive supporting reaction, 266
Postcentral gyrus, 177, 188, 220, 313
Posterior cerebral artery, 18, 45
Posterior funiculus–medial lemniscus system, 175, 181, 183
Posterior intercostal artery, 47
Posterior intermediate sulcus, 24
Posterior lateral sulcus, 24
Posterior median sulcus, 24
Posterior spinal artery, 24, 47
Postganglionic fibers, 148, 150, 230
Post-traumatic epilepsy, 316
Postural contractions, 125
Potassium, and steady potential, 97-98
Potential, action, 100
    after, 100, 103
    end plate, 111, 149
    excitatory postsynaptic, 111
    inhibitory postsynaptic, 112
    membrane, 97
    microphonic, 211
    miniature end-plate, 111
    receptor, 142
    recording of, 104-107
    resting, 97
    spike, 98
    steady, 97
Precentral gyrus, 160, 300, 304
Precentral motor cortex, 162, 164, 300-307
Precentral sulcus, 12
Preganglionic fibers, 148, 230
Preneural changes (influences), 63, 287
Pressure, blood, control of, 238-240
    intracranial, 52, 54
Pressure (deep touch), sense of, 138, 181
Primary cortical receptive area, 177
Procaine, 118, 252
Prosencephalon (forebrain), 12, 59, 286-299
Protanomaly, 204
Protanopia, 205
Proteins, 118, 119
Protoplasm, 67
Psychogalvanic reflex, 333
Pudendal plexus, 37
Pulse pressure, 239
Pump, sodium, 98
Puncture, lumbar, 51
Pupil of eye, 192
Purity of color, 203

Purkinje, J., 285
    cells of cerebellum, 277-278, 281
    fibers, 148
    shift, 200, 201
Purple, visual (rhodopsin), 196, 198-199
Purposeful acts, defects in (apraxias), 323
Putamen, 21, 292
Pyramid(s), 17
    decussation of, 160, 256
Pyramidal cells, 159, 305
    lesions, 170
    signs, 170
    system, 160-162
    tracts, 160-162
Pyruvate, 114

QUALITY (timbre) of sound, 212
Quastel, D. M. J., 121
Quastel, J. H., 121

RADIAL nerve, 254
Radiation, ultraviolet, 200
Radicular branches, 47
Rages, sham, 335
Rami communicantes, 40, 82, 231
Rami of spinal nerves, 33
Ramón y Cajal, S., 93
Ranson, S. W., 6
Ranvier, L., 93
    nodes of, 77
Rasmussen, A. T., 53
Reaction(s), arousal, 272, 298
    dynamic, 308
    hopping, 307
    of neurons to injury, 85-91
    placing, 307
    stress, 241
    supporting, 266
    tropic, 286
Receptive aphasia (sensory, auditory, Wernicke's), 330
Receptive areas, primary. See *Sensory areas*.
Receptor(s), 122-123, 135-144
    adaptation of, 143-144
    chemoreceptor, 136, 222
    exteroceptive, 135, 136-138
    for balance, 215-217
    for hearing, 208
    for special senses, 142
    in joints, 141
    in lungs, 142
    in skin, 136-137
    interoceptive, 135, 142, 239

Receptor(s) *(Continued)*
  mechanoreceptor, 136, 138
  nociceptor, 136
  olfactory, 221-222
  pain, 136-137, 142
  patterns, 326
  physiology of, 142-144
  potential, 142
  pressure (deep touch), 138, 181
  proprioceptive, 135, 138-142
  smell, 221-222
  stretch, 138
  tactile (light touch), 136
  taste, 219-220
  teleceptors, 135
  visual, 196
Red nucleus, 23, 258, 259-260, 267, 284, 293
Reflex(es), 123-133, 248
  abnormal, 132
  act (arc), 122-133
  after-discharge and, 129
  allied, 249
  antagonistic, 249
  attitudinal, 267
  auditory, 267
  autonomic, 238-240
  Babinski, 132, 168, 170, 250, 301
  behavior and, 130-131
  blinking, 264, 267
  body-righting, 309-310, 311
  clinical value of, 131-133
  conditioned, 332-333
  contralateral connections and, 127
  control of blood pressure, 239-240
  coordination of, 125-130, 248
  corneal, 264
  crossed extensor, 248, 266
  deep, 132
  general properties of, 122-134
  grasp, 301, 307
  groping, 307
  inhibition of (Sherrington's), 126
  intersegmental, 249
  ipsilateral connections and, 126
  labyrinthine-righting, 309
  labyrinthine tonic, 266
  light, 240
    tonic, 267
  local, 248
    sign of, 248
  myotatic, 124, 248, 266
    phasic type, 124, 248
    static type, 124-125, 248
  neck-righting, 310
  neck, tonic, 266
  of brain stem, 264
  of newborn, 301

Reflex(es) *(Continued)*
  optic-righting, 311
  pathological, 132
  psychogalvanic, 333
  pupillary, 240, 267
  respiratory, 269
  response to noise, 264
  rhythm of, 248
  righting, 309-311
  salivation, 240, 332
  scratch, 249
  segmental, 248
  special, 132
  specificity of, 248
  static, 124-125, 248, 266-267
    general, 266-267
    intersegmental, 266
    local, 266
    segmental, 248, 266
  stretch. See *Reflex, myotatic.*
  superficial, 131
  three-neuron, 123
  two-neuron, 123-125, 248
  types of, 123-125
  unconditioned, 332
  visceral, 238-240, 268-272
  visual, 267
Refraction of light in eye, 192
Refractory period, absolute, 102
  relative, 102
Regeneration, after peripheral nerve lesions, 89
  in nervous system, 86-87
Relative refractory period, 102
Renal ganglion, 40
Repolarization, 99
Representation of movements in motor cortex, 303-306
Reptiles, forebrain of, 289
Reserpine, 121
Respiration, control of, 268-271
Respiratory centers, 268-270
Response (reflex), Babinski, 132, 168, 170, 250, 301
  conditioned, 332-333
  contralateral, 127
  groping, 307
  local, to subthreshold stimulus, 109
Reticular activating system, 272, 298
Reticular formation, 24, 159, 217, 258, 259, 268, 272-273, 280, 293
Reticulospinal tracts, 159, 162, 260, 264
  excitatory, 162
  inhibitory, 162
Retina, 29, 191, 194-207
  binocular vision and, 205
  bipolar cells of, 197
  central connections of, 205-207

Retina (*Continued*)
  color vision and, 198, 203-204
  cones of, 195-199
  fovea of, 194, 205
  functions, 198-199
  ganglion cells of, 195
  grain of, 202
  macula lutea of, 194
  optic disk of, 194
  photosensitive pigments of, 196, 198-199
    rods of, 195-199
  vessels of, 194
  visual acuity and, 202-203
  visual sensitivity and, 201-202
Retinal arteries, 194
Retrograde degeneration, 87
Rheobase, 109
Rhinencephalon, 335-336
Rhines, R., 274
Rhodopsin (visual purple), 196
Rhombencephalon, 59
Rhythm, Berger (alpha waves of EEG), 297
Rhythm of reflexes, 248
Ribonucleic acid (RNA), 72, 118, 119
Ribosomes, 72
Righting reflexes, 309-311
Rigidity, decerebrate, 265
  in paralysis agitans, 311
Ritchie, J. M., 113, 189
Rods, of retina, 195-198
  olfactory, 222
Romer, A. S., 7
Roof nuclei of cerebellum, 24, 277, 281
Roots, spinal, 32-33, 78, 252
  dorsal, 24, 78, 172, 252
  ventral, 24, 81, 252
Round window, 209
Rubroreticular tract, 260
Rubrospinal tract, 260
Ruch, T. C., 6
Ruffini, A., 154
  endings, 138, 183

SACCULE, 215, 217
  macula of, 215
Sacral arteries, 47
Sacral plexus, 37
Sacrum, 10
Sadism, 335
St. Vitus' dance, 312
Saks, A. L., 319
Salivary glands, 31, 231, 268
Salivation, reflex, 240, 332

Salt as primary taste quality, 220
Saltatory conduction, 102
Sarcolemma, 149
Sarcoplasm, 144
Satellite cells, 78
Saturation of light, 203
Schadé, J. P., 94, 255, 338
Scharrer, B., 243
Scharrer, E., 243
Schildkraut, J. J., 121
Schultz, R. L., 55
Schwann, T., 93
  cells of, 78
Sclera, 192
Scotopic curve, 200
Scratch reflex, 249
Segment of spinal cord, 33
Semantic aphasias (higher level), 331
Semicircular canals, 215
  ducts, 215, 216-217
    cristae of, 216
Semilunar ganglion, 30
Sense(s) (Sensations)
  classifications of, 174
  compound, 324
  cutaneous, 135
  deep, 135
  exteroceptive, from skin, 135
    from subcutaneous and deep tissues, 181-183
    from viscera, 174
  general, and their afferent paths, 174-189
  kinesthetic (position sense), 182-183
  of balance, 215-219
  of color, 203-204
  of hearing, 208-214
  of pain, 136-137, 179-180, 181-182, 183-185, 315-316
  of position (kinesthetic sense), 182-183
  of pressure (deep touch), 138, 181
  of smell, 221-222
  of taste, 219-220, 262-263
  of temperature, 180
  of touch, 136, 138, 175-179, 181
  of vision, 198-205
  phantom limb, 185
  primary receptive areas and. See *Sensory areas.*
  projected, 183-185
  referred, 183-185
  somatic, 136
  special, and their afferent pathways, 190-225
  superficial, 135
  visceral, 136, 226-243
Sensitivity, visual, 201-202
Sensory aphasia (receptive, auditory, or Wernicke's), 330

Sensory areas (primary receptive areas), 177, 187-188, 206, 214, 220
  electrical activity of, 314
  extirpation of, 314
  secondary, 314
  stimulation of, 313-314
Sensory epileptic fits, 316-317
Sensory fiber. See *Afferent fiber.*
Serotonin (5-hydroxytryptamine), 120, 234
Sexual activity in spinal man, 252
Sham rage, 335
Sheath, myelin, 74, 79
Sherrington, C. S., 134
Sherrington's inhibition, 126
Shift, Purkinje, 200, 201
Shock, spinal, 247, 249
Sholl, D. A., 299
Showers, M. J., 7
Signs, pyramidal, 170
Simeone, F. A., 243
Sinclair, D. C., 154
Sink, in nerve conduction, 100
Sinoatrial node, 148
Sinuses, dural, 10
Skeletal muscle, 144
Skin, nerve supply of, 136-138
Skull, 9
Sleep, 272
Sleep spindles in EEG, 297
Smell, sense of, 221-222
Smithwick, R. H., 243
Smooth muscle, 144
Snyder, R. S., 285
Sodium, and steady potential, 98
  pump, 98
Somatic areas. See *Sensory areas.*
Sound, 212
  intensity, 212
  pitch, 212
  timbre (quality), 212
  waves, 213
Sour, as primary taste modality, 220
Source, in nerve conduction, 100
Space, epidural, 10
  subarachnoid, 10, 50
  subdural, 10
Spastic paralysis, 17, 306
Specificity of reflexes, 248
Speech (language) mechanisms, 328-330
  defects of (aphasias), 330-331
Spermatozoon, 56
Sperry, R. W., 338
Sphingolipids, 117
Sphingomyelin, 117
  lipidosis (Niemann-Pick disease), 117
Sphingosides, 119
Sphygmomanometer, 238
Spike potential, 98

Spina bifida, 65
Spinal, animal, 240, 247
  cat, 248
  dog, 248
  man, 240, 249-252
Spinal artery, anterior, 24, 46
  posterior, 24, 47
Spinal cord, 24-25, 244-252
  and autonomic nervous system, 230, 240
  as level of control, 158, 230
  blood supply of, 46
  cells of, 246
  cervical and respiration, 270
  connections with cerebellum, 280-281
  development of, 57-65, 253
  differences from brain stem, 256
  effects of extrapyramidal system on, 264
  enlargements of, 24
  fasciculi of, 25, 175
  functions of, 247-249
  funiculi of, 25, 162, 170, 187, 246-247
  gray matter of, 24, 158, 179, 246
  growth after birth, 65
  reflexes and, 248-249
  segments of, 245
  termination of in vertebral canal, 65
  tracts of, 246-247
  white matter of, 25, 246
Spinal ganglion, 32
Spinal nerves, 32-40, 82, 172, 252-253
  blood supply of, 46
  components of, 82, 253
Spinal roots, 32, 33
  blood supply of, 46
  components of, 78-81, 253
Spinal shock, 247, 249
Spindles, neuromuscular, 124, 138-140
  neurotendinous, 140
  sleep, of EEG, 297
Spinocerebellar tracts, 247, 280
Spinocervicothalamic system, 177, 181, 183
Spinothalamic tract, anterior, 175, 177, 187
  lateral, 179, 180, 183, 187, 247
Spiral ganglion, 31, 211
  organ (of Corti), 211
Splanchnic ganglion, 40
Spongioblasts, 61
Spot(s), blind, of eye, 195
  tactile (touch), 136
Spreading depression, 305
Staining, Marchi method, 87
  Nissl method, 93
  Weigert method, 76
Stanbury, J. B., 121
Stapes, 209

State(s), convulsive, 316-317
  spastic (hypertonic), 170
Stereognosis, 324
Sternocleidomastoid muscle, 32, 166, 261
Stevens, S. S., 224, 338
Stimulation, of motor areas, 303-306
  of sensory areas, 313, 314
Stimulus(i), 95
  and nerve impulses, 107-110
  subthreshold, 109, 249
  summation of, 249
Straus, W. L., Jr., 66
Strength-duration curves, 108
Stress, 241
Stretch reflexes, 124, 248, 266
Striate (visual) cortex, 206
Strings, auditory, 211
Stripe (band) of Gennari, 206
Stroke, 48
Strychnine, 150, 313
Subarachnoid space, 10, 50
Subcostal nerve, 37
Subdural space, 10
Subnormal phase, 102
Substance, Nissl, 69, 72, 74, 119, 294
Substantia nigra, 23, 258, 259-260, 267, 293
Subthalamic nucleus, 21, 292, 293
Sulcus(i), 12
  anterior lateral, 17
  central, 12, 300
  cingulate, 20
  lateral, 13
  median (IV ventricle floor), 20
  posterior intermediate, 24
  posterior lateral, 24
  posterior median, 24
  precentral, 12
Sulfatide lipidosis (metachromatic leuko-dystrophy), 117
Summation, spatial, 111
  temporal, 111
Superior cerebellar peduncle, 18, 260, 278
Superior colliculi, 16, 258, 267, 314
Supernormal phase, 102
Suppressor areas, 305
Supramarginal gyrus, 323
Suprarenal gland. See Adrenal gland.
Swallowing, 271
Sweat glands, 233
Sweet, as primary taste quality, 220
Sweet, W. H., 189
Sydenham, T., 319
Sydenham's chorea, 312
Sylvius (Jacques DeBois), 26
Symbolization, 328-329
Sympathetic ganglia, 40, 64, 231

Sympathetic system, 40, 230-235
  general functions of, 241-242
Sympathetic trunk, 40, 231
Synapse (synaptic junction), 74, 82, 110, 233
Synaptic transmission, 110-112, 233-235
Synaptic vesicles, 83, 111, 234
Syndrome, Brown-Séquard, 187
Systole, 238

TABES dorsalis, 185
Tactile discrimination and localization, 326-328
Tactile (touch) endings, 175, 326
Taste, 219-220
  buds, 220
  primary qualities of, 220
Tauc, L., 113
Taylor, N. B., 6
Tay-Sachs' disease (ganglioside lipidosis), 117
Tectobulbar tract, 258
Tectorial membrane, 211
Tectospinal tract, 259
Tectum, 259
Teleceptors, 135
Telencephalon, 12, 59
Telodendria, 82
Temperature, body, control of, 226-227, 236-237
  sense of, 180
Temporal lobe, 13, 315, 320
  and emotions, 336
  area 41 of, 214, 315
  lesions of, 336
Tendon of Achilles, 133
Terminal tremor, 284
Terminology, 1-3
Terms of direction, 3
Tetanus (tetanic contraction), 148
Thalamic animal, 301, 308
Thalamus, 13, 21, 188, 292, 293, 294
  basal ganglia and, 293, 311
  relationship with cerebral cortex, 314
Theory, Helmholtz, 213
  membrane or core, 100
  neuron, 91
  place, 213
  Young-Helmholtz, 204
Third ventricle, 19
Thrombosis, 48
  of middle cerebral artery, 330
Thudichum, J. L. W., 114, 121
Tickle, 136
Timbre (quality) of sound, 212
Time, excitation, 109
Tone, of color, 203
  of muscle, 125

Tongue, muscles of, 166
  nerve supply of, 32, 166
  taste buds of, 220
Total aphasia (expressive-receptive), 330
Touch, 136
  deep (pressure) 138, 181
  light, 136
  pathways, 175-179
  spots, 136
Tract(s), 158
  anterior corticospinal, 160
  anterior spinothalamic, 175, 177, 187
  corticobulbar, 164
  corticomesencephalic, 164
  corticopontine, 164, 282
  corticospinal, 160, 162, 187, 247, 258,
    278, 294, 301
  extrapyramidal, 162-163, 169, 187, 301
  in central nervous system, 158
  lateral lemniscus, 214
  lateral spinothalamic, 179, 180, 183,
    187, 247
  medial lemniscus, 177, 181, 183, 187,
    220, 258
  medial longitudinal fasciculus, 165,
    217, 258, 259
  olfactory, 14
  optic, 15, 29, 205, 259
  pyramidal (corticospinal) 160-162
  reticulospinal, 159, 162, 260, 264
  rubroreticular, 260
  rubrospinal, 260
  spinal, of trigeminal nerve, 179, 258
  spinocerebellar, 247, 280
  spinocervicothalamic, 177, 181, 183
  spinospinal, 247
  tectobulbar, 258
  tectospinal, 259
  vestibulospinal, 162, 217, 264
Tractus solitarius, 258, 263, 269
Tranquilizers, 121
Transmitters, 120, 233-235
  formulae of, 120
Transport, active, in steady potential, 97,
  98
Trapezius muscle, 32, 166, 261
Tremor, at rest, 311
  terminal (intention), 284
Triceps jerk, 132
Trichromats, 204
Trigeminal ganglion, 30
Trigeminal nerve, 17, 29, 166, 177, 282
Tritanopia, 205
Trochlear nerve, 15, 29
Tropic reaction, 286
Truex, R. C., 6
Trunk, sympathetic, 40
Tube, auditory, 211
  neural. See *Neural tube.*

Twitch, 148
Two-point discrimination, 326-327
Tympanic membrane, 209

ULNAR nerve, 185
Ultrastructure, 4
Ultraviolet radiation, 200
Unconditioned reflex, 332
Unipolar cells, 64, 73
  development of, 63
Unit, motor, 146
  of power, 212
Upper motor neuron lesions, 167-170
  of corticospinal tracts, 168
  of corticospinal and extrapyramidal
    tracts, 168-170
Utricle, 215, 217
  macula of, 215

VAGUS nerve, 17, 31, 166, 220, 231, 239,
  258, 261, 271
Vasomotor centers, 238, 239
Vasopressin, 237
Vein(s), 43
  of Galen, 1
Ventral rami, 33
Ventral roots, 24, 81, 252
Ventricles, 19, 50, 59
  fourth, 19, 258
  lateral, 19, 51
  third, 19
Ventriculogram, 52
Venules, 43
Veratrine, 104
Verbal aphasia (expressive, motor or
  Broca's), 330
Vermis, 18, 275
Vertebrae, 9-10
Vertebral artery, 18, 44-47
Vertebral canal, 9
Vertigo, 219
Vesicles, synaptic, 83, 111, 234
Vestibular division of vestibulocochlear
  nerve, 31, 258, 264, 281
Vestibular ganglion, 31, 216
Vestibular nuclei, 164, 217, 264, 281
Vestibular system, 215-219
  connections of, 217-219
  functions of, 219
  lesions of, 219
Vestibule, 215
Vestibulocochlear nerve, 17, 31, 211, 258
Vestibulospinal tract, 162, 217, 264
Villi, arachnoid, 51
Viscera, 227

Visceral activity, control of, 226-243
Vision, 191-208, 291
    binocular, 205
    color, 198, 203-204
    defects of, 207-208
    in primates, 291
    lesions of, 207-208
Visual acuity, 202-203
    angle, 202
    axis, 194
    pathways, 205-207
    purple (rhodopsin), 196, 198-199
    sensitivity, 201-202
Visual agnosia, 325
Vitamin(s), 118
    A_1 retinal, 198
    A_2 retinal, 198
    cobalamine (B_{12}), 118
    nicotinamide, 118
    pyroxidine, 118
    thiamin, 118
Vitreous body, 194
Volume conduction, 107
Vomiting, gastrointestinal movements in, 271

WALL, P. D., 189
Waller, A., 94
Wallerian degeneration, 87
Walls, G. L., 225
Walshe, F., 134, 173, 319

Waves, brain (EEG), 107, 272, 296-297
Weber, E. H., 337
Weber, W. E., 337
Weber-Fechner law, 328
Weigert, C., 94
    method of staining, 76
Weisenberg, W., 338
Wernicke, C., 338
Wernicke's aphasia (receptive, sensory, auditory), 330
White, J. C., 189, 243
White matter, 20
    composition of, 76
Willis, T., 54
    circle of (arterial), 15, 45
Wilson's hepatolenticular degeneration, 118-119
Windle, W. F., 94
Wollam, D. H. M., 55
Wright, W. G., 173
Wrist drop, 254
Wyburn, G. M., 189
Wyngaarden, J. B., 121

X-RAYS and retina, 207

YOUNG, T., 224
Young-Helmholtz theory, 204